Arduino Projects to Save the World

Emery Premeaux
Brian Evans

Apress®

Arduino Projects to Save the World

ISBN   978-1-4302-3623-8

ISBN   978-1-4302-3624-5 (eBook)

President and Publisher: Paul Manning
Lead Editor: Matthew Moodie
Technical Reviewer: Michael Turner
Editorial Board: Steve Anglin, Mark Beckner, Ewan Buckingham, Gary Cornell, Morgan Ertel, Jonathan Gennick, Jonathan Hassell, Robert Hutchinson, Michelle Lowman, James Markham, Matthew Moodie, Jeff Olson, Jeffrey Pepper, Douglas Pundick, Ben Renow-Clarke, Dominic Shakeshaft, Gwenan Spearing, Matt Wade, Tom Welsh
Coordinating Editor: Corbin Collins
Copy Editor: Nancy Sixsmith
Production Support: Patrick Cunningham
Indexer: SPi Global
Artist: SPi Global
Cover Designer: Anna Ishchenko

Distributed to the book trade worldwide by Springer Science+Business Media New York, 233 Spring Street, 6th Floor, New York, NY 10013. Phone 1-800-SPRINGER, fax (201) 348-4505, e-mail orders-ny@springer-sbm.com, or visit www.springeronline.com.

For information on translations, please e-mail rights@apress.com, or visit www.apress.com.

To my father: You handed me a screwdriver when I asked for action figures. Learning to solder before most kids my age had learned how to catch a ball had a profound affect on me. In a child's mind (at least to mine), being gifted with the ability to take things apart and put them back together held far more magic than any ball and glove ever could. First being shown by you, then being guided by you, and finally given trust and free reign to do whatever I wanted to do is what inspires me to this very day.

To my mother: You showed me how to fill the holes in the wall made by that screwdriver dad gave me. Actually, you showed me how to do (and cope with) all sorts of things. My heart is only half as big as yours, and yet even so, is sometimes more than I can handle.

To my sister and brother: You showed me what it REALLY means to lend compassion and to help strangers. TRUE compassion does not end with the singular act. Rather, singular acts completely change your entire outlook on life. Without the choices you both made, our family would be less whole.

To my grandparents: You valued education and you trusted me to make good use of mine. I never really returned. I hope you can accept this as one step towards "making good" on my promises.

To hackerspaces around the world, and Tokyo HackerSpace in specific: May you continue to inspire and enable young minds across the globe. May these communal "dream spaces" never be wiped from the Earth.

—Emery Premeaux

Contents at a Glance

Contents

About the Authors

■**Emery Premeaux** (a.k.a. "MRE") was raised on electronics and hamburgers. The need to disassemble mechanical and electronic devices is a genetic disorder passed on by his father. Soldering skills came before table manners. Formative years were spent putting model rockets into microwaves, searching for treasure with hand-wound electro-magnets, and building various Rube-Goldberg contraptions to catch "the monsters." An underlying theme of life in those early days was that technology was not only fascinating, but that nerdism could actually make one a hero. *The Goonies, Tron*, and *Revenge of the Nerds* were huge influences.

Eventually, so-called "adult reality" stepped in. So MRE started out on the "success quest." A series of jobs in the technical industry left him with a diverse set of skills, including, but not limited to cheating arcade and slot machines, building and maintaining incredibly complex robots that manufacture incredibly simple things, determining just what it would take to destroy a 3-story-tall, 200-ton piece of construction equipment, and answering the question "Can we measure that?"

After ten years, and nearly as many jobs in and around the electronics industry, MRE decided that, somehow, having an actual degree might do some good, so he went ahead and did that. It did him no good. Don't get him wrong, a degree is an incredibly useful thing to have. It's just that by the time he finished first an associate's and then bachelor's degree in electronics engineering, he was actually ready for something completely different. MRE now lives in Japan. He teaches technical English to Japanese engineers and normal English to normal Japanese kids. He is also a founding member of Tokyo HackerSpace, where he teaches electronics, Arduino, urban gardening, and leather and metal work to anyone willing to try something new. Visit his Web site at http://diy-scib.org.

■**Brian Evans** is an artist working in electronic media and Assistant Professor at Metropolitan State College of Denver, where he teaches multidisciplinary courses in art and design on topics that include spatial media, electronics, and 3D fabrication. Many of his classes use open-source hardware, including MakerBot and RepRap 3D printers and the Arduino electronics platform, in the creation of new works in art and design. His work has been shown at the Los Angeles Municipal Art Gallery at Barnsdall Park, the Orange County Center for Contemporary Art, and the University Art Museum at California State University, Long Beach. Evans was a resident and contributor to the Grounding Open Source Hardware Residency and Summit at the Banff New Media Institute in Alberta, Canada in 2009 and contributor to the Open Hardware Summit in New York in 2011. He received a BFA at Arizona State University in 2005, and an MFA at California State University, Long Beach in 2008.

About the Technical Reviewer

 **Michael Turner** was born in Coronado, California. He began programming in 1976 at the age of 12, and by the by the end of high school was taking master's level computer science classes. He joined the Navy in 1982, learning electronics and becoming a nuclear power operator and Submariner while serving on two submarines. After leaving the Navy Micael took various continuing education courses and earned multiple commendations, including three Special Service Awards with the Arizona District of the United States District Court. Michael current works for the City of Phoenix Police Department as a Senior I.T. Specialist maintaining and interfacing the primary RDBMS at the police department programming in C# and VB, as well as mainframe languages like ALGOL. He Is an avid hobbyist on the Arduino and .netmf platforms.

Acknowledgments

This book would not have been possible without the pushing and prodding from my support staff at Apress. In particular, Frank Pohlmann and Corbin Collins.

Special thanks to: Akiba (freaklabs.org) — it was your idea in the first place, Lauren and Chris Shannon. Thank you for the "sanity" space, and all the folks at THS. Pieter and the SafeCast crew, Ronnie — thanks for all the calculus, Mr. Toussaint — and all my teachers, friends, family, and so on. Additional thanks to: Mitch Altman, LadyAda, Hackers On A Plane. The stylish boys at Mogostyle.com.

Thank you to everyone who supported Japan and our efforts at THS: globalsolar.com, konarka.com, Carlos Miranda Levy and Relief 2.0, and everyone who made donations or volunteered.

Preface

In the year following the Tohoku earthquake and tsunami, I have been fortunate enough to be able to work alongside some incredible people in the open source community, doing extraordinary things. By now I am sure you are all well aware that the tsunami caused severe damage to the Fukushima dai-ichi (number 1) power plant. When the backup generators were swamped by the waves, the reactors began melting down.

Almost overnight, the cost of Geiger counters and Geiger-muller tubes skyrocketed. The price hike was not limited to Japan. A lack of ready supplies of Geiger counters caused a global price shock.

The Japanese government began radiation tests almost as quickly as the news pundits started making comparisons to Three Mile Island and Chernobyl.

It quickly became apparent to the hacker community that a few spot measurements taken outside government office buildings once a week were not going to cut it. Not that the Japanese government failed to step in and do its job, but until now the standard practices within the nuclear energy industry were limited to stationary sensors and limited readings. Essentially, the book would have to be re-written.

Only a few days after the quake, a few Tokyo HackerSpace members braved the dangers and ventured out to the space to have our usual meeting. Right away we began brainstorming ideas as to how we could help, by applying our technical skills to the current disasters (it was in fact multiple disasters). We got to work on solar-powered cell phone chargers, international pleas for donations and supplies, and coordinating with volunteers to provide crash space, food, and equipment for their trips up north.

In the first week, radiation was definately at the top of everyone's list.

About that time, Pieter Franken made contact with a group of people in the U.S., willing to set up and host a data server for collecting radiation data. In the beginning they could only aggregate all the independent sensors registered on sites such as Patchube, as well as independent servers. Even so, they quickly developed a radiation map far more sophisticated than anything the government could come up with. The advantage was many distributed sensors maintained by enthusiasts, willing to spend a bit of money and sweat to do it.

Once the Peter Franken-to-SafeCast-to-Tokyo-HackerSpace connection was made, the project exploded in scope. Akiba, one of our star members in the field of wireless sensor networks, quickly mashed up a portable Geiger counter system that logged readings to an SD card every 5 seconds. It does not sound like an amazing feat, but you must keep in mind that up till this point, the best the universities and government could come up with was to send ten people into an area. They each carried a Geiger counter, GPS receiver, camera, marking stick, and a clipboard. They were literally writing down GPS coordinates and timestamps on pieces of paper before jotting down the Geiger reading! Terribly inefficient to say the least.

Pieter got hold of the prototype, added his own touches to it, and the bGeigi was born. The bGeigi (or *bento geigi*; literally "lunchbox Geiger counter") contains an off-the-shelf, professionally calibrated Geiger counter connected to a wireless Arduino board. The Arduino reads the counts, reads a GPS receiver, and logs all the data to a memory card. In addition, it transmits the Geiger reading to a remote receiver.

The concept works like this: The bGeigi is mounted to a car, bus, or bicycle. It is battery powered and takes readings continuously every 5 seconds for up to 12 hours. You simply drive around, taking readings everywhere you go! By now, the SafeCast team has over a *million* readings throughout northern Japan. One volunteer has vowed to get readings on every street in his town.

Even in the early days of the SafeCast project, the resultant data maps were very telling and quite interesting to see evolve. Now that they have more than a million data points, you start to see the radiation cloud effect. As more data comes in, the true fallout pattern becomes more apparent. It's like assembling a jigsaw puzzle, only without seeing the box cover. So you really don't know what you will have till it's done. Each new puzzle piece reveals surprising perspective.

The team has not limited themselves to only road data. They make regular stops at homes, office parks, train stations, and other high-traffic areas. In fact, once the first bGeigi was complete, their first order of business was to collect readings in and around every public school in the affected areas. Children were the first priority. Through these field studies they have learned some interesting lessons about how radiation settles in and around a home. Certain materials are more prone to retaining radioactive materials. Areas around drainpipes often contain the highest concentrations (don't let your pets play or drink in the puddles).

A very interesting experiment involved measuring a family's yard soil before and after an attempt at cleaning up. They shoveled and bagged the first few centemeters of half their yard, then took readings on both areas. The results were significant. The undisturbed soil had readings that were highly disturbing (do a search for SafeCast on YouTube for the shock of a lifetime). The simple act of bagging the top soil had an incredibly positive affect. Unfortunately, other parts of the *new* home were contaminated in ways that were much more difficult to clean up, and the family felt their best option was to move.

The SafeCast model is the best example of citizen data in action. Individuals came together, applied open source thinking and tools to a national problem, and arrived at a solution that far outperformed the hertofore existing solutions. Their open and public data was at first debated and downplayed by some members of the scientific community, only to be fully backed by Keiyo University (one of the top three universities in Japan).

This "unorganized," "scientifically questionable," non-corporate, all-volunteer organization is currently deploying the largest radiation network in Japan. Until recently, funding was entirely private donations. With the backing of Keiyo and a few corporations that shall remain nameless, this group of concerned citizens is now providing reliable and consistant data to the scientific community and the public.

Eventually the government adopted a similar solution of high data rate mobile automated logging. Imitation is the best form of flattery.

All of our current models and understanding of the environment are based on a limited data set. We make grand predictions based on isolated sensors taking readings once a day. Our models can only get more accurate as we exponentially increase the number of sensors out there collecting data. But it is absolutely critical that this data be open.

Perhaps more important is that we enable each individual to participate in the collection process. The Arduino is perfectly situated to make this happen. As it becomes more acceptable for normal everyday people to be mobile science stations, smart phones will fill the role of data collector.

The next step for the bGeigi? The smart phone iGeigi. Then the world!

CHAPTER 1

Saving the World...

...One Arduino at a Time!

Every scientist or engineer begins life as a hacker. In order to discover something new, one must often BUILD something new. Fortunately for the "non-scientists" among us, that paradigm puts us on even ground!

For instance, temperature was once only a relative term: "Eh… it's hotter than yesterday, isn't it?" Finally someone with a workshop, some raw material, a bit of time on his hands, and a great bit of creativity invented the thermometer. Suddenly humanity had the ability to quantify "hot" and "cold" in a universal manner that could be understood across continents. Even more fantastic was the ability to record and compare these facts, year after year. Eventually, with a large enough data set, humanity was able to make reasonably approximate *predictions*.

All this from one man's ingenuity: simple spheres of glass filled with various mixtures of oil and other liquids, suspended in a tall glass of water.

Fast-forward several hundred years. We now have the ability to measure so many phenomena that we can not only predict outcomes but also examine complex ecosystems, understand the cause and effects of changes within them, and have learned to reduce the negative effects—and sometimes eliminate them completely. More than any other technology, *sensors* (which provide the ability to quantify something) help scientists and everyday people save lives, save resources, and save the world.

It is with this premise that the book you now hold came about. By volunteering a small amount of their time and effort, normal people should be able to participate actively in scientific data gathering that benefits the greater good. If we can benefit ourselves along the way, even better!

The Arduino fits into the picture by positioning itself as the "bridge" between humans and sensors. Never has it been easier to learn about microcontrollers, understand sensor technology, and write code. The Arduino makes it all easy by providing a simple hardware and software platform that runs on any desktop or laptop computer. Furthermore, the programming language in which you write the code that is to run on the Arduino is an easy C-like language called Processing, which automates all of the difficult hardware tasks for you. Finally, a standard electronic interface based upon the "shield" concept makes working with complex hardware a simple matter of plugging in the optional boards. With some basic electronics knowledge, you can even build your own shields to serve customized purposes.

This book covers several sensor types. In addition, we will interface these sensors to the Arduino through a series of progressively complex methods. Initially, simple sensors will be connected directly to the Arduino inputs or via a breadboard. Once a circuit is verified, we will then build the interface circuits on prototyping shields or perf board.

With the primary circuitry complete, we will develop the project into its final form, adding support systems such as power supplies, switches, and jacks, as well as the all-important housing to protect the sensor system from environmental conditions.

It's All About Sensors

The main theme of this book is constructing Arduino projects that focus on sciences. In particular, this book has a very strong "green focus." What will make these projects possible are *sensors*, which are devices that respond electrically to a physical change. Often this response is a change in resistance. For example, a flex sensor will vary its resistance based on how much bend is applied to it. Essentially, the sensor converts one analog (physical) condition to another analog (electrical) condition, such as temperature to resistance or impact pressure to voltage.

By itself, a microprocessor (which lives in a digital world) cannot understand analog values. Resistance or voltage means nothing to a microprocessor. We need some way to convert these values into the ones and zeros of computer language.

At this point, I think we need to define how a microcontroller such as the one built into the Arduino board differs from a microprocessor. In fact, a microcontroller *is* a microprocessor. However, it has several key differences from the one lurking inside your laptop or desktop. A microcontroller has had several useful peripheral devices built inside the chip casing, along with the CPU.

A microcontroller has RAM, ROM, serial ports, and digital inputs and outputs. All these might be familiar to you already. After all, your personal computer has all the same devices. However, it is important to note that these peripherals are built *into* the chip instead of sitting on the side. Therefore, they are much more limited than their desktop PC counterparts. Where a traditional PC might have gigabytes of RAM, a microcontroller might have only a few kilobytes.

There is one peripheral device built into the microcontroller that we will focus on again and again throughout this book: the *analog to digital converter*, or *ADC* for short. As its name implies, the ADC connects the analog world to the digital world, converting the signals into something the CPU can understand and work with. Before moving on, let's take a moment to look at the ADC more closely.

Arduino's Analog to Digital Converter (ADC)

We will be using the analog to digital converter (ADC) extensively throughout the book. The Arduino has an ADC tied to six inputs (labeled Analog0–Analog5). A few of the projects might utilize all six inputs. We might even wish for more! It is the job of the ADC to sample a voltage at the specified input pin, transcribe that voltage to a byte value, and finally deposit that value into a variable you specify in ram.

Essentially, the ADC does nothing more than makes a comparison. It compares the voltage presented at the analog input to another voltage presented at a reference input.

■ **Note** The analog reference is considered the highest expected voltage that a signal will present to the analog input. The input will not be damaged by any voltage that is 5 volts or less, but anything above the reference voltage will be reported as the maximum value.

You have a few options regarding the analog reference voltage. For instance, you could choose to utilize the Arduino's primary voltage supply as the reference. This is an easy solution, and is the default. It will be either 5 volts or 3.3 volts, depending on your board. It does have a drawback, though. It is not so stable. When running on batteries, for example, the supply voltage (and thus the analog reference voltage) will drop over time. Also you might experience dips and sags if your project switches high-current devices such as relays or servos.

Another option is to utilize an internal reference voltage. You have a few options as to what that voltage might be, depending on the Arduino CPU you own. This reference voltage is dependent on internal conditions of the Atmel CPU and is thus very stable. It will be either 1.1 volts or 2.56 volts.

Finally, you might provide your own voltage directly. This voltage can be anywhere from 0 to 5 volts. It should never exceed 5 volts, and it is recommended that you take extra precautions when using the Aref pin directly.

Conversion Process

Imagine for a moment that the voltage presented at the input is placed on a bar graph. This bar graph has 1024 increments, and the 1024th increment represents the maximum input voltage. Because computers count starting with zero, the 1024th value is actually read as 1023.

Assuming that the operating voltage of the Arduino board is 5 volts, and that we are using the default analog reference, the byte value 1023 (starting from zero) must represent 5 volts (actually 4.995 volts). It is fairly easy to see that 2.5 volts would be represented by the byte code 512, but what about the others?

■ **Tip**   If we were to take the maximum input voltage of 5 volts and divide it by 1024, we would find that each increment of the byte code represents about 4.8828 millivolts. So, if we want our software to determine the voltage of the analog input, all we need to do is multiply the byte code by 4.8828 millivolts.

Notice that because the ADC can count only in 4.8828-millivolt increments, it must round up or down to the nearest increment. For example, 2.750 volts is between byte values 563 and 564. Byte value 563 represents a voltage of 2.747, while 564 represents 2.752 volts.

Changing the Voltage Reference

We can increase the resolution by utilizing either an internal reference voltage or by providing our own lower voltage reference on the Aref pin.

In Table 1-1, each Arduino model has slightly different options for analog reference voltages. All Arduinos have, by default, the system voltage as the reference, which is 5 volts in most models. Some models have lower operating voltages, such as the Lilipad. Be sure to check the operational voltage of the board before calculating the ADC increment size.

As for internal reference voltages, 1.1 volts is somewhat hard to use with most of the sensors described in this book. Many won't operate at all in that voltage region. This reference voltage is useful in special circumstances, but beyond the scope of this book.

The 2.56 volt reference is quite practical, but it is only available on the Arduino Mega, and possibly the rare ATMEGA8-based devices.

For these reasons, we use the default reference as much as possible throughout the book. However, it can be useful to provide your own lower reference voltage. If you were to lower the reference voltage to the ADC, you would have to modify the sensor circuit and software so the data scales properly. To determine the voltage increment of your own analog reference voltage, simply divide it by 1024. Also, be sure to provide an absolutely stable reference voltage. The best way to do this is to build a dedicated voltage regulator for the analog section. This is relatively straightforward with standard LM78xx linear regulators.

More information about the analog reference can be found here: http://www.arduino.cc/en/Reference/AnalogReference

Table 1-1. Comparison of Various Analog Reference Options for Arduino Boards

Mode	Board	Voltage	Increment Voltage
DEFAULT	ALL	Depending on board 5 Volts or 3.3 Volts	5 Volts = 4.88 mV 3.3 Volts = 3.22 mV
INTERNAL	ATmega8, 168, 328–based boards	ATmega168, 328 = 1.1V ATmega8 = 2.56V	1.1 Volts = 1.07 mV 2.56 Volts = 2.50 mV
INTERNAL1V1	Arduino Mega only	1.1 Volts	1.07 mV
INTERNAL2V56	Arduino Mega only	2.56 Volts	2.50 mV
EXTERNAL	ALL	0 to 5 Volts	Aref / 1024

Voltage Dividers

The ADC can only measure a voltage; it cannot measure resistance or current (at least, not directly). Many sensors will output a voltage directly, but not all. Some sensors are purely resistive. For example, a light dependent resistor (LDR) changes its resistance due to light striking its surface. In such a case, we will need to convert this resistance to a voltage before we can send it to the ADC. It's really quite easy, using a simple circuit called a voltage divider (see Figure 1-1).

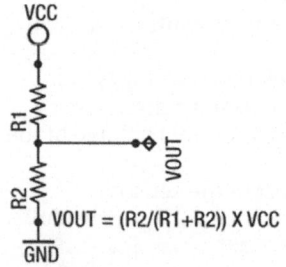

Figure 1-1. The voltage divider circuit

Look at Figure 1-1 and imagine that a 5-volt source (the same as the Arduino ADC reference voltage, or CPU power supply) enters from the top. As the voltage passes through the first resistor, some of it is "used up." As the voltage continues into the next resistor, by the time it reaches the end of the line (returns to the power source), it will equal zero. Thus, the second resistor *must* use up whatever voltage remains after the current passes through the first resistor.

Perhaps now it is becoming clear that the voltage at the middle, where both resistors meet, is the result of the ratio between the two resistors. If the two resistors are precisely equal, it hopefully is intuitive to imagine that the voltage output will be precisely half of the input. Likewise, if the top resistor is very small compared with the bottom resistor, very little will be consumed by it. So we could expect that the voltage at the center will still be quite large. If, however, the top resistance is quite large, while the bottom resistance is small, we can expect that the voltage at the middle will be closer to zero.

Let's try it out with a quick example. Assume that R1 = 10 ohms, and R2 = 90 ohms. Also assume that VCC = 5 volts. Plugging those values into the equation should yield 4.5 volts at VOUT.

Unfortunately, we are not done. We now need to consider the current passed and power dissipated by those two resistors. The two resistors are in a series, so the total resistance is 100 ohms. Using Ohm's Law (V=IR, or in this case, current = voltage/resistance), we see that they pass 50 milliamps (mA). Although this might not seem like much, power dissipated = current X voltage. Multiplying 50 mA with 5 volts means we must dissipate 250milliwatts. Most through hole resistors will run quite hot. They are rated at either 250mW (which would blow instantly) or 500mW (which would run quite hot at half its maximum power rating).

Let's try again. This time, choose significantly higher values. For example, let's try 10k and 90k. Running the numbers again, we get 100k total resistance, 50 microamps, and 250 microwatts. *Much better.*

The ideal variable voltage divider is the *variable resistor* (also known as a *potentiometer*, or just *pot*, but you might best recognize it as a volume knob on your stereo). The pot can sweep from maximum resistance all the way down to zero resistance. This means that we can drive the voltage all the way down to zero and all the way up to 5 volts.

Unfortunately, most sensors are not simple. Typically, the sensor would occupy the place of one resistor in the voltage divider, and we must select the appropriate resistor for the other position.

Deciding in which position to place the sensor as well as selecting the companion resistor can be a bit of a mental challenge. It is partially dependent on the minimum and maximum range of the sensor as well as personal preference.

Imagine that the photo sensor is in the top position. It could drop its resistance to zero, and thus the center point might go as high as 5 volts. However, even at maximum resistance, the bottom resistor would still prevent the center point from driving all the way down to zero volts. If the resistor positions were reversed, the inverse would apply.

Imagine a sensor with a minimum resistance of zero, and a maximum resistance of 500 ohms. Place the sensor in the top position, with the fixed resistor in the bottom position. Now, when the sensor is at its minimum of zero, the voltage to the ADC would be 5 volts. As the sensor resistance rises, the voltage to the ADC will decrease. However, because the sensor maximum resistance matches the fixed resistor, the voltage to the ADC will never go below 2.5 volts

We need to keep this small issue in mind when we set up our sensors. We must ask ourselves how we wish the sensors to react (should the sensor be on top, or bottom?), and what is the practical output voltage range from our circuit (should the fixed resistor be larger, smaller, or equal to the maximum resistance of the sensor?). We need to have at least a basic understanding of what to expect before we attempt to interpret the data given to us by the ADC.

A Strategy for Prototyping Sensor Systems

When we build up a sensor system (or any Arduino project, for that matter), it is important to have a clear plan of action. A consistent framework for initially exploring and ultimately verifying our sensor code before integrating it into a larger project is essential.

I have broken the process down into five key stages:

1. You must research and understand the sensor's operation.

2. You will need to determine the appropriate equations to convert the sensor's output to valid data.

3. You should write a simple Arduino program, called a *sketch*, to operate the sensor and verify that your equation works properly.

4. After that, you will want to verify that the data is correct and possibly calibrate your sensors to known calibration sources.

5. Finally you can integrate the sensor code into your primary project.

When building remote battery-operated sensors, you will also want to consider what methods you can employ to reduce power consumption.

Understand the Sensor

Our first task is to get a good idea about how the sensor works (or at least, how we are to interface with it). The best resource is to study the data sheet provided by the manufacturer carefully. Certainly, there is a lot of confusing material in any data sheet, but thankfully most of it is not necessary to get the basic system up and running. We want to pay particular attention to any reference schematics, written descriptions of theory of operation, and equations that describe the relationship between sensor resistance or voltage and the phenomenon we are attempting to measure.

Theory of operation is particularly important. While many sensors are quite simple (needing only to read the voltage output), some sensors require a series of steps to be taken before we can read the sensor. Gas sensors for instance require that a heater be turned on for a specified period of time, and then turned off. Then, after an interval, we must turn on the sensing element and wait another period of time. Finally, we can read the sensor value.

Figure Out the Equations

After understanding the basic operation of the sensor, we must check the data sheet for any equations we need to perform in order to get the data we need. If we are lucky, the data sheet will spell it out in black and white, with a statement like the following:

$$Vout = some\ equation$$

We will need to rearrange the equation so that the result can be deposited into a variable in the unit of measure we want:

$$Unit\ of\ measure = rearranged\ equation\ including\ Vout$$

Unfortunately, many data sheets lack the required equation (perhaps the manufacturers assume it must be obvious, when in fact is far from it). In such a case, we have no choice but to study the sheet carefully and attempt to decipher what we should do. I often find it helps to do a web search for more information or sample projects in such a case. Another option is to contact the manufacturer directly for assistance via e-mail.

Also, referring to the section concerning the ADC, we need to actually replace any instance in the equation of Vout with an equation that relates the ADC count to a voltage. Certainly, such an equation could get quite confusing rather quickly. Thankfully, many sensors are designed to operate on a simple linear scale, which simplifies the initial equation for us. Generally, we will end up with something like this:

$$\text{Unit of Measure} = ((\text{ADCcount} \times 4.8828 \text{ milli-volts}) - \text{Yoffset}) / \text{coefficient}$$

Write a Sample Serial Sketch

Once I have a good idea about how the sensor works and I sit down and wrestle with the math (I *hate* math!), I find that the best first step in building the application is to write a very simple sketch to output information to the serial monitor.

From the Arduino integrated development environment (IDE), go to File ➤ Examples ➤ Basic and load the `AnalogReadSerial` sketch. Now save it with a new name. I usually use the name of the sensor device, such as **LM35-test**.

We can now modify the sketch to read the sensor on Analog pin 0 and output data to the serial monitor. Right away you might want to adjust the default sketch just a bit. In fact, I have modified my own sketch and saved it back to the original example, so my modified version loads every time.

I adjusted the serial port speed down to 9600. Your version can be set at the maximum transmission speed (115200). This is what I would call massive overkill. Really, you have no need to be transmitting most data at such a speed. I have found that the higher data rates are not always reliable, especially when you move your hardware around to various computers. When troubleshooting the reason why you are getting garbled messages on the screen, it is always better to start slowly and ramp it up until you hit the limitations of your equipment.

The other item I changed was to add a delay to the end of the loop. Normally, I don't suggest using the `delay()` function, but in this case all we ever want to do is read one sensor and report it. Because it is only a test, and we have no critical tasks to take care of, using a delay is certainly acceptable here. The reason I highly recommend a delay is because without one, the Arduino will read and spit out data from the ADC as fast as possible. The text will literally be flying by, and the serial monitor buffer will quickly fill up, causing slower computers to lock up. Set the delay to at minimum 500 milliseconds. My personal choice is 1-second intervals.

Now it's time to start testing out your sensor. You might want to take it slow at first (let's avoid the black smoke). If the sensor does not require any particular sequence of events to take place in order to complete a successful read, I will simply leave the sketch as is. After hooking up the sensor, I like to just check that I am getting raw ADC values, and that they fluctuate in an expected manner, based on the sensor type. So, assuming that I am using a new temperature sensor for the first time, I will look at the raw ADC values and make sure that as I warm the sensor, the numbers go up, and as I chill the sensor, the numbers go down. This will satisfy the need to verify the sensor is in working order and that I know roughly how to use it. From here, you can rapidly build up a complete sensor application. Just take the ADC data and pass it through a function to perform the required calculation and print it to the serial port.

Put the Sensor Through its Paces

Now that the code is done, you really need to verify that it is in fact working properly and reporting *accurately*. It might be a bit difficult to compare your sensor directly with a commercial product. After all, that *is* the reason we built our own in the first place: commercial products can be either too expensive or not suitable to our requirements. But it is important to at least know you are close.

The solution is easy if you are lucky enough to have an instrumentation retail shop that is able to rent out calibrated sensors. Simply compare the two sensors and make adjustments to your software until they both agree. It's not enough to compare them at only one data point. You should attempt to simulate a typical environment for the sensor, as well as both extremes. In the temperature sensor example, you should compare ambient room temperature in your refrigerator (which is usually very stable), and near some heat source. Only after you become quite familiar with the sensor's variations over the entire range can you be confident in your ability to interpret the data it reports.

If you have no calibration source for your sensor, you might want to contact the vendor for some ideas or scour the Internet. Sometimes solutions come in unusual forms or from your own ingenuity. For example, while attempting to calibrate a gas sensor, you might have to build your own vacuum jar so you can directly control the calibration environment.

Integrate the Code into the Project by Building Sensor Functions

Once you are satisfied that your code is working well and reporting reasonably accurate data, you should modify your code to make it more modular. The goal is to make it as reusable as possible. If the sensor requires a series of steps to be performed, contain the sensor read process in one function that returns raw ADC data.

The calculations required to convert the ADC data into units of measure should be contained in a second function. If there are several devices in the family that require different values for parts of the equation, these should be included as variables passed into the function. This makes the function universal to the whole family of devices and allows you to easily change devices simply by passing a new constant into the function.

You could take it a step further by learning a bit about writing libraries. Building a series of devices into a library will make it very simple to use any number of them in any project, simply by importing the library and calling the functions.

Consider Power Saving Whenever Possible

If the sensor has the ability to be turned off or disconnected in any way, you should consider using the feature whenever possible. For devices powered by a wall outlet or the USB port, it really does not matter. However, when building field devices, which need to operate on batteries or solar panels for long periods of time, any bit of power you can save will help.

Many devices without a power saving feature can still be shut down to conserve power. Simply assign one digital output of the Arduino to act as a power switch to all your external hardware. Route the power for these devices through a transistor, with the gate tied to the digital output pin. When you are ready to take a measurement, all you need to do is set the output to high to turn on all your sensors. Such a design will incur some warmup delay, which varies from sensor to sensor, so you need to take that into account when writing your code.

Supplies and Tools Needed

Before we really get going, I think we should talk a bit about the prototyping tools you will need to get started. Obviously, you will need at least one Arduino. You have a lot of options, but some are better for sensor networks than others.

When choosing an Arduino (or team of Arduini?) you should ask the following questions:

- Will my project be operating on batteries?

- Will my project need to communicate over a distance?

- How many analog inputs will I need?

- What are the environmental conditions my project will operate in?

- Will my project be connected to a PC or network?

- Will I need to store large amounts of data?

Some projects will require special attention to some or all of these questions. In such cases, I will do my best to provide advice in choosing the best Arduino for the project. In other cases, the choice of Arduino will not matter much, and you can use any device you like.

In addition to parts required for individual projects, your shopping list should include these:

- Several Arduino prototyping shields

- Jumper wire kit

- Wires with pins on one end and sockets on the other

- Small breadboard (several might be nice)

- 6-pin header sockets, with *long* pins

- 8-pin header sockets, with *long* pins

Finally, you will need the following additional tools and supplies:

- Soldering iron, solder, and stand

- Diagonal cutters (nippers)

- Needle nose pliers

- Electric drill and drill bits

- Screwdriver set

- Adjustable wrench

- Set of jewelers' files

- Electrical tape

- Heat shrink tubing of various sizes

- Silicone glue or hot melt glue gun
- Razor knife

Building the BreadboardShield

One tool I have found to be invaluable in preparing the projects in this book is what I call the BreadboardShield. You can make one yourself using a standard Arduino prototyping shield kit, a set of replacement shield sockets with long pins, and a mini breadboard, as shown in Figure 1-2.

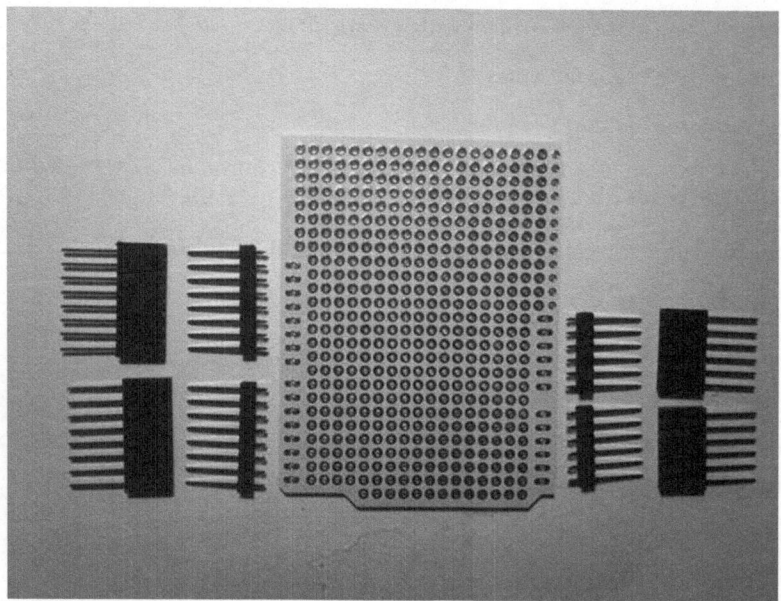

Figure 1-2. A typical prototyping shield with original pin headers. Replace them with sockets.

Arduino prototyping shields usually come with header pins that don't include the female sockets on top. This means you can't stack another shield on top of the prototyping shield. I usually replace the header pins with my own set of sockets with long pins so I can stack additional shields on top.

You should buy at least one set (2 each) of 6- and 8-pin sockets. Having several sets will come in handy. It is always better to have them in stock rather than putting your project on hold while you go shopping.

Start by laying the shield over an Arduino and inserting the socket pins through the shield and into the Arduino sockets. This will confirm orientation of all the pins, and that you have the board right side up instead of upside down. Trust me; nothing is more frustrating than trying to pull the sockets off after you soldered them into the board bottom up!

Next, pull the shield off the Arduino and carefully turn it over onto the table, keeping the sockets in place, as shown in Figure 1-3. You should now be able to solder the pins easily. I suggest that you only solder one pin for each socket at first. You can then test fit and adjust sockets in your Arduino. If everything fits fine, solder the rest of the pins in place. If not, heat the solder joint of any socket not in alignment and make adjustments till it fits properly.

Figure 1-3. *Preparing to solder the sockets*

The next step is to locate your mini breadboard and remove one of the power strips, as shown in Figure 1-4. Usually these boards are held together with a wide piece of double-sided tape on the bottom. You will need to cut this tape with a razor knife.

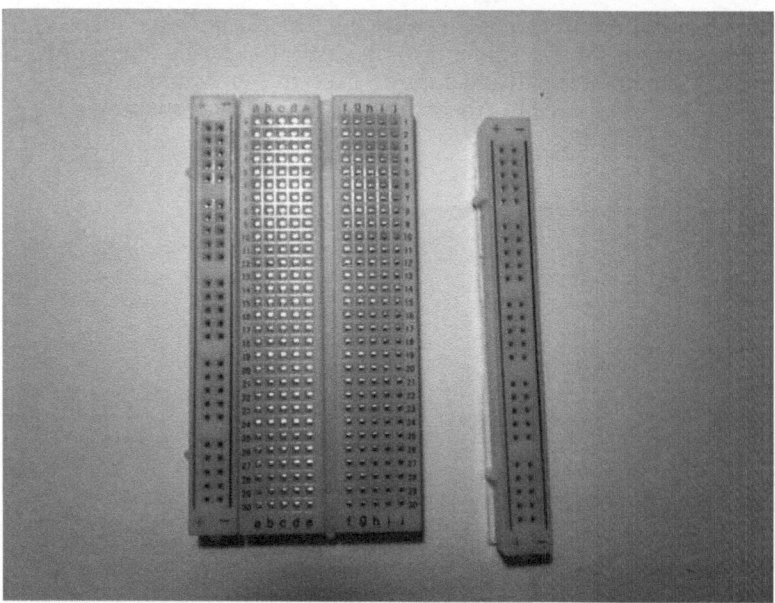

Figure 1-4. Cutting one power strip away from the mini breadboard

Once the mini breadboard has been separated, test fit the piece between the sockets of the prototyping shield. Notice that the side of the breadboard might have some plastic nubs to align the board into the board next to it. You might need to cut these nubs off with a pair of nippers.

If all fits well, peel the backing off the double-sided tape and stick the breadboard down onto the shield. Be sure to check the alignment of the breadboard as you do so, such that the end over the power connector and USB port of the Arduino does not hang out too much. It will make it more difficult to plug and unplug the Arduino. You also want to be sure that the VCC and GND pins on the Arduino are next to holes on the power strip of the breadboard, rather than at an angle to them. The completed BreadboardShield is shown in Figure 1-5.

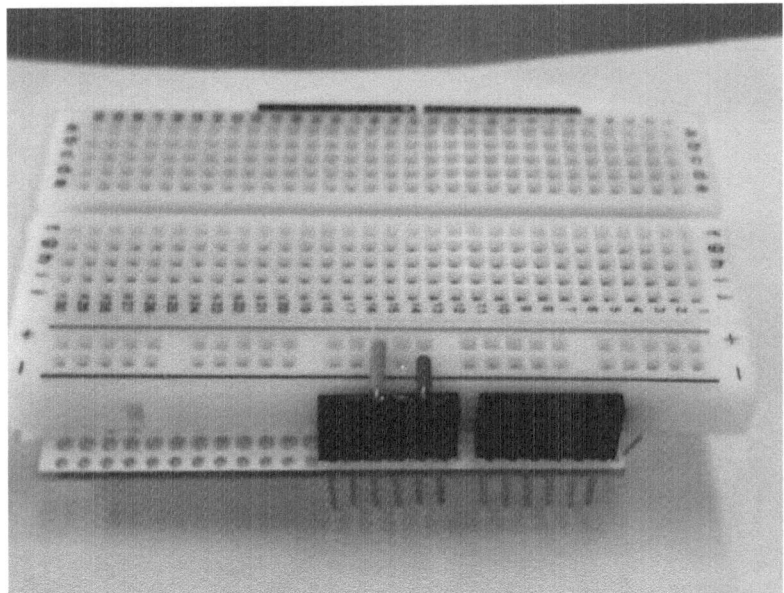

Figure 1-5. Completed BreadboardShield with power jumpers installed

I use this shield pretty much constantly to prototype Arduino projects. Only after the hardware is fully tested do I go ahead and solder the parts down to a prototyping shield. This way, I have a lot of freedom to move things around, try different parts, or completely reconfigure the circuit.

Summary

The Breadboard Shield is your new best friend! Once you become comfortable using it, you will start virtually every Arduino project (and not just the ones in this book) with this shield. If you find a box large enough to hold an Arduino with the shield attached, and some extra headroom for wires and components mounted in on the breadboard, you can assemble a very nice travel kit for experimenting on the go.

After verifying your project on the breadboard, you can finalize the design and build it directly onto another prototyping shield, or have a printed circuit board made.

Now that we have assembled our parts, supplies, and tools, we can start building our own environmental lab equipment.

Let's start saving the world!

CHAPTER 2

Spider Temps

A Temperature Measurement Tool with Six Legs

In environmental projects, we often want to measure the temperature of something. Actually, we often want to measure the temperature of many somethings!

Let me give you an example. My apartment has a loft, and thus the living room space has a very high ceiling. We all know that hot air rises. In the winter, the loft sleeping space is quite warm and comfortable, but the living room and kitchen are ice cold. To make matters worse, I have a double wide sliding glass door to the patio, with single-pane windows (I loathe Japan's building codes).

I would really like to be able to compare several temperatures at once, so that I can get a really good idea of the "heat bubble," as well as heat losses throughout the apartment. Then, I can use this information as a baseline, while I try out different ideas to more efficiently manage the airflow and heating in my apartment, and thus more efficiently manage my costs. Hey, I love saving a few bucks by reducing my utility bills. It is a tiny impact on the environment, but if we can all analyze our living spaces and learn to decrease our utilities, it will add up.

This is just one simple example of how you can use simultaneous temperature data. Another possibility might be measuring river temperature upstream and downstream of a sewage runoff. Fish and other aquatic wildlife are very susceptible to temperature variations. Knowing the temperature at several data points in and around the runoff could help officials better understand the effects.

The following project starts off relatively simply. It is always easier, when working with new hardware, to build up in stages. After getting one temperature sensor up and running, it becomes quite simple to get five more working. At this point, you will have a pretty useful tool that will help you to measure six temperatures at one time. In fact, it does not necessarily need to be temperature. With some simple modifications, you can measure six of any sensors you have in your arsenal. Temperature is certainly the most obvious sensor choice, but not your only option.

We then add a display to make it more portable and easier to handle (it's hard holding a laptop in one palm and controlling a large array of sensors with the other).

Finally, we will box up the device in a field-ready form.

The Hardware

There are many ways to measure temperature, but I like to keep things simple. For most environmental measurements (ambient air temperature, weather data, and the like) I prefer silicon temperature sensor ICs. They have a lot of advantages over thermistors and thermocouples. For one thing, silicon sensors are incredibly easy to interface. In most cases, you simply need three wires. One wire provides power, one for ground, and one provides the signal input to the Arduino analog pin. Also, these sensors are usually manufactured to be as linear as possible around the specified temperature range. This means that calibration is incredibly simple, and the mathematics required to determine the temperature is basic algebra. Easy for us! Easy for the Arduino!

In addition, silicon sensors are quite cheap. Of the two options presented here, one is about a dollar each, while the other is as low as 3 sensors for a dollar!

We will be using either the LM35 sensor, made by National Instruments, or the MCP9700 sensor, made by Microchip. See Table 2-1 to help you decide the sensor (or combination of sensors) you think will best suit your needs. The "Determining Temperature Equations" section explains the coefficient and offset in more detail later.

Table 2-1. *Comparison of Two Temperature Measurment ICs*

Manufacturer	Part Number	Range (Degrees C)	Accuracy	Coefficient (mV/C)	Offset (mV @ 0C)
National Semiconductor	LM35D	+2 to +150	+/- 0.2 @ 25C	10	0
Microchip	MCP9700	-40 to +125	+/- 2 @ 70C	10	500

It should be noted that the LM35 series has several ICs in the family, designated with a letter. Each part has different operating ranges and zero degree offsets. If you are using something other than an LM35D, you should study the data sheet carefully.

The most obvious points to consider when choosing the best temperature sensor for your application are temperature range and accuracy. Notice that although the MCP9700 has a much lower operating temperature (which might be important for winter weather monitoring), it is less accurate than the LM35D. With an accuracy of plus or minus 2 degrees, there is a potential error in reading by as much as 4 degrees Celsius. Microchip provides an appnote to help you increase the accuracy to as little as plus or minus .02 degrees, but it is an advanced project and beyond the scope of this book.

The zero degree offset is not a set-in-stone figure. We know that the slope (coefficient) is 10 millivolts per degree Celsius. Thus, it is reasonable to assume that in the case of the MCP9700, which has a minimum temperature of -40 degrees, it would measure zero degrees at or around 400 millivolts. In other words, it must move from -40 to 0, in 10-millivolt increments per degree (40 x 10 = 400). However, the table shows that the offset is 500 millivolts. There is a 10 degree difference. When the analog to digital converter (ADC) is reading very close to zero degrees, it might have trouble reading accurately. The sensor has been "pushed" up the scale by 10 degrees such that at its extremes, it is still within the accurate "window" of most analog converters.

Parts List

Here is the parts list for this project:

- Any Arduino

- Breadboard or prototyping shield

- 6 x LM35D or MCP9700 Temperature sensors (or a combination of both)

- At least 6 meters of 3-conductor cable (cut into 6 equal lengths)

- Small diameter heat shrink tubing (should fit over wires within the cable)
- Miscellaneous build materials depending on your own plans (see text)

Optional

The following items are optional for this project:

- Single row header pins
- 2 x 20 LCD
- Project box
- 5 volt Boost regulator, such as from SparkFun or AdaFruit
- AA x 4 battery case

Building It

Figure 2-1 shows the details of the temperature probe.

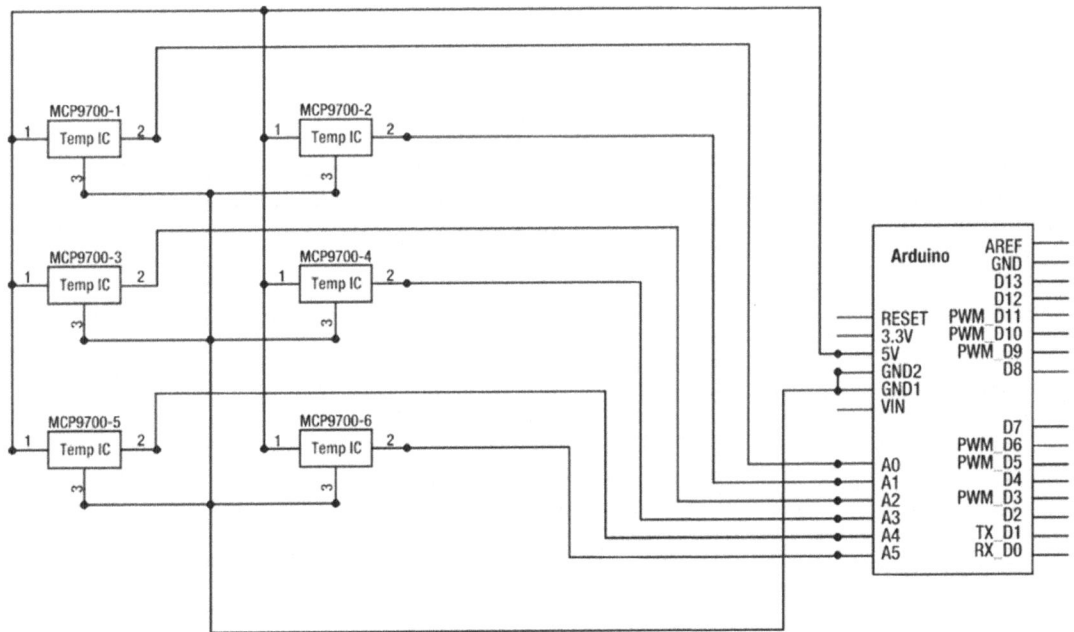

Figure 2-1. SpiderTemps six–sensor temperature probe

If this is your first time looking at a schematic, trust me, it is less complex than it at first appears. What looks like wires going all over the place in the schematic actually translates to a simple set of connections in real life. The breadboard helps us tremendously by providing a set of *busses* that allow several wires to be plugged into a row, and thus all be connected together.

Notice in the schematic that pin 1 of every sensor is connected to the 5-volt pin. Also, pin 3 of every sensor is connected to Ground. Finally, pin 2 of each sensor goes to a different analog input.

The sensor looks like any standard small transistor. By referring to the data sheets, you will find that the pin functions are the same with both sensors. Hold the sensor with the pins down and the flat face toward you, and consult Figure 2-2. The left pin needs 5 volts input. The right pin should be connected to Ground. The center pin is the output and connects directly to an Arduino analog input.

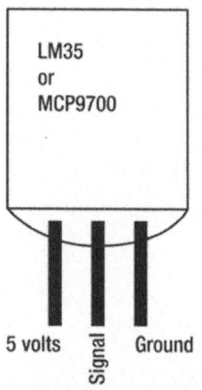

Figure 2-2. Temperature IC pin names

The build for this project is quite simple in principle. We want to solder several meters of 3-conductor cable to each of 6 temperature sensors. When cutting the cables, be sure to match the lengths of all six as closely as possible. We want to maintain consistency from sensor to sensor. Going the extra mile now will save us a lot of trouble later in the field.

Also, be sure to take note of which conductors are soldered to which pins on the temperature sensor IC. It might help to tape small "flags" onto each wire, opposite the sensor, on which you have marked the pin name.

There are two things to consider about your cabling (and thus how you attach the sensors to any objects). First, try to keep all the sensor leads about the same length. It is not so critical for short lengths, but as the cables become quite long, cable resistance might become a factor. Two sensors measuring at the same location, but with drastically different cable lengths, can actually report different values.

The other issue to consider is shielding. It would be ideal to use shielded cable, but 3-conductor shielded cable is not exactly easy to find. It is not critical, but I have found that with cables over a few meters, noise on the sensor line caused by nearby electrical devices and power lines can interfere with the measurement. When unshielded lines are coiled up, the measurement is very stable, but when stretched out, it could end up reading plus or minus one or two degrees Celsius.

You have several options when planning how to build the sensor cables. If you have raw wire or you have salvaged wire from category 5 network cable (as I have done), you could do the following:

- Solder directly to the sensor and apply heat shrink tubing (see Figure 2-3).

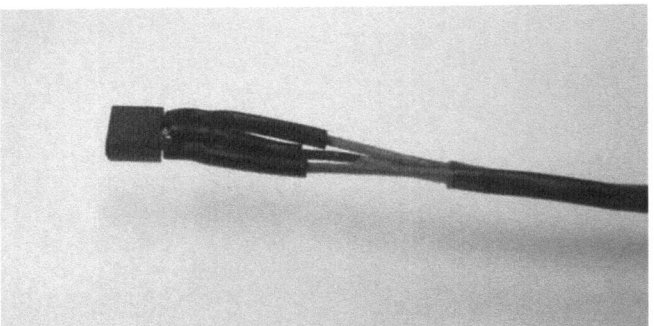

Figure 2-3. A temperature IC soldered to a 3-conductor cable with heat shrink applied

- Take a more practical route of soldering a 3-pin female header on the sensor end, so that you can easily swap sensors attached to the cable, as shown in Figure 2-4. Be sure to use heat shrink tubing to insulate and protect the solder joints (not shown in Figure 2-4).

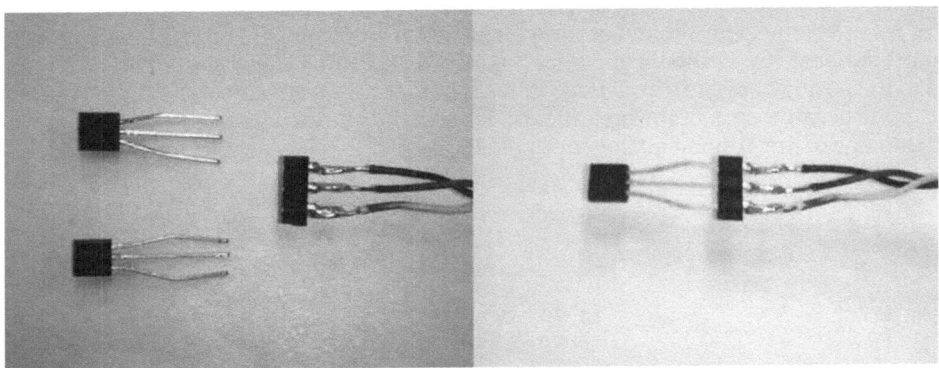

Figure 2-4. A 3-conductor cable soldered to a three pin female header. Thus, we can easily try out an assortment of sensors on this one cable.

If you intend to submerge your sensors, you should invest in cable with a round outer jacket. Also, ask around for water–resistant shrink tubing. It has a special material on the inside, which melts and flows around the connection as the tube shrinks, creating a watertight barrier. Finally, add a larger diameter shrink tube of the same water-resistant type over the entire cable to sensor connection, covering half of the sensor body.

Never submerge the sensor in corrosives such as acids, rubbing alcohols, oils or (God forbid) radioactives. The casing is plastic and will not withstand that sort of treatment.

You will also need to consider how you want to attach the cable to the Arduino. I offer two suggestions. The first is demonstrated in Figure 2-5. Cut two sections of standard header pins (0.1 spacing). One section is two pins wide, while the other is a single pin. The single pin should be soldered to the signal wire of the sensor, while the two-pin section is soldered to the positive and ground wires of the sensor.

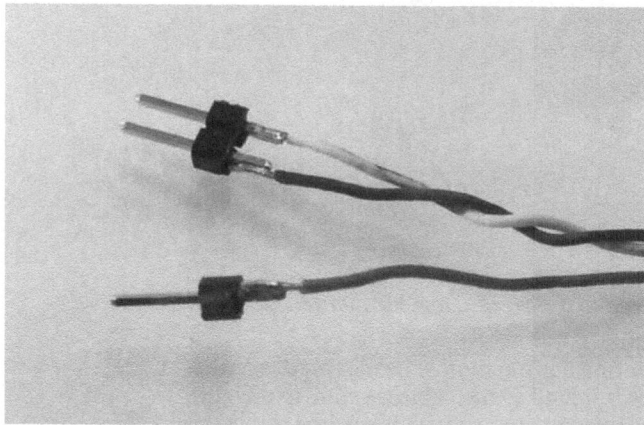

Figure 2-5. The Arduino end of the cable is soldered to male header pins. They can be inserted easily into the breadboard shield.

Next, we will connect power and ground for each sensor by plugging those header pins into the breadboard power strips, as shown in Figure 2-6. We will also attach a wire from the 5-volt pin on the Arduino to the positive power strip. Then connect another wire from any of the three ground pins on the Arduino to the negative strip of the breadboard. Finally, the output wire from each sensor will be plugged into one of the Arduino analog input pins.

Figure 2-6. *The cable is inserted in the breadboard shield, which has been stacked onto a FreakDuino board. Note the power connections from the shield socket to the breadboard.*

This is where building the breadboard shield really pays off. By attaching a 2-pin header to the power wires, and a single-pin header to the sensor output wire, it becomes a snap to connect to the breadboard. Simply plug the power header into the power rows and the single pin header into the analog input.

Another method is demonstrated later in the chapter. It is more appropriate for a semipermanent instrument design, built into a case. Look ahead to Figures 2-11 to 2-13 if you are curious.

Mechanical Build

There are a number of ways in which you could use the basic setup. You could configure the sensors to collect data as individual point sources, a linear group, or a two-dimensional group.

For example, let's assume you want to measure the gradient in temperature from floor to ceiling of a vaulted room. In this case, you might attach each sensor at three-foot intervals along a long pole, and stand the pole upright in the center of the room. You now have a vertical temperature gradient meter, as shown in Figure 2-6.

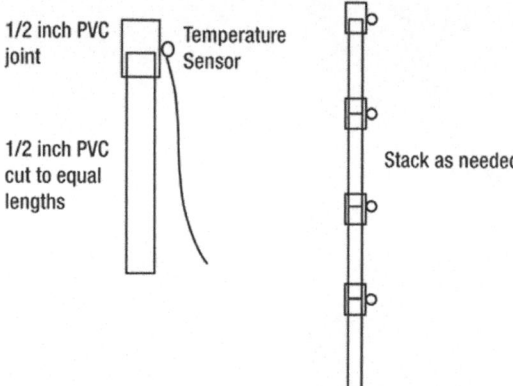

An expandable linear temperature probe kit

Figure 2-7. An example of an expandable boom made from PVC pipe fittings and loaded with temperature sensors in equal intervals

Another build option might be to use PVC pipe fittings to build a large grid so that you can measure a large flat surface (such as a wall or large window) or to study how warm air from a single point source mixes with a larger volume of cold air in a confined space.

You might even choose to not build the sensors onto a frame at all, so that you can place the temperature sensors in various locations, such as one outside the window, another directly on the inside surface of the window, a third sensor on the opposite side of the room, with a fourth sensor directly in front of your heater or air conditioner.

Determining Temperature Equations

Remember algebra class? If so, you might hit upon the linear equation in Figure 2-8, where m is the slope of a line, and b is the point at which the line crosses the Y-axis.

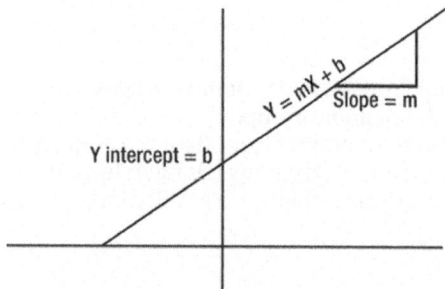

Figure 2-8. Trying to remember high-school algebra

In temperature sensor terms, the slope is referred to as the *temperature coefficient*, and the Y intercept (+- b) is the *zero degree offset*. The zero degree offset simply states that "at zero degrees, the sensor will output Y millivolts." Thus, voltage output by the sensor would be related on the vertical axis (Y), while temperature is related on the horizontal (X) axis. In the case of the MCP9700 sensor, with an offset of 500 millivolts, our equation would be:

```
Y = 10X + 500
```

Now let's solve the equation for X, so that we can find the temperature, when we know the voltage (Y):

```
X = (Y - b) / m
```

Or

```
X = (Y - 500) / 10
```

After looking at several types of semiconductor temperature sensor, I arrived at the following general equation to be used in code:

```
Temp = ((val * ADCmV) - TempOffset) / TempCoef
```

At first glance, this does not look anything like the linear equation above. Trust me, it is. Remember that in order to know Y, we must multiply the value given by the ADC (`val`) by a constant (`ADCmV`), which represents the voltage portion that each increment of the ADC value represents.

The Arduino analog input will divide a voltage presented at the analog input into 1024 pieces. If our input voltage range is 0 to 5 volts, each piece represents 5 volts/1024 pieces, or about 4.8828 millivolts per piece. Keep this number in mind because you will use it nearly every time you utilize the analog input.

By multiplying the ADC byte code (`val`) by the `ADCmV` value (4.8828), we arrive at the measured voltage at the analog input. We next need to subtract from this voltage the zero degree offset. Finally, we divide by the slope to arrive at the temperature in degrees Celsius. This equation will work with nearly all linear temperature sensors (and perhaps many other types of linear sensors as well).

Test Code

When you work with a new sensor, your first sketch should be to run some basic validation on your equations. With that in mind, open the `Examples/Basics/AnalogReadSerial.pde` sketch and save it back as a new project; it will look like Listing 2-1. Name it **MCP9700-test**, **LM35-test**, or something similar.

Listing 2-1. AnalogReadSerial.pde Sketch

```
void setup() {
  Serial.begin(9600);
}

void loop() {
  int sensorValue = analogRead(A0);
  Serial.println(sensorValue, DEC);
}
```

Go ahead and upload it to the Arduino. Connect the first temperature sensor to analog 0 and run the serial monitor. Verify that you are getting the ADC data in the window, and that the value remains steady. Now warm the sensor by pinching it between your fingers. The ADC value should increase. If possible, put the sensor into a freezer and verify that the ADC values drop. This test simply outputs the raw ADC data to the serial monitor, but provides us with a very quick opportunity to verify that we have connected the sensor properly, and that it functions as expected.

Now that the basic hardware validation is complete, let's move on to the exciting part: converting the ADC value to real data (temperature) and printing it to the window. Add the following variables to the top of the code (note that the temperature offset will need to change, according to Table 2-1; I have highlighted it in bold):

```
int TSensor = 0;        // temperature sensor ADC input pin
int val = 0;            // variable to store ADC value read
int TempOffset = 500;   // value in mV when ambient is 0 degrees C
int TempCoef = 10;      // Temperature coefficient mV per Degree C
float ADCmV = 4.8828;   // mV per ADC increment (5 volts / 1024 increments)
float Temp = 0;         // calculated temperature in C (accuraccy to two decimal places)
```

Finally, modify the loop function:

```
void loop()
{
  val = analogRead(TSensor);                    // read the input pin
  Temp = ((val * ADCmV) - TempOffset) / TempCoef;   // the ADC to C equation
  Serial.println(Temp);                         // debug value
  delay (500);
}
```

After uploading the new version, you should again verify the values printed to the screen. This time you should be reading degrees Celsius. For the moment, we can ignore most of the decimal places. Later, we will cut these off. The final code is shown in Listing 2-2.

At this point, it would be good to have a traditional thermometer around to compare your sensor with. Again, place both the sensor and the traditional thermometer into a cold environment (such as a freezer or refrigerator) and compare the results after a few minutes. A possible heat source for the opposite end of the scale is a hair dryer.

Listing 2-2. Temperature in Degrees Celsius Sketch

```
int TSensor = 0;        // temperature sensor ADC input pin
int val = 0;                    // variable to store ADC value read
int TempOffset = 500;   // value in mV when ambient is 0 degrees C
int TempCoef = 10;      // Temperature coefficient mV per Degree C
float ADCmV = 4.8828;   // mV per ADC increment (5 volts / 1024 increments)
float Temp = 0;                 // calculated temperature in C (accuraccy to two decimal
places)

void setup()
{
  Serial.begin(9600);   //  setup serial
}
```

```
void loop()
{
  val = analogRead(TSensor);                    // read the input pin
  Temp = ((val * ADCmV) - TempOffset) / TempCoef;        // the ADC to C equation
  Serial.println(Temp);                         // display in the SerialMonitor
  delay (200);
}
```

Basic SpiderTemps Code

Now that we are totally confident in the sensor and our equation, as well as how the code should handle the sensor, we can move on to scaling it up. Again, we will do this in stages, but we will take much bigger steps.

The first stop is to read six sensors at once and print them to the screen in a reasonably nice fashion. Connect six sensors to the Arduino, as illustrated in Figure 2-1. Also, let's start with a blank sketch.

As always, the first thing we need to do is set up some variables. The first line of the code creates six variables, one for each ADC input. The next two variables are the 0 degree Celsius offset values, as defined by the temperature sensors you intend to use:

```
int ADC0, ADC1, ADC2, ADC3, ADC4, ADC5;
int MCPoffset = 500;
int LM35offset = 0;
```

Following that, we need to set up the serial port for debugging. We will output all six values in the serial monitor:

```
void setup() {
  Serial.begin(9600);
}
```

There are two functions in the program, in addition to the mainline. The first function (getADC) simply performs the analogRead function on all analog inputs and assigns the byte code to each variable:

```
void getADC() {
  ADC0 = analogRead(A0);
  ADC1 = analogRead(A1);
  ADC2 = analogRead(A2);
  ADC3 = analogRead(A3);
  ADC4 = analogRead(A4);
  ADC5 = analogRead(A5);
}
```

The second function (calcTemp) takes the ADC value, as well as the desired offset as inputs, and outputs a temperature in degrees Celsius, using our equation:

```
float calcTemp (int val, int offset) {
  return ((val * 4.8828) - offset) / 10;
}
```

It is always a good idea to break up the process into two functions like this. More-elaborate sensors can have tricky timing constraints or a complex interface. It is much easier to figure out what is going wrong if you isolate the read function from the convert and output functions. You can divide and conquer each aspect of the process in the case of failure, first validating a good read, secondly validating the conversion, and finally validating the print function. You could simply output the value at each stage to the window. Usually, the faulty function becomes obvious.

If all three of these stages were integrated, it would be terribly difficult to try and isolate a problem. There would be no way to break into the loop. Much longer and more complex code will be hard to sift through, and it would be really difficult to expand or scale back the project for other purposes the future.

So, starting in the `loop` function, the first thing we do is call `getADC` to fill the variables. Next, we want to call the `calcTemp` function for each temperature. Notice that I dynamically created the variables `temp0` through `temp5`. I could have just as easily defined them at the top of the code listing with the rest of the variables.

When we call `calcTemp`, we pass into the function both the ADC variable, as well as the desired offset. Both the LM35 and the MCP9700 use the same equation, but different 0 degree offsets. So, by calling this function individually, we can actually mix and match sensors quite easily, by simply changing which offset we pass to the function.

```
void loop() {
  getADC();
  float temp0 = calcTemp(ADC0, LM35offset);
  float temp1 = calcTemp(ADC1, LM35offset);
  float temp2 = calcTemp(ADC2, MCPoffset);
  float temp3 = calcTemp(ADC3, MCPoffset);
  float temp4 = calcTemp(ADC4, MCPoffset);
  float temp5 = calcTemp(ADC5, MCPoffset);
```

Our last major task is to output the temperature data to the serial port and then wait a moment before doing it all over again. To print the data to the serial port, we use the `Serial.print` function. Notice that we also insert a double space between each value to make reading the data easier on the eyes. For the final piece of data, we use `Serial.println`, so that after printing the data, we get a line feed, putting us on a fresh line in the terminal for the next loop.

```
  Serial.print(temp0, 0);
  Serial.print("  ");
  Serial.print(temp1, 0);
  Serial.print("  ");
  Serial.print(temp2, 0);
  Serial.print("  ");
  Serial.print(temp3, 0);
  Serial.print("  ");
  Serial.print(temp4, 0);
  Serial.print("  ");
  Serial.println(temp5, 0);

  delay(500);
}
```

Notice that for each `Serial.print` command we send the variable, followed by a zero. This zero sets how many decimal places we want to present. We need to use floating-point numbers through the temperature equation (since we are doing some division). Thus the output variable must also be able to contain a decimal place. However, we might not always want to see the decimal places. Do you care that the temperature is 19.30376 degrees, or is 19 degrees just fine for you? You could easily change this value to show two, three or even eight decimal places. However, let's refer to the accuracy column in Table 2-1. The LM35D is accurate down to 0.2 degrees, so you might think that showing one decimal place of accuracy makes sense. Unfortunately, this is not entirely true. Consider that there is inherent error in the conversion from analog to digital (remember the "step size" of each size is 4.8828 mV). Errors add up.

With plus or minus 0.2 degrees, *plus* the rounding error or the ADC due to step size, the error could be as high as plus or minus 0.25 degrees (a full half a degree in total error!) Thus, displaying decimal places, even for the LM35, is somewhat misleading. Listing 2-3 shows the finished sketch.

Listing 2-3. Code Listing for the Basic 6 Sensor System

```
/*
SpiderTemps 6 sensor
Arduino projects to save the world

This sketch reads all six analog inputs, calculates temperature(C) and outputs them to the
serial monitor.
*/

int ADC0, ADC1, ADC2, ADC3, ADC4, ADC5;
int MCPoffset = 500;
int LM35offset = 0;

void setup() {
  Serial.begin(9600);
}

void loop() {
  getADC();
  float temp0 = calcTemp(ADC0, LM35offset);
  float temp1 = calcTemp(ADC1, LM35offset);
  float temp2 = calcTemp(ADC2, MCPoffset);
  float temp3 = calcTemp(ADC3, MCPoffset);
  float temp4 = calcTemp(ADC4, MCPoffset);
  float temp5 = calcTemp(ADC5, MCPoffset);

  Serial.print(temp0, 0);
  Serial.print("  ");
  Serial.print(temp1, 0);
  Serial.print("  ");
  Serial.print(temp2, 0);
  Serial.print("  ");
  Serial.print(temp3, 0);
  Serial.print("  ");
  Serial.print(temp4, 0);
  Serial.print("  ");
  Serial.println(temp5, 0);

  delay(500);
}

void getADC() {
  ADC0 = analogRead(A0);
  ADC1 = analogRead(A1);
  ADC2 = analogRead(A2);
  ADC3 = analogRead(A3);
  ADC4 = analogRead(A4);
```

```
  ADC5 = analogRead(A5);
}

float calcTemp (int val, int offset) {
  return ((val * 4.8828) - offset) / 10;
}
```

Test It Out

Before trusting that the output values are correct, you should thoroughly test the sensors. Ideally, you would attach them all to a singular object so that the thermal mass of the object ensures that each sensor is measuring the same temperature. Next, measure the object with a known calibrated thermometer and compare it with the measured output. Another (simpler) option is to insert all the sensors into your refrigerator, along with an accurate thermometer. After a few minutes, compare the values from your sensors to the thermometer.

At this point, you should write down the differences in temperature. You might even want to increase the decimal places to 2 just to be sure you have good data.

With this information in hand, we will modify the preceding code to include a calibration point for each sensor. Without a calibration for each, we would not be able to trust the hardware when it says that one end of the probe is cold while the other end is hot. When dealing with air temperature gradiants, plus or minus two degrees is a rather large difference. We really need to know that all our sensors are reading on the same scale.

SpiderTemps, Take Two: Calibration

As it turns out, there are a couple of solutions to the calibration problem. We will take the easy way out and simply do it in software. To calibrate the sensors in software, we simply need to add or subtract some value from the final result produced by running the temperature equation.

■ **Note**   This is not quite scientifically accurate, and both National Instruments and Microchip offer guides to writing equations for a more scientific approach to calibration. You can certainly take up the reading and implement their suggestions, but it is beyond the scope of this book.

We can easily add a simple calibration value to the equation. We then add this variable to the list of variables to be passed into the calculation function. Finally, we define a set of calibrations somewhere at the top of our code.

Add a block of variables to the top of the code, with one for each analog input, like this:

```
float calibration0 = 0;
```

We should also change the list of tempX variables from being created within the mainline to being created at the top of the code so we can use them within function blocks. This will become important later when we add a display to the system. By being defined directly in the loop function, they were only available for that one function. You can make this change by removing the float data type names from loop:. So the following line:

```
float temp0 = calcTemp(ADC0, LM35offset);
```

becomes this:

```
temp0 = calcTemp(ADC0, LM35offset);
```

Then add the following line to the top, along with the calibration integers:

```
float temp0, temp1, temp2, temp3, temp4, temp5;
```

Finally, we modify the calculation function, but to do so, we also need to modify the code that calls the function for each analog input. We want to add the calibration value to the list of parameters passed to the function, as well as to add it to the equation. First, modify the calling functions in the main loop, just after the getADC function call. You should call the calcTemp function six times, like so:

```
temp0 = calcTemp(ADC0, LM35offset, calibration0);
```

Next, modify the calcTemp function to read in the calibration data sent by the calling code:

```
float calcTemp (int val, int offset, float cal) {
  return (((val * 4.8828) - offset) / 10) + cal;
}
```

With the ability to add or subtract some small amount to each sensor on an individual basis, we can adjust each sensor so that they all read the same value when in close proximity to each other.

Begin calibrating by placing all sensors in close proximity. They should now be evaluating the same body of air and thus the same temperature. You will need to check the readings against a known constant, such as a professional-grade thermometer.

Note the reported temperatures, and calculate the difference between the reported temperatures and the known temperature. Input this difference in each calibration point in the code. Finally, upload the new version to the Arduino and verify accuracy.

You might want to expand this code so that the user can input the calibration data directly in the serial monitor window, rather than manually adjusting the code. The final version is shown in Listing 2-4.

Listing 2-4. Software-calibrated Version of SpiderTemps.

```
/*
SpiderTemps 6 sensor plus software calibration
Arduino projects to save the world

This sketch reads all six analog inputs, calculates temperature(C) and outputs them to the
serial monitor.
*/

float temp0, temp1, temp2, temp3, temp4, temp5;
int ADC0, ADC1, ADC2, ADC3, ADC4, ADC5;
int MCPoffset = 500;
int LM35offset = 0;

float calibration0 = 0;
float calibration1 = 0;
float calibration2 = 0;
float calibration3 = 0;
float calibration4 = 0;
```

```
float calibration5 = 0;

void setup() {
  Serial.begin(9600);
}

void loop() {
  getADC();
  temp0 = calcTemp(ADC0, LM35offset, calibration0);
  temp1 = calcTemp(ADC1, LM35offset, calibration1);
  temp2 = calcTemp(ADC2, MCPoffset, calibration2);
  temp3 = calcTemp(ADC3, MCPoffset, calibration3);
  temp4 = calcTemp(ADC4, MCPoffset, calibration4);
  temp5 = calcTemp(ADC5, MCPoffset, calibration5);

  Serial.print(temp0, 0);
  Serial.print("  ");
  Serial.print(temp1, 0);
  Serial.print("  ");
  Serial.print(temp2, 0);
  Serial.print("  ");
  Serial.print(temp3, 0);
  Serial.print("  ");
  Serial.print(temp4, 0);
  Serial.print("  ");
  Serial.println(temp5, 0);

  delay(500);
}

void getADC() {
  ADC0 = analogRead(A0);
  ADC1 = analogRead(A1);
  ADC2 = analogRead(A2);
  ADC3 = analogRead(A3);
  ADC4 = analogRead(A4);
  ADC5 = analogRead(A5);
}

float calcTemp (int val, int offset, float cal) {
  return (((val * 4.8828) - offset) / 10) + cal;
}
```

Adding a Display

We now have a very useful tool for measuring gradients or zones of temperature. However, we are tied to the computer to do so. This can be incredibly frustrating, especially with a short USB cord. At best, you have to somehow securely fasten the temperature probe setup and have a stationary place to sit down and read the data. What we need is an all-in-one unit, complete with its own display.

The first thing we should do is consider what size of display we will need. If each sensor needs 2 or 3 digits for whole degrees (remember that -10 degrees requires 3 characters), a decimal point, and two decimal places, we need 5 to 6 characters per sensor, plus a pad between sensors of 1 character. I think the only decent option here would be a 20-column by 2-line display, as shown in Figure 2-9. Sensors 1 through 3 can be displayed on the top line, and 4 through 6 can be displayed on the bottom line.

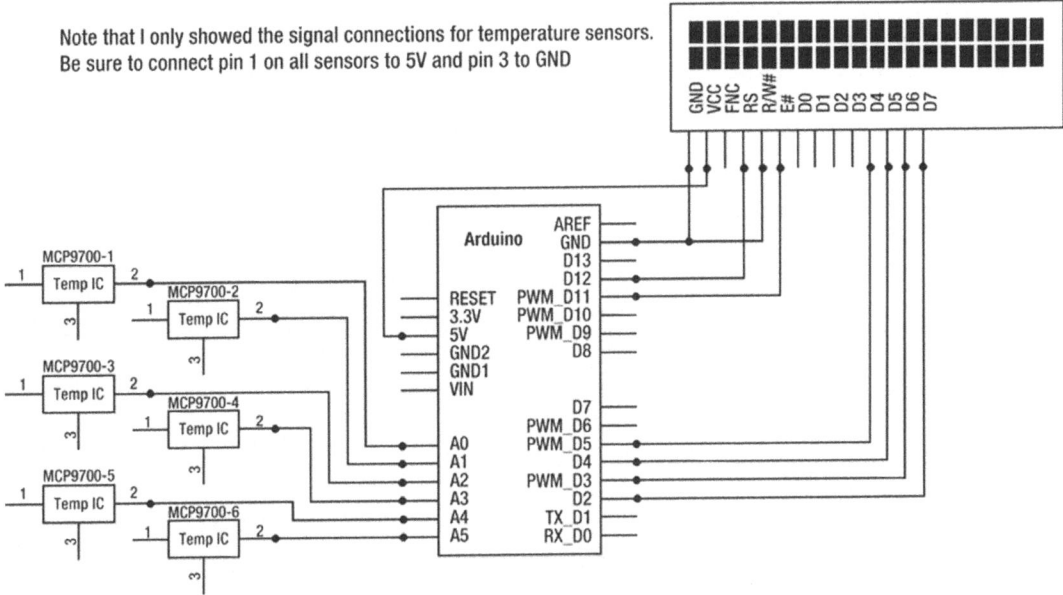

Figure 2-9. Adding an LCD display to the SpiderTemps project

Note that I have not included the power supplies for the temperature sensors in Figure 2-9. I want to draw attention to the LCD side of the schematic. The left half remains the same as in the previous schematic.

■ **Tip** When choosing an LCD screen, be sure to check the data sheet for the correct pin numbers. There are various LCD communications options available (for example: Serial, SPI, I2C, and parallel). The `LiquidCrystal` library expects that you will utilize a "character" LCD with a parallel connection, and that it be HD44780 controller–compatible. These LCDs can operate in 8-bit or 4-bit mode. The library operates in 4-bit mode by default. The best mode is 4-bit mode because it requires only 4 data pins and 2 control pins (for a total of 6 pins) from the Arduino.

To get started, we first need to initialize the library by including it like so:

```
#include <LiquidCrystal.h>
```

We then need to create an object of the LiquidCrystal type. We could call it anything we want (such as Display or Face), but the typical convention is simply to call it lcd. While creating the object, we also need to define the pin connections for the six pins that connect to the LCD.

As noted in the previous tip, we can operate in 4-bit mode to save pins. Thus we need four data pins for the LCD from the Arduino. We also need a few additional control pins. The Enable (E) pin acts as a switch to notify the LCD that data is available on the data pins. Register Select (RS) instructs the LCD to consider the data either as a register address or instruction code. These two pins are critical for maintaining proper communication with the LCD.

A third control pin on the LCD is the Read/Write (RW) pin. When this pin is low, we can write text to the screen. When it is high, we can read back the data from the LCD into the Arduino. This feature is rarely (if ever) used, and therefore is not included in the default setup of the library. However, you will need to be aware of the pin, and tie it low by connecting it to the ground pin on the Arduino. Finally, we need to apply power to the LCD. Connect the LCD ground (often labled *VDD*) to the Arduino ground and the LCD positive supply (often labled *VSS*) to the Arduino's 5-volt pin.

With the pins in place, we can now define them in the Arduino sketch. When we create the LiquidCrystal object in code, we use this format:

```
LiquidCrystal name(RS, Enable, D4, D5, D6, D7)
```

Thus the following line would start a LiquidCrystal object named lcd, using Arduino pin 12 as the RS, 11 as the Enable, 5 as D4, and so on:

```
LiquidCrystal lcd(12, 11, 5, 4, 3, 2);
```

■ **Tip**　If your LCD screen does not display anything after resetting the Arduino, check the connections carefully. In particular, be sure that RW is connected to ground. Without this connection, the LCD will never show any text.

With the object created and the pins in place, we need only start the object and start writing to the screen. lcd.begin(20, 2) designates the size of the LCD screen. In this case, the screen is 20 columns wide, with 2 rows.

We won't see any more LCD code until we call the lcdPrint() function. Sending text to the screen is no different from sending it to the serial port, except that we use the name of the LiquidCrystal object rather than the serial object; for example: lcd.print() instead of serial.print(). One thing to watch out for is lcd.println(). Although it is a valid function (as far as the compiler is concerned), it often ends up causing garbage on the screen. A better choice is to stick with lcd.print() and manually move the cursor and clear the screen. We can perform the clear screen function with lcd.clear(). Positioning the cursor is accomplished with lcd.setCursor(Y, X), where Y is the horizontal position and X is the row.

■ **Tip**　When using the LCD, it is always a good idea to clear the screen and write fresh text instead of simply overwriting existing text. Doing so often causes unexpected results. For example, the LCD currently shows something like "This is long text", and you want to overwrite "Short text" on the screen. Without clearing the screen, the result would be "Short textng text."

In Listing 2-5, I have moved some things around to utilize functions as much as possible. The main loop is now simply a short series of function calls. This method of verifying code, and then compartmentalizing it, makes it much easier to port the code to other applications later. Also, future modifications to the project are simple because you can focus on small blocks of code instead of worrying about what effect one small change will have on the rest of the program.

Listing 2-5. *SpiderTemps with an LCD Screen*

```
/*
  SpiderTemps - LCD
  Arduino projects to save the world

  This sketch reads all six analog inputs, calculates temperature
  and outputs to the serial monitor.
  It also displays them on an attached 20x2 LCD
*/

#include <LiquidCrystal.h>
//LCD pin setup
//            (RS, Enable, D4, D5, D6, D7)
LiquidCrystal lcd(12, 11, 5, 4, 3, 2);

// working variables
int ADC0, ADC1, ADC2, ADC3, ADC4, ADC5;
float temp0, temp1, temp2, temp3, temp4, temp5;

// sensor offset constants
int MCPoffset = 500;
int LM35offset = 0;

// sensor calibrations
int calibration0 = 0;
int calibration1 = 1;
int calibration2 = 0;
int calibration3 = 0;
int calibration4 = 0;
int calibration5 = 0;

void setup() {
  Serial.begin(9600);
  lcd.begin(20, 2);
}

void loop() {
  getADC();
  calcLoop();
  serialPrint();
  lcdPrint();
  delay(2000);
}
```

```
void calcLoop(){
  temp0 = calcTemp(ADC0, MCPoffset, calibration0);
  temp1 = calcTemp(ADC1, MCPoffset, calibration1);
  temp2 = calcTemp(ADC2, MCPoffset, calibration2);
  temp3 = calcTemp(ADC3, MCPoffset, calibration3);
  temp4 = calcTemp(ADC4, MCPoffset, calibration4);
  temp5 = calcTemp(ADC5, MCPoffset, calibration5);
}

void getADC() {
  ADC0 = analogRead(A0);
  ADC1 = analogRead(A1);
  ADC2 = analogRead(A2);
  ADC3 = analogRead(A3);
  ADC4 = analogRead(A4);
  ADC5 = analogRead(A5);
}

float calcTemp (int val, int offset, int cal) {
  return (((val * 4.8828) - offset) / 10) + cal;
}

void serialPrint(){
  Serial.print(temp0, 1);
  Serial.print("   ");
  Serial.print(temp1, 1);
  Serial.print("   ");
  Serial.print(temp2, 1);
  Serial.print("   ");
  Serial.print(temp3, 1);
  Serial.print("   ");
  Serial.print(temp4, 1);
  Serial.print("   ");
  Serial.println(temp5, 1);
}

void lcdPrint(){
  lcd.clear();
  lcd.setCursor(0, 0);
  lcd.print(temp0, 1);
  lcd.setCursor(7, 0);
  lcd.print(temp1, 1);
  lcd.setCursor(14, 0);
  lcd.print(temp2, 1);
  lcd.setCursor(0, 1);
  lcd.print(temp3, 1);
  lcd.setCursor(7, 1);
  lcd.print(temp4, 1);
  lcd.setCursor(14, 1);
  lcd.print(temp5, 1);
}
```

Battery Powered?

The next logical step is to build a self-contained device. By operating the device over a battery pack we can be truly mobile, but first we need to do a little experiment. We need to find out how our sensors will respond on battery power. It is possible that as the battery voltage drops over time, the sensor readings will be affected. This is an experiment you should try with any sensor systems you build.

Start by loading the temperature test sketch into the Arduino. It needs to report temperature on only one analog input (refer to the "Test Code" section of this chapter. Now, we need to simulate a situation in which the supply battery has dropped. We can do this by attaching a variable resistor to the supply input of the sensor, as shown in Figure 2-10.

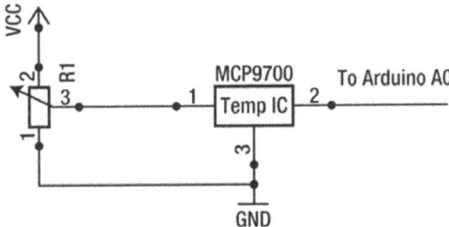

Figure 2-10. The temperature sensor low supply voltage experiment

Fire up the Arduino serial monitor and observe the temperature readings as you turn the knob on the variable resistor. Notice that the readings remain constant for a large portion of the dial, but suddenly they become unstable, decreasing quickly until finally reading zero, or even a negative temperature.

As the voltage supply to the temperature IC decreases, it attempts to compensate until the voltage drops below a certain threshold. The cutoff voltage is very important for us to know because it helps us to choose the best battery supply for the project, and we can know when our readings are no longer reliable.

Using a multimeter set to the voltage setting, measure the voltage coming out of the variable resistor. Do so by touching the black probe of the meter to the ground connection of the variable resistor, while touching the red lead to the center pin. Now sweep the knob again, looking for the point in which the measurement is no longer stable. Note the voltage readings on the meter. It is above this point that we need to maintain a voltage to the sensor.

We can now modify Table 2-1 with this new data to produce Table 2-2:

Table 2-2. Updating Table 2-1 with Minimum Voltage Data

Manufacturer	Part Number	Range (Degrees C)	Accuracy	Coefficient (mV/C)	Offset (mV @ 0C)	Minimum Operating Voltage
National Semiconductor	LM35	+2 to +150	+/- 0.2 @ 25C	10	0	3 volts
Microchip	MCP9700	-40 to +125	+/- 2 @ 70C	10	500	1.7 volts

This data concludes that we should have no problems operating the temperature sensors on batteries. Even a 2–cell AA pack (3 volts), while not okay for the LM35, *will* keep the Microchip part in operation for quite a while before readings become unstable.

Unfortunately, this is only half the problem. What happens when the voltage supplying the Arduino (and thus the ADC) dips below 5 volts? When the ADC reference dips below 5 volts, it will no longer be comparing the analog input to a stable reference voltage. Therefore, it will be reporting inaccurate data. You must provide some sort of stable voltage to the analog reference pin.

Your best solution would be to utilize an Arduino with a boost converter (such as the FreakDuino). A boost converter accepts a lower voltage input, and boosts it to a higher voltage. A typical example in the case of an Arduino is to take an input from two AA batteries, which total 2.4-3 volts, and boosts it to 5 volts. Boost converters have a wide operating range below the required voltage, so that even as the battery supply drops, the Arduino and ADC reference remain at 5 volts for as long as possible. The Freaklabs Freakduino is one such example of an Arduino with a boost converter on board. Another option is to use a standalone boost converter to power the board, such as SparkFun's lithium polymer battery booster (`http://www.sparkfun.com/products/10255`). There is a trade-off, however. All boost converters exchange current for voltage. This has the effect of dramatically reducing the overall time of operation on batteries. In other words, to get 5 volts out of a 3–volt battery pack, either the pack must drain faster or the circuit must be very considerate of current requirements.

Boxing It Up

When using the temperature array indoors, the bare board might be suitable for most applications; very little can be damaged, other than knocking the cable leads loose from the Arduino board. To increase reliability, you might consider building a prototyping shield with screw-down or spring-loaded terminal blocks to attach the cables.

You might want to box up the device. I placed mine inside a cheap plastic case from the dollar store, but you can use any project box that suits you as long as it is large enough to house the Arduino plus the prototyping shield, as well as a battery pack. If you intend to use the LCD, you will also need to have plenty of space to mount it as well. If you plan on using the project for extended monitoring outdoors, be sure to choose a box with a watertight seal and rubber grommets for any outside connections.

After choosing a box, you need to decide just how you intend to connect sensors to the device. I used 1/4-inch stereo phono plugs and jacks (look at your headphones for your portable media device). I suggest that you buy panel mounted jacks, as shown in Figure 2-11. They are much easier to work with than PCB mounted parts.

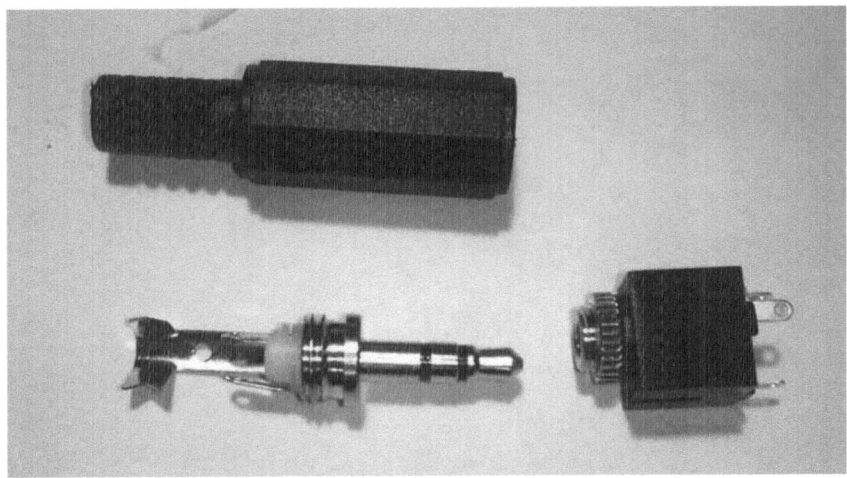

Figure 2-11. 1/4-inch phono plug, plug jacket, and panel mount jack

You should use a multimeter to confirm the corresponding pins on the jacks to the location on the plug. I chose to place the negative connection on the large ring toward the base of the plug, the signal output on the middle ring, and 5 volts on the tip of the plug. This way, 5 volts is the final connection to be made when plugging in a sensor. This will protect it (as well as your Arduino) from short circuits as you plug it in while power is applied.

1. Start by marking the location of the Arduino, battery case, and headphone jacks. You might also want to include a power switch as well.

2. After testing that everything will fit without crashing into each other, drill holes in the box for the mounting screws of the Arduino.

3. Using hexagon standoff posts, screws and nuts, mount the Arduino in place. Now is a good time to double-check that there is room to spare above the Arduino. We need some space for cabling, as shown in Figure 2-12. You can see the copper wire power rails and their cables, which loop over into the right connector. The analog inputs are connected on the left. This case has five analog input sockets and a power switch on the far left.

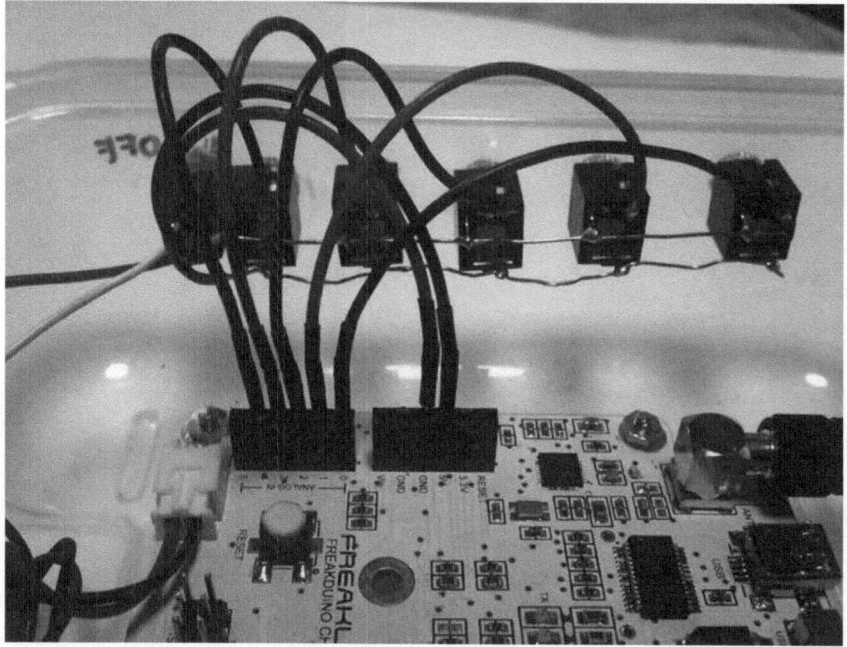

Figure 2-12. Internal connections of the SpiderTemps box.

4. Next drill and mount the panel jacks. Align them such that the pins all face the same way.

5. Strip a long strand of solid core wire and thread it through all the positive posts of the panel jacks. Do the same for the negative posts.

6. Now solder each post to the stripped wire. Add a bit of jacketed wire to the end of both the positive bus and negative bus, so that you can easily plug them into the breadboard. I used wire with a machined pin soldered to the end that will fit into the breadboard.

7. Finally, solder a similar wire with machined pins to each signal output pin on the panel jack. You can now plug the power pins into power sockets, and attach each sensor input to the analog inputs of the Arduino, as shown in Figure 2-13.

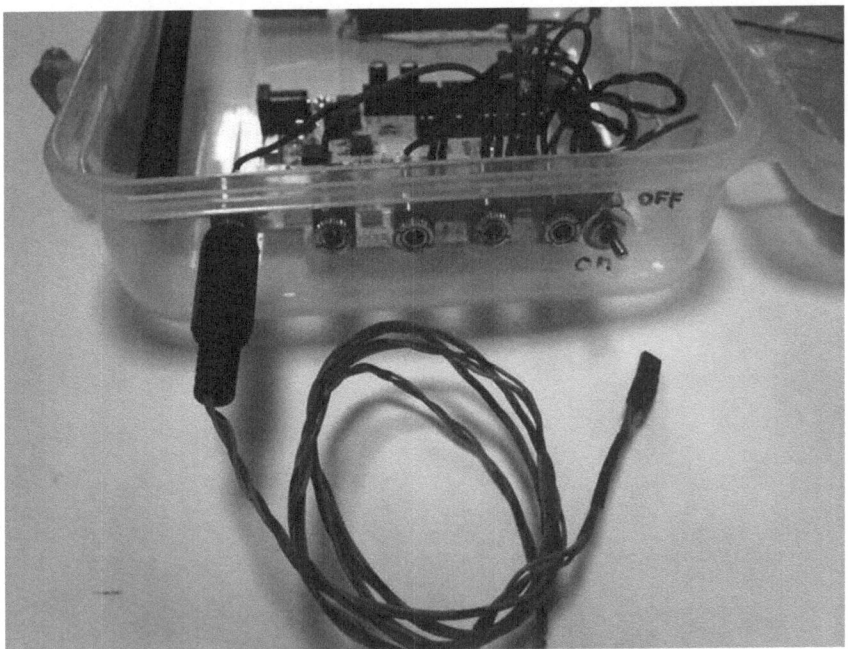

Figure 2-13. The SpiderTemps case with a probe inserted

Making Mods

This chapter featured several variations on the same basic theme. It demonstrates the versatility of both the Arduino platform and available temperature sensor ICs well. An excellent extension to the project would be to write a Processing sketch that reads the data and saves it into a file that can be accessed by a spreadsheet and graphing program, such as Microsoft Excel. Or invest some additional time in learning the Processing IDE and system, and write a data visualization application to better suit your own needs. For more about Processing, data logging and visualization, take a look at Chapter 6.

The unit could also benefit from data storage or a wireless communications upgrade and long–life battery pack. In the river waste water example, mounting the Arduino temperature probe unit near the wastewater outlet, and sending data wirelessly to a more physically secure location which contains the computer system would be a logical solution.

Finally, take a look Chapter 5, where we cover the online service Pachube, for a way to share your temperature data around the world.

Conclusion

Having the ability to measure several temperature readings in various locations simultaneously allows you to characterize and model the environment much more effectively. You can examine the effects of temperature flow in and around an environment, and start actively making deductions and decisions based on this information.

We found that the solution to simultaneous measurement is actually quite simple. You could apply the same code to virtually any array of like sensors, by simply changing the code and equations within the `calcTemp` function.

This chapter set out to put the design process model outlined in Chapter 1 into action. We took baby steps at first, in order to confirm functionality and our fundamental understanding of the sensor technology. We then were able to aggressively build upon that foundation to create incredibly powerful variations in a relatively short period of time.

Now that you have this powerful data acquisition hardware on your tool belt, you will start to see many applications for its use. Be sure to mention it the next time your local environmental or ecology organization has a tricky temperature measurement problem.

CHAPTER 3

Jungle Power

Keeping an Arduino Alive in the Field

One aspect of electronic sensors deployed in the field that is quite difficult to deal with is that of power management. Sensors obviously need electrical power to operate, but it is usually impractical to run long power cables out to the sensor's location. Often, there isn't even a power grid to connect up to. This leaves relatively few practical options.

Most often, field sensors are powered by battery sources. This gives them a limited operational life span. Your equipment can operate only as long as the battery pack has power. To be more accurate: only as long as your battery pack has enough power to keep the sensor going. When the voltage in the pack drops below a certain threshold, the sensor system shuts down, even though there is still some remaining "juice" in the battery cells.

In the not-too-distant past, remote sensor equipment was often bulky, heavy, and required a lot of power to keep operational. It also usually had limited recordkeeping time. This resulted in field scientists contriving various incentives to get their lab assistants to trek out into the forest, up the mountain, or to other uncomfortable locations to serve as pack mules. The battery packs required for long-term service were difficult to transport, to say the least.

But technology marches forward. We live in a new era of lightweight, high-current battery packs. Solar panels are getting more efficient. Adding to the power input advantage, voltage boost circuits let us suck every last milliamp of power out of battery cells.

Microcontrollers are now packing a heavy punch in tiny packages. They require very little power and less physical space. Most offer some sort of "sleep" mode to consume even less power.

The sensors are smaller, lighter, and more accurate. MEMS micro machines have replaced complex mechanical sensors. The interface circuitry required has been minimized by placing as much of it as possible on the sensor chip.

With all this miniaturization, the costs have been driven down as well. In the past, the idea of installing a sensor system with no intention of ever retrieving it later would be unheard of. No one could justify the thousands of dollars lost. Now, it is quite practical for a scientist to design and install a system in a very remote location, with no intention of ever returning. The "throw away" cost is often less than $100. For that money, they could have a reasonably sophisticated instrument.

By adding radio communications, there is no need to install communication lines or return to the instrument to pick up the chart logs or swap out data storage media. They can have live, real-time data. Now we can install hundreds of instruments like this in a location, for the cost of what just one instrument would have been, 10 years ago.

In this chapter, we will explore several key concepts required to keep an Arduino "alive" and unattended for several days, weeks, and possibly months. In particular, we will need to determine the energy requirements of the Arduino-based sensor and match a battery pack to the system. We will also need to add a charging system, in the form of a solar panel (or two). You could also charge the battery using energy harvesting from other environmental sources, such as wind, hydroelectric, or biological power. Finally, we can take steps to assure that we extend the battery life as much as possible, by putting the Arduino to sleep in between readings and using an alarm clock to wake it up at predetermined intervals.

Diverse Power Sources

The key to self-contained, long-term instrumentation is a diverse power source structure. Batteries are all well and good (and form the primary source for nearly every field instrument), but they have one serious drawback: time. When building your system, you must always evaluate how long you expect a fully charged pack to last. It is finite. We can prolong and possibly even eliminate this drawback altogether by adding natural recharging solutions such as solar power. Granted, long exposure to heat and cold, as well as a bit of humidity and condensation, will *eventually* render the battery pack permanently dead. Thankfully, this will happen much further down the timeline if we include solar recharging than if we simply threw in a few alkaline cells and called it "done."

Whenever you think of renewable or free energy sources, perhaps only a few options come to mind. You might think of windmills and solar panels. Or perhaps you think of a big hydroelectric dam, or even a nuclear power plant. But there are also other less-known options such as energy harvesters.

Doing a few Google searches can lead you down some interesting roads. When doing searches for generator– or turbine–based power systems, it is helpful remember this basic guide:

- A *pico system* is a small system, just about right for charging a small portable battery pack, such as the ones we will be using in our Arduino project, over the course of a day.

- A *micro* system is larger. It is suitable for a home, provided you are very energy-conscious. It should charge an automotive-sized battery cell over the course of a day.

- Doing a search without the terms *pico* or *micro* will bring up systems larger still. You are now getting into the industrial-sized systems that are capable of powering large homes.

These terms apply on a totally different scale when talking about energy harvesting. By definition, energy harvesters work with incredibly small currents.

Solar Power

The most obvious free source of energy to recharge your sensor's battery is a solar panel. It is a relatively simple option, cheap, and requires no mechanical parts that could break.

Solar has a few minor drawbacks. Remember that it has a possibility of working for only half the day; it generates electricity only when the sun is shining down on it. You will need a space clear of trees and buildings that would cast a shadow on your panel. You will also need to aim the panel in the most optimal position. In the northern hemisphere, this means aiming the panel generally toward the south. Close to the equator, the panel can lay flat. As you approach the poles, you'll need to dramatically increase the angle.

Finally, the sun is constantly moving. This means that unless we have a sun-tracking mechanism, we will have to accept that the panel will perform optimally for only a short period of time. Between the hours of 10 a.m. and 2 p.m. are usually the most optimal energy-generation times for a stationary solar panel.

Wind Power

Another power option is a wind turbine. You might be thinking that a large windmill would be impractical. A few years ago, you might have been right. But we are living in exciting times. Manufacturers have found that small compact renewable or free energy systems are big business.

Doing a Google search for "pico wind turbine" will yield hundreds of products in the sub-$300 range, which output 8 to 12 volts at 100 mA. These small systems are perfect for adding a bit of recharge to your remote sensor.

Wind is not a steady and reliable recharging source. Some days, it is gusting and blowing, while other days it is still. As part of an overall energy plan, however, wind can be an excellent addition to a sensor site.

Water Power

If your sensor site is near naturally running water, a pico hydro turbine is the best choice. It tops wind and even solar due to its consistent nature. Even if the water flow is not year-round, it will remain consistent for days on end. With the exception of unforeseen rains or drought, a river bed is quite predictable, so power output will be mostly constant. It provides power at night when solar is no longer affective. A pico hydro system will not suffer the surges and lows that a wind system must contend with.

Energy Harvesting

Energy harvesters convert energy from ambient sources. Vibrations in the ground, salinity of water, or the difference of temperature between two masses are all ambient sources that can be tapped for energy.

An energy harvester often operates in ultra low currents, cumulatively storing the current until it has reached a usable level for the device. It does not necessarily need to be a low-current system, though. The key to a good harvester system is to look to the natural environment for a source of mechanical or thermal energy.

To get started with energy harvesting, you might want to check out SparkFun's LTC3588 breakout board.

Three Sides to Every (Power) Story

Having a robust and diverse power input section is not enough. Regarding power management, there are three sides to the story: input, regulation, and usage.

On the input side of the story, we have the bulk energy generation or storage medium. This could be a "wall-wart" power supply, batteries, a super capacitor, a solar panel, or a combination of several energy sources.

Current from the energy source is passed through a voltage regulation device. The purpose of the regulator is to set the voltage from the energy source to a level compatible with the Atmel microcontroller and other electronics in our project.

Finally, we can utilize the energy provided by the power source through the regulation circuits. In most projects you might not be too concerned about how much current it draws. However, in the case of remote sensor sites, you must always be aware of your current usage and how to minimize it in order to maximize the sensor's "uptime."

Input (Batteries, Charge Controllers, and Free Energy)

For the moment, let's assume our sensor system will be battery-operated with some additional charging source, such as a solar panel. We have a few considerations to take into account. Primarily, we have three systems at play: battery, charge input source, and charge controller.

First we must decide our battery pack chemistry, voltage, and current. This decision will determine what sort of charge controller we will need. Finally, we must match the charging input to the system. By far, the simplest solution is to use a system based around modern lithium polymer packs. You can buy a pack and charge controller as a set. The charge controller is often mounted as a breakout board, with a connection for the battery pack, an input for the charge voltage (your solar panel), and an output to the Arduino.

A far less efficient but still serviceable system is composed of standard sized NiCD or nickle metal hydride (NiMH) cells and a simple charge circuit (see Figure 3-1). All that is required is a solar panel, diode, the batteries, and a battery case. The batteries and panel are in parallel, while the diode is placed between the panel and the pack, so current cannot flow from the pack into the panel. As long as the voltage output of the panel exceeds the pack (by about 2 volts), and the current demands do not exceed that of the panel output, it will feed current into the system. This current will be split up, going either into the battery pack as a charge or to the Arduino. Thus, you will want to size the panel so the current exceeds the Arduino requirements, while the remaining current has a maximum output of about 1/10th of the current output of the battery pack.

The rule of thumb for charging these kinds of batteries is 1/10th (or C/10 in the battery world). To charge the battery pack at 1/10th its rated current requires 16 hours of charge time. Obviously, this is totally impractical with a solar panel. It receives optimal sunlight for only four hours per day, from 10 a.m. to 2 p.m. Thus, a totally ideal system would require four days to fully charge the battery pack.

For example, suppose that we have a 2xAA–sized 1000mAh battery pack that is rated at 1.2 volts per cell. With cells in series, our pack outputs 2.4 volts. While the voltage required to charge the battery changes over time, you will need to make available at least 2.4-3 volts. It will require C/10, or 100mA, for 16 hours. At 200mA, it would require only 8 hours, but we might be trading overall life of the battery for a quicker charge time.

A 3 volt solar panel would be ideal for this battery pack. If our project needs 150mA of current during operation, we need to provide a solar panel that outputs at least 250mA at 4 volts to charge the batteries and power the project during sunlight hours.

This has not yet taken into account that the forward voltage drop of the diode could be as high as 0.7 volts. Thus, we really want a panel of 3.7-4 volts to be sure we can fully charge the batteries.

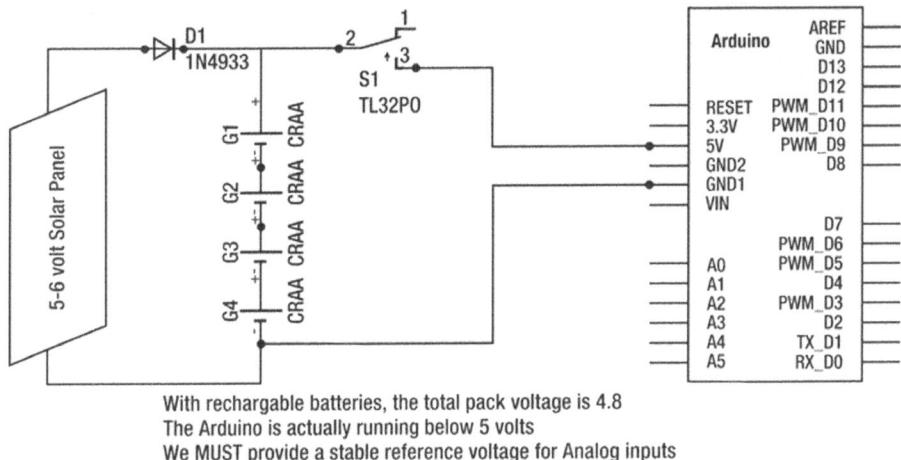

With rechargable batteries, the total pack voltage is 4.8
The Arduino is actually running below 5 volts
We MUST provide a stable reference voltage for Analog inputs

Figure 3-1. *A simple solar recharging Arduino project*

Regulation Options

Having solved the input problem, the next problem we encounter is that of regulation. This is the area in which the standard Arduino kind of fails the test. Don't get me wrong; it is awesome for prototyping and even some commercial applications. It makes a very flexible and robust lab tool (the subject of this book). Unfortunately, it was never really designed with a lean power diet in mind. Building field-ready, long-duration instruments for harsh environments was never at the top of the list.

So, the regulation circuitry on most Arduinos and Arduino clones was never optimized for such a case. They are not particularly efficient when running off of batteries. Thankfully, the open source community is pretty good at keeping in mind that we, as users, are never going to follow all the rules. Thus, there are a variety of clones, each with its own intended use in mind. There are clones designed for radio use, data logging, low power, or really tight spaces. Later in the chapter, we will explore a few of the available options that are well suited for wireless sensors. However, don't let that be the end of the discussion, New clones are popping up all the time. It pays to do some research before selecting a clone for your project.

Operate at 5 Volts from a Higher Voltage Source

This is certainly the easiest option. If you don't mind the inefficiency of the onboard regulators, you can use a battery pack made up of AA, C, or D cells, with a supply voltage over 5 volts. Simply wire it up to a barrel plug as shown in Figure 3-2, and plug it in as you would an external wall wart power supply. Because the onboard regulator requires *more* than 5 volts to operate, you will need to be sure you have a battery pack that provides at least 5.5 volts to the barrel plug.

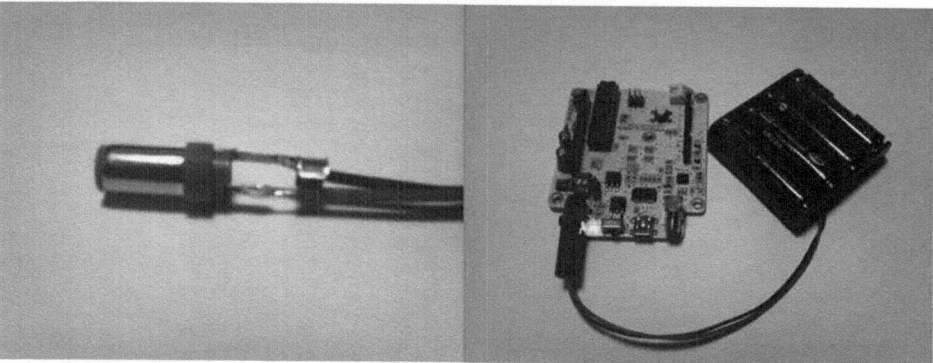

Figure 3-2. A simple power solution for a mobile Arduino

The whole power system will need to be designed around the idea that you are operating the Arduino in its most-convenient yet least-efficient modes. Consider that when using standard off-the-shelf NiCD or nickle metal hydride (NiMH) batteries, they are no longer rated at 1.5 volts like their alkaline counterparts. At 1.2 volts each, you need at least 5 cells to get over the 5 volt mark (plus regulator overhead) needed to power the Arduino.

The other possibility is to provide your own 5 volt regulated source. It is often the case when using specialized batteries like Lithium Polymer, that the pack will have its own control board. In such a case, simply connect the 5 volt output of the controller to the 5 volt pin on the Arduino. This will bypass the onboard regulators.

Another option might be a DC-to-DC converter. This is an example of a switching power supply and is incredibly efficient at cutting higher voltages down to a precise 5 volt supply without wasting valuable current as heat. However, they are considerably more expensive (10 to 20 times) and are bulky devices.

Operate at Lower Voltages

First, it is important to know that while the Arduino system specifies a 5 volt supply, it can actually operate as low as 3.3 volts (and in some cases, 2.5 volts). This is very important for a number of reasons. For example, you can power the Arduino off of lower voltages However, when doing so, you must remember that analog input circuitry will be affected, and you will need to account for the voltage differences, not just in your hardware design, but in your code as well.

Use a Boost Converter to Operate on 5 Volts with a Supply Less than 5 Volts

A *boost converter* is a specialized style of voltage regulator, that actually allows us to input *less* voltage than we require to power our electronics. One rendition of this project will connect two AA batteries, supplying 3 volts, to a boost converter. The boost converter will then supply 5 volts to the Arduino. You will find that even as the voltage output of the battery pack dips well below 2 volts, it is still supplying 5 volts to the Arduino. It manages to do this, but at a loss of current. The available current will quickly drop as the voltage remaining in the pack drops below 1 volt.

SparkFun sells an excellent boost converter/energy harvester module in the form of a general-purpose power supply board named the "LiPower–boost converter."

Also, many hackers are familiar with AdaFruit's MintyBoost project, which takes the input of just two AA batteries and charges a smartphone. This project could easily be repurposed for powering an

Arduino. The MintyBoost is a perfect complement to AdaFruit's solar LiPo charger kit. Together they provide a complete 5 volt solution for the Arduino. Simply connect the output of the solar LiPo kit to the input of the MintyBoost, the output of which connects directly to the 5 volt pin of the Arduino.

Finally, by the time this book goes to print, you should start seeing a lot of breakout boards for the LTC3108 and LTC3588 on the market. These chips can harvest energy as low as 20mV and boost it up to 3.3 volts or more.

Selecting Your Sensor Node Arduino

Some Arduino clones have built-in boost converters, whereas others do not. Some are capable of operating down to 2.5 volts. It is very important in this case that you check carefully the specs of the device you have chosen (see http://arduino.cc/main/hardware for original Arduino boards). In addition, you should consider whether it is possible to disable onboard power indicator LEDs. The LED actually consumes more power than the CPU does!

When using the Uno, for example, you need to supply more than 5 volts to the power jack (or VIN pin) in order to power the onboard 5 volt regulator. While this is a modern regulator, and relatively efficient, it is still consumes too much power for low-powered systems. Unfortunately, the power LED cannot be disabled unless you have some skill modifying surface mount circuit boards.

The best option for the Uno is to buy a separate boost regulator circuit and connect its output to the 5 volt pin on the board, which bypasses the 5 volt regulator on board. We can then power the boost regulator with two AA batteries, making a lower-powered Uno. Because we are operating the Arduino CPU at 5 volts, we don't have to worry about mucking up the analog inputs.

A really good option for low-power systems is the Lilipad. It takes the opposite approach to power regulation: It has none! You will need to be extra cautious that you power it up properly, not exceeding 5.5 volts and observing correct polarity. The advantage with it is that you can operate down to 2.7 volts, meaning that two AAs will happily get the Lilipad going. However, in so doing, you will have to account for this voltage difference when working with analog inputs.

Another option with very similar specs as the Lilipad is the ProMini series. These are available from SparkFun. You have the option of 5 volts or 3.3 volts, as well as a number of clock frequencies. Be sure to check carefully the voltage expected. It is marked on the bottom of the board.

I recommend the Mini over the Lilipad due to its pin payout. It is laid out like a large IC, having 12 pins on each side. It fits standard chip sockets, making it much easier to prototype with than the Lilipad. Also, it is roughly half the size.

Arguably the best original Arduino option for low–power sensor systems is the Fio. It includes a lithium polymer cell input connector and charger. This is great because you don't have to worry about the charging system. Simply plug in the battery, connect solar cells to the VIN input, and the charger will handle power management. The Fio runs down to 3.35 volts, as well as giving you 14 digital I/O and 8 analog inputs. It also includes an Xbee socket for radio communications. The Fio had some of the lowest current measurements out of any of the devices tested for this book.

My personal recommendation for low-cost wireless applications is Freaklabs' Freakduino (http://www.freaklabs.org). I use it extensively throughout this book, and chose it as the build example for this chapter. It is available as a kit form with many options. See Figure 3-3 for the bare system, which does not include the boost circuitry and DC input jack. (In Figure 3-3, the optional boost regulator electronics are missing from the right of the digital pin sockets.)

The Freakduino has several advantages suited to wireless sensor applications. For one thing, it includes an onboard boost regulator. Regardless of how low the input voltage is, you will have a steady 5 volts for all your analog sensors. It even has an optional 2xAA battery pack that can be attached to the bottom side. In addition, the onboard LEDs can be disabled via dip switches.

FreakLabs also offers a case-mounted version with a rubber jacket, which lets your project resemble a meter or other handheld device.

Figure 3-3. FreakLabs' Freakduino-Chibi wireless Arduino clone.

The most important feature of the Freakduino, however, is the onboard radio. For about the same price as an Uno, you get a boost-regulated Arduino with integrated radio. The radio conforms to similar specifications as Xbee, but runs an open source stack. Also, depending on your configurations, it could cost less to buy two Freakduino-Chibi boards instead of two Arduinos, Xbee shields, and Xbee radios.

Chibi boards are sold with several optional add-ons (the boost regulator is one). Figure 3-1 illustrated the bare kit. Available kit upgrades include the complete boost circuit components, a bottom mounted battery case, or a professional project case complete with rubber boot.

As always, every product has its drawbacks. For one, the Chibi radio is unlikely to be compatible with an Zigbee network, even though they talk over the same airwaves. Another point to consider is that the Chibi has not been power-optimized. It is meant more as a radio testbed than an actual deployed sensor. If you intend to have an evolving network, you might want to stick with a Zigbee/Xbee solution. Further, Chibi boards are not always in stock at the Freaklabs.org web shop. With standard NiCD or

NiMH batteries in the pack, you can attach solar cells (through a diode) to the white DC jack, and they will charge the batteries. If you choose more–advanced battery technology, such as LiPo, simply leave the AA battery pack off and connect the output wires of the battery management circuit to the white DC jack.

Unfortunately, FreakLabs is a one-man show. This means stock is not always available. This is especially true now (2011) because the owner is hard at work on the SafeCast project.

If you are unable to get your hands on a Chibi, another board of equal prowess is the Dangerous Prototypes Stalker, available from Seeed Studio. Some might argue that the Stalker is superior to the Chibi. In my opinion, it just depends on your plans.

The Stalker (see Figure 3-4) is an all-in-one solution to the wireless sensor network problem. In fact, if you were to purchase a full Stalker kit, you would have accomplished every objective in the build of this chapter simply by placing your order!

The Stalker uses the much smaller ATMEGA328P chip to free up more board space and operate at 3.3 volts. In addition, it has a built-in LiPo charging circuit, with a solar panel and battery inputs. It comes with a real-time clock (with super capacitor backup supply), SD card socket, and an Xbee socket for wireless connectivity.

The board is well thought out. All the options have solder pad jumpers that can be cut to disable features and soldered to reenable them later if need be. These include all the onboard LEDs. Being able to disable them will save a lot of current.

Another excellent feature of the Stalker is that it has a level shifter to interface 3.3 and 5 volt devices.

The only frustration I have with the Stalker is the lack of onboard USB support. This makes sense, though, when you consider that most of the time that USB chip would be draining your valuable current resources. However, with no onboard USB support, you are forced to buy an additional programming dongle, buy an FTDI cable, or make up your own programming solution. This frustration is worth it in the end, though, because you will have a very lean, mean, sensor machine.

Figure 3-4. The Dangerous Prototypes Stalker V2, with LiPo battery, solar panel, XBee radio, and a USB XBee dongle

Tips to Optimize Your System for Longer Battery Life

The third critical factor for ensuring that your remote sensor will continue to report data for as long as possible is to actively manage power usage. There are a number of approaches, and you might employ several of them together to squeeze the most performance out of the system.

Lower the Operating Voltage

The most obvious choice is to operate the Arduino and sensors at lower voltages (refer to the preceding section). It is not always a practical option (for example, some sensors can only function at 5 volts), but when it's possible, you should certainly consider it. In so doing, you must take into account that a different operating voltage will affect the overall system design, and have particular consequences in the Analog input section of your design. Thankfully, one benefit of a lower voltage is that you will gain resolution on the analog to digital converter (ADC). Refer to Chapter 2 for more information. When you divide 3.3 volts instead of 5 volts by 1024 slices, you get a much smaller voltage value per ADC count.

You need to make a few changes to both your circuit design, as well as code in order to ensure that you can accurately read the analog input voltage when working with batteries. (Refer to Chapter 1 and Table 1-1).

In particular, you should take the following steps:

- Place the following code in the Setup() portion of your code:

  analogReference(type as specified in Table 1-1)

- Recalculate your conversion equations using the new increment voltage from the table.

- If you are using an external reference voltage, supply a stable reference voltage (like that from a regulator or Zener diode) to the Aref pin on the Arduino of the specified voltage.

Using a Zener Diode to Drive Aref

When operating at a lower voltage, you have two options to handle the analog reference. First, you could use the internal reference option if it is available on your board. You will need to check the ATMEGA chip used on the board and find out what the internal reference voltage is for that IC.

Your other option is to provide it with a stable voltage reference. The easiest way to do so is using a Zener diode, which is a specialized diode meant to be operated in reverse (reverse biased). The Zener diode sinks to ground any voltage above it's voltage rating. Thus, if you had a 2.5 volt Zener diode, and placed 3 volts across it, the diode would short 0.5 volts to ground. You would measure 2.5 volts across it, even though your supply is outputting 3 volts.

Obviously, this "short circuit" will cause a lot of current to flow. So to control it, we can add a resistor to the circuit, which limits the amount of current flowing through the diode. We only need about 10mA for the diode to begin working.

Even with an appropriate resistor, 10mA is a lot of waste when our goal is to use as little current as possible. For this reason, they are not ideal in ultra–low power solutions because they create a short circuit for any voltage over their reference setting.

Fortunately there is a very simple solution, shown in Figure 3-5: the Zener diode is powered from a digital output! The Aref pin will not require much current to do its thing. As long as we don't use the Zener reference voltage for anything other than our analog system, we can simply tie the voltage input to a digital pin. When we want to take an analog measurement, we set the digital pin high, wait a few moments for the analog system to warm up, take our measurement, and then set the digital output back to low again.

You must be certain that your analog sensors will not consume more than about 40mA. If you have power-hungry sensors, you should consider a "proper" voltage regulator instead. An LM7803 voltage regulator could be switched on via a digital output, using a transistor (similar to Figure 3-5).

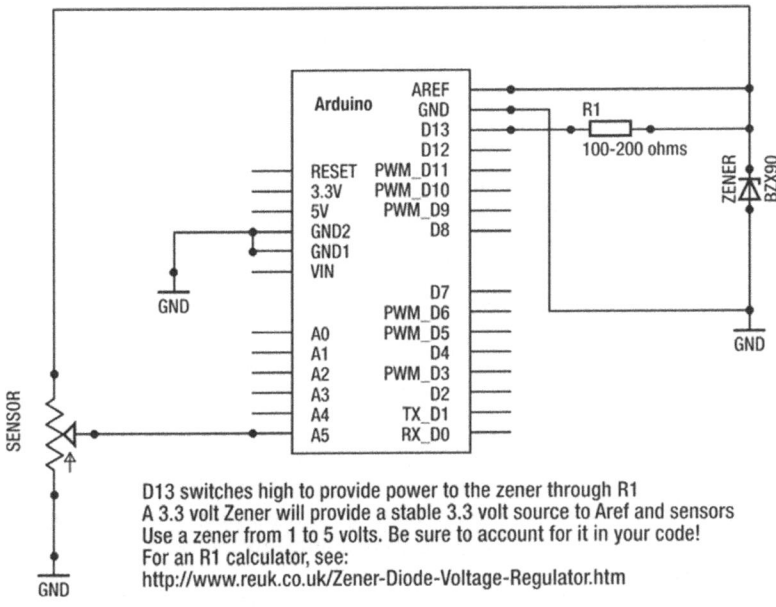

D13 switches high to provide power to the zener through R1
A 3.3 volt Zener will provide a stable 3.3 volt source to Aref and sensors
Use a zener from 1 to 5 volts. Be sure to account for it in your code!
For an R1 calculator, see:
http://www.reuk.co.uk/Zener-Diode-Voltage-Regulator.htm

Figure 3-5. A simple AREF stable voltage source is switched on by a digital output.

Another option for lowering current consumption is to switch off power to sensors and external circuitry when not in use. A perfect example is a weather station. The only sensors that must be actively monitored every few seconds are the anemometer and wind vane. Gusts of wind can blow in at any moment. However, temperature, humidity, and rainfall are rather stable. These sensors can be placed on a schedule, being checked every 5 minutes. During the "down time" between checks, it would be helpful if you could cut the power to the sensors.

Depending on the sensor type, this could easily be accomplished by using a transistor to cut power to the sensors. Any general-purpose transistor will do.

See Figure 3-6. A digital output from the Arduino is set to HIGH, at which point the NPN transistor is switched on due to the pin being connected to the transistor's base through a current limiting resistor. Current will now flow from VCC (the Arduino 5 volt pin) through the analog sensors, through the transistor, to ground. To turn off the transistor, switch the digital output to LOW.

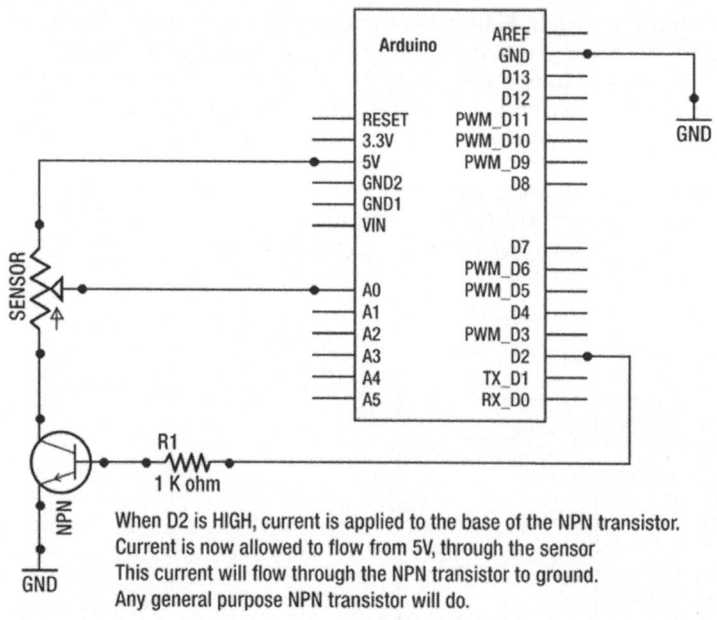

When D2 is HIGH, current is applied to the base of the NPN transistor.
Current is now allowed to flow from 5V, through the sensor
This current will flow through the NPN transistor to ground.
Any general purpose NPN transistor will do.

Figure 3-6. One way to switch off sensors while the Arduino is sleeping.

Putting the Arduino to Sleep

The final option is to tell the Arduino to take a nap. This option is possible only when your sensor package does not need to be on standby, waiting for something to happen. If you will be taking readings at regular intervals, it is a fantastic way to save lots of power. A system with appropriate sleep schedules can run for several months on just two AA batteries.

To get a good handle on the powerful sleep modes, we need to do some research outside the normal scope of the Arduino integrated development environment (IDE). The Arduino language is based largely on the AVR GCC compiler, and there are a lot of hidden GCC header and include files behind the scenes that get linked into your program when you hit the compile button in the IDE.

Of particular interest are the `power.h` and `sleep.h` files. These files are buried down in the IDE directory (try looking into `hardware\tools\avr\avr\include\avr` if you are curious) and are quite complex. Fortunately, you can easily find a summary of the functions; one site that documents the GCC header files well is `http://www.nongnu.org/avr-libc/user-manual/modules.html`. Finally, the Arduino Playground has an excellent sleep tutorial at `http://www.arduino.cc/playground/Learning/ArduinoSleepCode`.

Five sleep modes are made available by the sleep.h file:

- `SLEEP_MODE_IDLE`

- `SLEEP_MODE_ADC`

- `SLEEP_MODE_PWR_SAVE`

- `SLEEP_MODE_STANDBY`

- `SLEEP_MODE_PWR_DOWN`

The `PWR_DOWN` mode gives the most power savings.

In addition to the sleep modes, the `power.h` file provides a way to switch off every hardware peripheral built into the Atmel CPU. They can be switched individually by calling them by name. For example, `power_adc_disable()` will shut down the ADC, whereas `power_adc_enable()` will turn it back on.

Rather than turning on and off peripherals individually, `power_all_disable()` and `power_all_enable()` will switch every peripheral at once. Be careful with this one because one or more peripherals might actually be needed to wake back up. For example, instructing the Atmel to wake on a serial event, only to shut down the serial devices would cause the chip to never wake up from sleep.

To get the Arduino to wake up from a deep sleep, the only solid option is to use one of the two external interrupt pins. They are digital pins 2 and 3 (labeled 0 and 1, respectively, for the purposes of attaching an interrupt). The code `attachInterrupt(0, DoThis, LOW);` will call the function `DoThis` whenever the interrupt 0 (digital pin 2) goes low. It is important to understand that this is not a wake up command. The `DoThis` function will get called any time the pin goes low. If you want to utilize the `DoThis` function only immediately after a wakeup, you should use the corresponding `detachInterrupt` command.

By adding a real-time clock (RTC), we can give the Arduino an alarm clock. Before putting the Arduino to sleep, we instruct the RTC to wake it up at a particular time. The RTC will signal the Arduino via an interrupt pin attached to interrupt 0 or 1 (digital pin 2 or 3).

An interrupt is a way for a program or a piece of hardware to demand attention from the microcontroller. It's like that nagging kid in the back seat: it can't be ignored! We can set the Arduino sleep mode to "Wake on Interrupt" via the interrupt pin.

When selecting an RTC, we need to be absolutely certain that it has an external interrupt pin. There are many popular clock chips available *without* this much-needed pin. It has no way of setting an alarm or signaling the Arduino to wake up.

This is one area in which the Stalker board has a clear advantage over many other Arduino clones on the market. It has a built-in RTC with supercapacitor power supply backup, and the all-important interrupt pin prewired to the appropriate Arduino pin.

■ **Caution** The I2C bus of the Arduino is located on pins A4 and A5. If you are using the I2C bus in your project (such as for an RTC), keep in mind that you will only have analog inputs available on A0-A3. Also, the Freakduino-Chibi radio uses A2 and A3 for SPI. Therefore, only 2 analog inputs are available (that of A0 and A1).

Get Rid of LEDs Wherever Possible

Perhaps the hardest task of optimizing an Arduino for low power is to minimize your reliance on LEDs. Consider that a single LED adds about 20mA. Obviously, it is critical to be able to shut them off or remove them if shutting them off is not possible.

Unfortunately, we are attracted to LEDs. We rely on the power LED to indicate to us that the Arduino is on. We rely on the LED attached to pin 13 to indicate a heartbeat from the CPU. We rely on the transmit and receive LEDs to indicate messages being sent.

This reliance on status LEDs is something we will have to break with if we want to have long-lasting sensor nodes. But we don't have to get rid of LEDs completely. For example, setting a heartbeat LED on pin 13 to be active only when the Arduino is awake or once every 5 seconds is a good balance between power conservation and satisfying our "need to know."

If you are not transmitting messages constantly, you can likely leave the status LEDs alone. Because they are on only for brief moments, it should not hurt your power budget too much.

The real waster here is the power LED. You might want to leave it in place during design and debugging, but before sending the sensor out to the field, it should really be removed. You might need to desolder the LED from the board. If you like, you could hack the LED back on with a bit of hot glue, some wire, and a tiny switch. That way, you can switch the LED on during debugging, and cut it off for field work.

Fortunately, if you choose either the Chibi or Stalker boards, the LEDs are fully configurable via switches or jumpers. Another good reason to consider them when selecting a field sensor.

The Build

The following project should be looked at as just one example of a system you could build up. In this example, I am using a Freakduino-Chibi board with built-in boost converter. I am running the Chibi on just 2 AA rechargeable batteries, yet the boost converter allows me to operate at 5 volts and not have to worry about a stable reference voltage for the analog section. The complete system is illustrated in Figure 3-7.

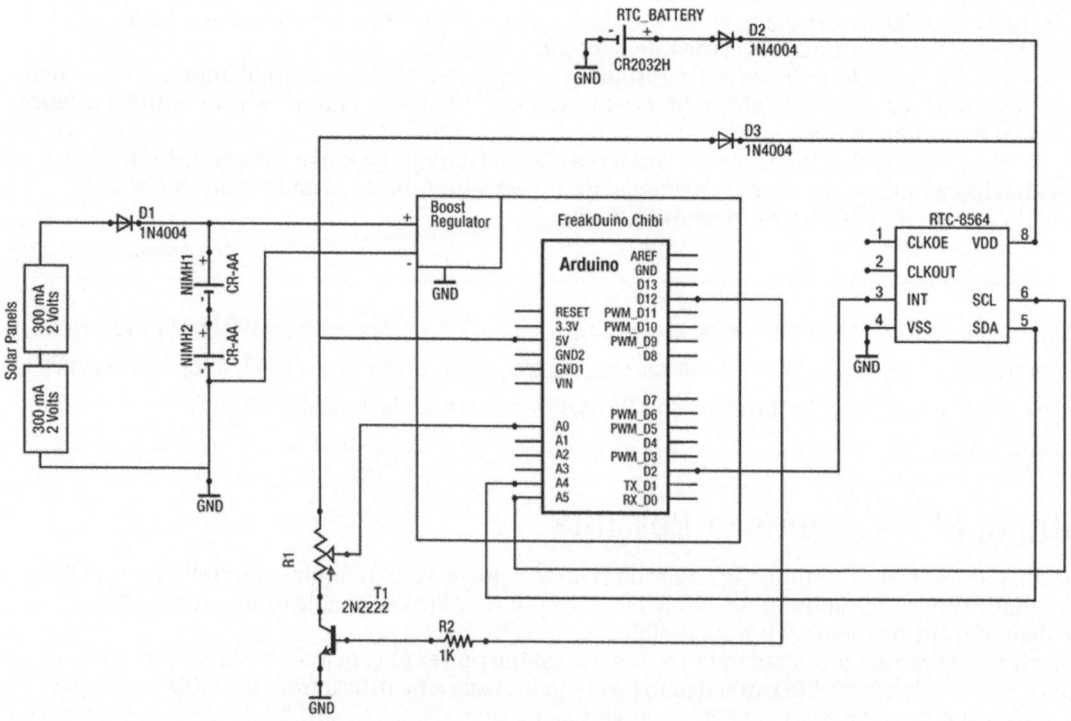

Figure 3-7. A complete sensor node, capable of solar charging, RTC-controlled sleep, and sensor power shutdown

I am also adding a very simple solar charge system using two panels and a diode. I have mounted everything in a cheap plastic box, intended to be a mobile prototyping system for wireless sensors. By adding 1/4 stereo phone jacks and cables, I have a clean exterior connection for simple analog sensors.

Finally, I stacked on a breadboard shield, onto which I can prototype circuits, such as the real–time clock system, sensor–power switch circuits, and additional analog conditioning.

You are surely going to choose different combinations of hardware, depending on what you have available, as well as ease of setup. I have chosen only one board to act as an example of the kind of system you could build, but you should look at it as only an example, and not the only way to do it. I chose to use the Chibi because it is sort of a middle ground board. Had I chosen the Stalker, this would only be an exercise in software and mounting because all the hardware work is essentially done for you. Had I chosen an off-the-shelf Arduino Duemilanove, we would be here all day hacking away, trying to optimize it.

Having commented on which Arduino to select and your power options, I leave those choices up to you. You might need to make some modifications to this example project based on the choices you made, and I will try to touch on those as they come along. However, the following project should work with just about any combination of hardware and power supply. Pay attention more to the method and understand that your parts can vary.

Obviously, hardware choice will drastically affect your code. Thankfully, much of it will be hidden behind libraries, but again consider this only an example of how to go about the process of bringing up your first low–power remote sensor. In particular, the RTC and sleep code will need your own special touch to get up and running.

Parts

For this project, you will need the following:

- An Arduino (Stalker, Chibi, or ProMini series are suggested).

- Boost regulator module or LiPo charge controller (optional, depending on the Arduino board you have).

- Battery pack (and possibly matching charge controller module).

- Solar panel/s.

- RTC8564 RTC module (or any I2C clock module with alarm and interrupt output).

- Coin cell battery and case for RTC backup battery (ex: CR2032 battery). Required only if your RTC module does not already have one.

- Weatherproof case large enough to contain components.

- Some sensors (I will simply use variable resistors on the remaining analog inputs to demonstrate a worst case example).

- Two general purpose diodes.

- Drill and various hand tools.

- Screws and nuts, or standoffs, to mount the Arduino in the case.

When choosing solar panels and super capacitors, you need to take into account the battery pack and operating voltage you have chosen. To charge the batteries, you need to provide a higher voltage from the solar cells. I will explain my system as an example.

In my case, I am using two AA batteries. Because they are rechargeable and their output is 1.2 volts each. So in series, my battery pack puts out 2.4 volts. The pack goes to an onboard boost circuit, which runs the Arduino at 5 volts. Because I am running the Arduino at 5 volts, I don't need to worry about changes in the analog input circuitry or code.

I chose two solar panels that output 2 volts at 300mA each. I wired the solar cells in series, so that I have a 4-volt, 300mA solar array. In order to protect the panels from reverse voltage from the battery, we need to install a diode on the positive side. Any general-purpose diode rated for more current than your panels provide will be fine. Keep in mind that a typical diode requires about 0.7 volts to forward bias. Thus this must be subtracted from the solar panel voltage output. After the diode, my 4 volt panel actually provides about 3.3 volts. This is nearly 1 volt more than the battery pack, so it should be acceptable.

I then tied this array to the battery pack in parallel. Under the noonday sun, with an idling Arduino, 4 volts (really 3.3 volts) from the solar panels is enough to charge the pack and power the Arduino. However, keep in mind that I only have 300mA coming from the cells. Assuming that the Arduino is turned off, and my batteries are high-capacity NiMH (such as 2100mA), it would take more than 7 hours of full sunlight to fully charge completely drained batteries. (It represents 2100mA divided by 300mA, which does not take into account that there is some overhead charging time. Remember that C/10 actually takes about 16 hours.) Obviously, with the additional load of the Arduino, the charge time increased dramatically. So I will need to be very stingy on how long I allow the Arduino to stay awake.

Finally, my RTC did not come with a battery backup circuit. I added my own in the form of a coin cell battery and holder. The schematic for this is much the same as the solar panel, except that we want to arrange it so that voltage from the Arduino supply does not flow into the coin cell, and vice versa.

To do that, we can use two diodes, one per power supply. Refer again to Figure 3-6. When power is applied to the Arduino, 5 volts passes through D3 to supply the RTC. This voltage is far above the voltage supplied by the small coin cell battery, so D2 is affectively blocked. When power is cut to the Arduino, D2 is now free to conduct, allowing the coin cell to keep the RTC alive, even though the Arduino is shut down. D3 prevents the coin cell from attempting to power up the Arduino. This will maintain the time and date for at least a few days.

Build Process

To complete this build, we will go through several steps. Keep in mind that in some steps your options will depend on what Arduino configuration you use. At the end of the process, I will demonstrate how to cut power to sensors when not in use, as well as using the RTC to put the Arduino to sleep and wake it back up. The steps we will follow are these:

- Preliminary test measuring the current draw of your system at full work load

- Determining operational duty cycle

- Calculating the expected battery requirements and life

- Calculating solar panel requirements

- Building the final system

I will outline the steps and provide further detail in the sections to come. It is best to read the whole chapter first, then come back here and follow the guide step by step. This is a process you will use many times as you build your own sensor networks.

Measuring Current Draw

We cannot select battery packs and solar panels until we have built the primary focus of our project and taken some current usage measurements. The first thing we need to do is to determine our worst case scenario regarding the current draw of our application. We need to know how much current the whole system will require when it is doing the most work. From this figure, we can calculate the minimum (worst case) uptime of the system. This is vital because if we want to ensure that the project will fulfill the requirements, we must design it so that this minimum uptime meets or exceeds the total uptime expected of the experiment for the duration of its lifetime.

Step 1: Building the Primary Focus of the Hardware

We start by building the primary hardware. At this time, we don't need to worry about the power sources. We are only interested in the Arduino, sensors, clock, and other bits and pieces. If you plan on having a user interface or data-logging hardware, go ahead and build them as well. Likewise, if it will be connected to a network or utilize wireless communications, get that up and running. In other words, get the project to a functional and complete state, but don't worry about mounting and power just yet.

If you have not thought of a specific project yet, I will present a sample system in the form of a variable resistor. By connecting a current meter to the power supply, I can observe current usage as I vary the knob position (and thus the resistance of the sensor). With the current meter installed, I can also get a feel for how much current the Arduino uses when it is idle, reading sensors, transmitting the data, and finally going to sleep. With those numbers in mind, I can better assess how often I need it to take readings.

Keep in mind that the code presented in this chapter, while functional, should be viewed as an example of how you can manage power issues. You will need to implement the functions into your own projects on a case-by-case basis.

Step 2: Inserting the Current Meter

Now that we have a functional project, we need to cut into the power connection so that we can insert a current meter. The power must flow *through* the current meter in order to measure current draw. We have a number of options, depending on how you plan on powering the project. The first question we need to ask is this: What will the operating voltage be?

If you plan to use the USB cable in your application, it is unlikely you are concerned with current usage, solar cells, and battery packs. I only mention this because if you are using the cable for debugging purposes, now is the time to "cut the cord." You will need to switch your debug connection to a wireless connection or temporarily comment out those sections in code while you measure the current usage. The USB cord will take over powering the Arduino, and you will not be running on batteries and solar cells.

Barrel Jack Method

If you will be powering the Arduino through the barrel jack, you will need to provide more than 5 volts on the jack. Also, keep in mind that the onboard regulator is not so efficient, so you will be consuming more current than using an independent regulator or boost converter.

1. Begin by gathering parts. You will need an AA battery holder for 4 or 6 batteries. You will also need a barrel jack that fits the Arduino. You can either get one you solder yourself, or one with wires already attached (by cutting it off a dead wall wart supply for example). If you choose to solder them yourself, you will need a bit of additional wire (preferably red).

2. Connect the negative terminal of the battery pack to the wire or pin on the plug that corresponds to the outside ring of the plug (see to Figure 3-2).

3. Now connect a bit of additional wire to the pin that corresponds to the inside hole in the plug.

4. Refer to Figure 3-8 (right). Load up the battery pack, plug it into the Arduino, and touch the two red wires together, completing the circuit from the positive terminal of the battery pack to the center hole on the plug. The Arduino should power up and get to work.

5. To connect your current meter, connect the red meter probe to the battery pack's positive terminal and the black meter probe to the positive wire from the plug.

Figure 3-8. Left: Unmodified 5-volt battery pack with barrel jack; right: cutting into the cable to insert a current meter.

Battery Wedge

Another method of measuring current draw is to use a battery case *wedge*. By placing a nonconductive material into the battery case between one cell and the spring contact of the case, you can cut into the circuit loop. Now you only need to complete the circuit again.

A simple way to do this is to use a small bit of thick paperboard. With the battery-to-spring-contact connection cut by the paperboard, insert the needle probes of your multimeter into the case on either side of the paperboard, so that one probe touches the battery tab, while the other touches the spring contact. You now have a complete circuit through the meter.

A far superior way to do this is to construct your own proper wedge, as shown in Figure 3-9. (In that figure, a small piece of double-sided PCB with two clip leads attached is inserted into a battery case. The clip leads are clipped to the probes of a current meter.) If you can cut copper clad circuit board, you should have no problem with this. Find a bit of clean copper circuit board, which has copper plate on both sides. Cut a small piece about 1 centimeter wide and 1 1/2 centimeters long.

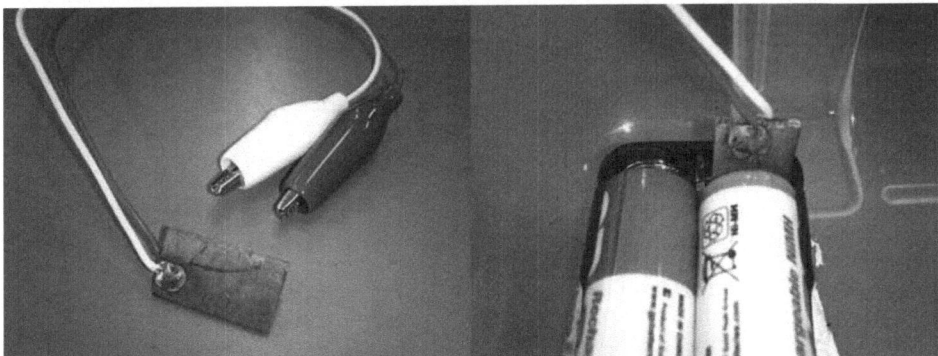

Figure 3-9. A battery wedge.

Now take a wire with small crocodile clips on both ends and cut it in half. Strip the insulation from the wire and tin the ends. Returning to the piece of copper board, scrub both sides clean with an abrasive cloth or sponge, and put a small bit of solder on both sides. Holding a wire to the board, touch both the wire and the solder lump to solder the wire to the surface of the board. Do this for both sides.

To use the wedge, just place it up against a spring contact before inserting a battery. Now clip each crocodile clip to one of the meter probes. You now have a hands-free current wedge.

■ **Caution** Exceeding the current rating of your meter (usually around 200 to 300 mA) will blow the fuse in your meter. Typically the Arduino is not likely to do this; the user is most likely to cause this frustration. A prototyping environment, with dangling wires and a hard-working engineer poking around, provides plenty of opportunities for there to be a temporary dead short across the battery pack. Be especially careful with a LiPo pack because it is not as forgiving of these sorts of transgressions as AA batteries. The most frustrating issue is that you will need to replace the fuse inside your meter. Be sure to buy a pack of 5 or 10 fuses and keep them handy.

Independent Regulator or Boost Converter

If you are using a boost converter or an independent regulator, you will need to construct a custom cable. Carefully read the explanation for the barrel jack method. You need to measure the current between the battery pack and the boost circuit board. This might be difficult or impossible if the battery pack and boost circuit board are one contained unit.

You will want to connect the 5 volt output of the circuit directly to the 5 volt pin on the Arduino rather than to the barrel jack. This will bypass the regulators, preventing them from being a power drain on your supply. You might need to cut the red wire of your battery pack, take your measurements, and then patch it back up. This is obviously not an ideal solution. A better solution is to insert some stiff wire into the holes of the battery connector and devise some method to connect them to the socket on the charge controller board. This is unfortunately a bit challenging, and I do not have a clean method for doing this (at least not one I am willing to demonstrate in public!).

Step 3: Taking Readings

When you have the assembled Arduino and clock breadboard shield, as described in the following "Assembly" section, and have loaded the code in Listing 3-1, you can take the readings.

1. Set the multimeter to measure DC current. It is usually best to set it to the highest setting first; then walk the knob down the scale for more accuracy after you have an initial feel for how much current the system is using. Be sure that the probes are connected to the correct jacks on the meter. Connect the red probe to the battery power lead and the black probe to the Arduino power lead.

2. Power up the Arduino and make sure everything is working properly. If not, immediately disconnect it and double-check your connections. Also, make sure the fuse within the meter did not blow. If it did, there is a serious problem, and the Arduino was drawing a very high amount of current.

3. Once you are satisfied that everything is in working order, begin by establishing any communication connections you have.

4. Measure current usage when the sensors are at their extremes. If you build the variable resistor circuit, turn all the pots in one direction so that they read 0. Record the current draw in a table.

5. Turn the sensors all the way in the opposite direction to read 1023 and record the current draw here as well. Fully exercise your project, so that you have strong familiarity with its current usage.

You might find it helpful to have some baselines to compare your readings with sort of like the benchmarking software you might have used on a PC, in which it compares your system to that of several other configurations. I took a few base readings of several Arduino and Arduino clone devices. The first reading is that of default configuration current consumption with a "do nothing" code. I simply uploaded the "basics/bareminimum" sketch to each device and measured its current running on a 4 cell AA battery pack. Rather than inject the power through the regulator using the barrel jack, in order to maintain consistency and fairness, I connected straight to the 5 volt pin of the Arduino shield socket. This has the affect of bypassing any regulators and boost circuits. I assumed that in the case of Uno like clones, readings would be pretty similar. The results were a bit surprising (Table 3-1).

Table 3-1. *Current Consumption of Several Arduino Clone Varieties, Running the Bare Minimum Code*

Device and Condition	Current (mA)
Stalker V2	17.8
Japanino	28.7
Chibi V1	39.3
Chibi V2	35.7
Chibi V2 with all LEDs off	26.5
Uno (Surface mount version)	60
Uno (Dual inline package version)	57.4
5 volt Pro Mini	24
3.3 volt Fio	4

In Table 3-1, all devices are running at 5.5 volts except the Fio.

The largest consumer of current in an Arduino–based wireless sensor node is the radio, followed by LEDs. Some might say that in normal operation in a wireless sensor system you should not need the LED (although looking at a circuit board without LEDs and wondering if it is "alive" is incredibly frustrating).

This is one of the reasons I like both the Chibi and Stalker boards. In the case of the Chibi, onboard LEDs can be switched off easily. In the case of the Stalker, you have to cut jumpers and resolder them later if you want the LEDs back, but the capacity is there to make your own decisions.

I suggest that you leave them enabled while prototyping and doing initial testing. When you are ready to walk away from the sensors for good, disable the LEDs.

Determining Operational Duty Cycle (Arduino Takes a Nap)

We can extend the uptime considerably by implementing a duty cycle. Essentially, we put the Arduino to sleep when we don't want to take a reading. In many situations, this is perfectly acceptable. In others, not so much. It is up to you (as the designer) to make the best determination.

Let's take a simple example: temperature. If you measure ambient air temperature for a weather experiment, you likely won't need to take a reading more than once every 5 to 10 minutes or so. This puts you in a really good situation for an extended uptime. The Arduino wakes up for only a few seconds every 10 minutes. Perhaps the Arduino will be awake no more than about 12 to 24 seconds every hour.

On the other hand, if you measure the temperature of a stream just past an industrial waste dump, in order to characterize damage to the ecosystem, you should measure much more often; perhaps once per minute. In this case, the Arduino will be awake 120 seconds every hour.

Optimizing the duty cycle of the project will help us to also optimize power usage over long periods of time. Once we know how much "awake time" we can expect in any given hour, we can predict how long the batteries will last.

The Real-Time Clock (RTC)

An RTC is an integrated circuit with a built-in oscillator. The circuit and oscillator are tuned so that the IC can accurately calculate the time with a high degree of accuracy. The IC has a bit of smarts added to it, and can calculate and then communicate the year, month, date, and day of the week in addition to hours, minutes, and seconds. Some RTCs also include additional features, such as an interrupt output, and multiple alarm modes such as a countdown timer or a specific time alarm.

When powering the time clock, it is a good idea to provide it with two sources. It is not necessary when building up your system, but should be installed before sending the system out to the field. The primary source will be the same power source for the rest of your circuit. A secondary backup battery will keep the clock running even when the system power is completely drained or removed. When system power is restored, the clock has kept the time accurately due to the backup battery. This is very useful feature if your sensor needs to be mobile. After completing an experiment in one location, you can shut it off, install it in a new location, and trust that the clock will not need to be reset.

Many modules provide a backup battery connector (and possibly the battery itself) on the board. Others do not. If the connector is not provided, you will need to build a small support circuit. You do not want the backup battery to try powering the Arduino, in case that system power is drained. You can stop this from happening by inserting a couple of diodes between the two power supplies.

In this project, I chose to use the Epson RTC8564, mounted on a small PCB with all the support parts, as shown in Figure 3-10. The PCB adapts the surface mount chip to a through hole package perfect for use on a breadboard. It also adds the required capacitors. It does not however provide a backup battery supply connector.

Figure 3-10. RTC8564 clock module before and after soldering the termination resistor and interrupt LED jumpers

If you cannot find an RTC8564 module locally, you should consider one based on the R8025, which is used in the Stalker board. That way, the existing Stalker library should work with your board. Another option is the DS3234. It uses SPI rather than I2C, but there are libraries available to make use of it. See Figure 3-11.

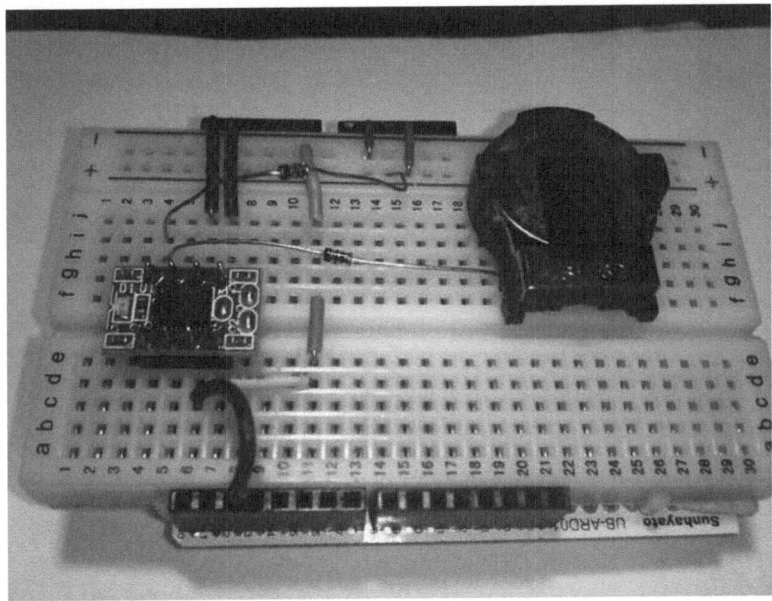

Figure 3-11. Assembling the clock and coin cell backup battery on the breadboard shield

The RTC8564 is an I2C wire interface. I2C is a two-wire communications standard that simplifies intercommunication between multiple intelligent devices. Briefly, the Arduino acts as the bus master, and several devices can be connected to the same two wires to act as slave devices. This means we can connect a whole lot of hardware to the Arduino using just two pins.

Unfortunately, the two pins required for I2C communications on the Arduino also happen to be analog input pins. Therefore, when using the I2C bus, we get only four analog inputs. This is not usually a problem because you can string many more sensors up to the I2C bus pins than you could if you used them strictly as analog inputs.

If you choose to use a different module than the RTC8564, please take into account the following points:

- It *must* be an I2C wire interface for this project to work.

- It *must* have an alarm and interrupt output (DS1307 does not work).

- You need to compare the data sheet of the part you choose with that of the RTC8564, and make some adjustments to the code:

  - Check the I2C address of the device you are using. Not all RTCs use the same device address.

  - Also, check the registry map of your device and compare it with that of the RTC8564. The registry map shows in which address each element of the time and date are stored, as well as the configuration bits for the clock.

- In theory, all I2C clocks will work roughly the same. However you might need to change the order in which you assign time storage variables from the date returned by the clock. For example, one clock IC could return hours, minutes, and then seconds. Another clock could return seconds, minutes, and then hours.

External Interrupts

An *interrupt* is like an alert to the CPU, which tells it to stop whatever it is doing and pay attention. Something important is happening. The CPU will save its current state and then switch to processing whatever interrupt occurred. Once finished, it can reload the saved state and pick up where it left off.

There are two kinds of interrupts: internal and external.

- An *internal interrupt* is usually caused by a timer. For example, the `millis` function uses one of the internal interrupts to trigger an action every millisecond (that of updating the counter).

- An *external interrupt* is hardware-based. It usually occurs on a digital input. For example, a robot might use an interrupt for a ledge detector. When approaching a cliff or stair, the edge detector will signal the CPU of impending doom. If the CPU does not respond immediately, the robot might tumble down.

One feature of the sleep function is that it can be woken up by an external interrupt. If we tie this external interrupt to an alarm clock, we can wake it up at predetermined times.

The RTC has an interrupt pin. In this case, it is an output. We can set an alarm time within the RTC, and on the designated time it will change the state of the interrupt pin. By feeding this pin into the external interrupt pin of the Arduino, it can listen in for that state change. This has the effect of waking up the CPU.

After completing its tasks for this wake cycle, we have two options to set the wake up time:

- We can set a timer, which will trip the interrupt every X seconds or minutes. This is convenient because we can set it and forget it. Every 30 seconds or 5 minutes (whatever we set it to), the clock will wake the Arduino.

- We can choose a very specific time and instruct the clock to wake the Arduino at that time. To do this, we need to make sure we first calculate the wake up time and load it into the clock before going to sleep; otherwise, the Arduino will go to sleep without an alarm, and never wake up.

Both options are useful in different situations. For example, a periodic sensor (or application here) is more likely to use the timer mechanism. An automatic watering system for a garden would need a specific schedule and thus use the second option. A later project in this book does just that.

More about Batteries

There are a lot of options when it comes to battery chemistry. Because we plan on charging the batteries over time, we avoid regular alkaline cells. For ease of use, nothing beats NiCD packs. They can be charged easily, and are not picky about how you do it. So long as the voltage input exceeds the voltage output of the cell, it will charge. They are not immune, but relatively resistant to overcharging. Finally, NiCD cells are quite cheap.

Other battery chemistries, such as lithium polymer or lithium ion cells are much more fragile. You will need to research safe operating temperatures and compare them with the experiment's environment. In addition, they will require specialized charge circuits designed for that particular chemistry and power output. Be sure to purchase the matching charger when buying cells.

Batteries are rated in milliamps per hour (mA/h). Essentially, it is the amount of current the fully charged cell can discharge under full load for the duration of one hour. That is not to say that the voltage or the current will remain constant for that hour. By the end of that hour, the cell is essentially depleted and must be recharged.

Also, the cell will most likely be damaged. Rechargeable batteries should not be discharged below a rated minimum (depending on chemistry, it is somewhere around half the C rating). NiCD and NiMH might survive a few "deep cycles" but will most surely die after a few rides. Lithium polymer will be permanently damaged by only one full discharge. Thankfully, most LiPo packs have built-in protection circuits to avoid this problem.

So taking into account that we should not discharge the cell to more than about half the rated voltage, it becomes clear that we must be careful that our estimates might be a bit optimistic.

Choosing Solar Panels

When choosing a solar panel (or combination of panels), you want to consider both the voltage output and current. You must choose a panel so that the voltage output exceeds that of the battery pack and that will provide more than enough current during peak current draw.

Assuming that you have a battery pack made up of two AA batteries in series, you have between 2.4 and 3 volts output, depending on the battery chemistry. In order to charge this battery pack, we need to provide at least 3.5 volts to it via the solar panel. Panels come in a range of voltages and currents, but the typical panel will either be a 5 or 6.5 volt panel. For example, the dark panel shown with the Stalker board in Figure 3-4 is a 5 volt panel at 100mA. However, the panels shown in Figure 3-12 are 2 volt panels at 300mA each, wired in series.

Figure 3-12. Solar panels mounted to the outside of a plastic box

When selecting a panel, find one with a current output exceeding the maximum current draw of the Arduino. (A rule of thumb is at least 100mA over the project requirements). This ensures that when the sun is out and the panel is doing all the work, It has 100mA to spare to pump into the batteries. With NiCD or NiMH, you should not exceed the current capacity of the cells divided by 10. If you have a 2100 mAh cell, a 200 mA panel is ideal. On the other hand, if you are using a LiPo pack with a charge controller, you can use a panel array generating upward of 500 mA or more. Be sure to check the specifications of the charge controller for maximum input current before proceeding.

Assembly

Now that you have collected all the parts, looked over data sheets, and become familiar with the clock's operation, it's time to start the final assembly. You have a few steps to complete and you can do them in practically any order you feel like. Here is my build process:

1. Solder the leads of the solar panel and mount them to the case.

2. Complete the wiring harness for the power supply system.

3. Glue the battery case in place.

4. Drill holes and mount the Arduino.

5. Drill holes and mount sensors (in my case, I chose panel mount 1/4 inch stereo sockets, into which I can plug sensors soldered to plugs).

6. Build the clock circuit on a breadboard shield or solder directly to a prototyping shield.

Prepare the Solar Panels

When soldering the leads to the panels, be sure you leave plenty of length. Also, it helps later if you use twisted pair wires or two conductor cables. It keeps the leads to each panel together. Also be sure that you can easily identify which wire is positive and which is negative. Using red and black cable is a very good idea.

1. Figure out where you will attach the panels and their orientation. If possible, set them so that both sets of leads can enter through one hole in the case. Mark the location with a marker if you need a guide mark.

2. Drill a hole large enough for both the wires to pass through.

3. Insert the leads and pull them through.

4. Now position the panels in place. You can use hot melt glue or silicon caulk to hold them in place and create a watertight seal to the case.

5. Be sure to glue over the seam where the two panels come together. I advise doing a temperature test on the chosen glue first. Some silicon glues melt in direct sunlight. I chose hot glue because I could be certain that the melting temperature is well above typical ambient temperatures.

Wire the Power Supply Subsytems

With the panels in place, you can begin to wire the power supply circuit:

1. Split the wire pairs from each panel a bit, so that you can solder the series connection between them.

2. Solder the positive wire from one panel to the negative wire of the other panel. Cover this joint with electrical tape.

3. You should now have a positive wire from one panel and a negative wire from the other panel hanging free. Identify the positive wire; you need to attach the diode to this wire.

    Take a close look at your diode. One end will have a black or white stripe painted around it. Solder the *opposite* end of the diode to the red wire. Now solder another length of red wire to the end with the stripe. Cover the whole assembly with tape.

4. At this point, it might be nice to test your panels. Take the case and a multimeter out into the sun. Place the case down on the ground with the panels facing up.

5. Connect the red probe of your multimeter to the wire coming from the diode. Connect the black probe to the other wire. Set your meter to read DC voltage. Verify that the panels output the expected voltage.

    If so, move along to the next step. If not, double-check the connection between the panels, as well as the diode connection.

Mount the Battery Case and Connect the Supplies

Depending on the connection you have available on the battery case, you could complete this step a number of ways. For instance, I had a 9 volt battery snap on the 2AA case. I opted to solder wires directly to the snap rather than purchase a connector with leads. If you have a battery case with wires, this step is actually quite easy.

1. If you have a lot of room in your case, consider mounting a terminal strip, in which you can easily insert all the positive wires into one terminal and screw it down tight, making a connection.

2. If you don't have enough space, you will have to make do by banding the wires together and making one large solder joint and then covering it with tape.

3. Connect the solar panel leads to the battery case. You can use a clip or solder directly to the snaps. Be sure you connect red to red (positive to positive) and black to black (negative to negative).

4. Finally, add a power lead from these two junctions of wire to the DC input jack provided on the Arduino. Here you will need to make a decision about how you want to connect to the Arduino. It really depends on the Arduino you are using.

I added a super capacitor to my power circuit. This is purely for my own use and is not necessary for your project. It allows me to operate the project without batteries.

Now is another good opportunity to run through a systems check. Insert rechargeable batteries (NiCD or NiMH) into the case and flip the power switch on the Arduino. It should power up. If not, double-check all your connections.

Now take the kit out into the sun. Turn off the Arduino, remove the AA batteries, and then turn the Arduino back on. The solar panels should be outputting enough power to run the Arduino. If not, double-check the connections. If your panels have any chance whatsoever of charging the batteries, they must at least be able to power the Arduino on their own.

Install the Sensors

I used a set of 1/4-inch stereo sockets to connect my sensors. You are familiar with them as the same plug you insert headphones into. This is a convenient plug because it provides three connections to the outside of the case. We need power, ground, and the sensor signal to pass through the case to our external sensor, so it is a logical choice.

When considering jacks or connectors, avoid pcb mount connectors. Unless you know precisely where the shield board will sit in the case, it is very hard to line up the drill to put the holes in the correct place. Instead, use panel jacks, which mount in the hole drilled in the case, and have wires coming off the inside to connect up to the Arduino. Thus you can mount the jacks anywhere you want.

On close inspection of Figure 3-13, you will see that I mounted five jacks, even though we have only four free analog inputs. I also mounted an external power switch. This simply cuts the positive wire before going into the Arduino. It's just more convenient than opening the case to turn the sensor node on and off.

Figure 3-13. This shot shows the RTC mounted in the box, with four analog inputs connected.

When installing the jacks, one trick I found that helped a lot was to orient them all the same direction. I then striped one long length of wire and soldered it to each of the positive legs on the jacks. I then did the same for the negative legs. Thus, I had one solid "bus bar." I then soldered lengths of wire with pins attached to insert into the breadboard shield or directly into the Arduino header.

Build the Clock Circuit

The I2C communication bus requires two termination resistors at the end of the chain in order to work. Many I2C modules come with the resistors on board and have jumpers that you can install or small solder pads that need to be connected. If you find that your clock data appears to be random, be sure that the jumpers are installed or the pad is soldered.

My initial tests with the RTC8564 module appeared promising. I had modified the Time library from the Arduino Playground and thought that I was getting good time data. Strangely, every once in awhile, the time would reset. What is worse, the clock did not maintain the time when the Arduino was reset, even though the power to the clock was never disconnected. Finally, I tried a series of other libraries, and was finding that they reported bizarre data as well.

After a few hours of head scratching, I called in the special forces. Yep. I phoned a friend. The first thing he said was "check your termination resistors." Long story short, be sure the jumpers or solder pads are connected!

I decided to go ahead and solder the interrupt LED pad as well. It helps a lot when debugging the hardware. I can tell right away that the interrupt and alarm function on the clock is functional, just by watching for the LED to flash. I can always desolder the pad when I am ready to deploy if I feel I need to save a little more power.

Connecting the clock module should be fairly straightforward if it has onboard termination resistors. Figure 3-14 shows one way to accomplish it. Simply attach power and ground to the breadboard power strips. Next, connect the SDA pin on the clock module to the SDA pin on the Arduino, which is analog pin 4. SCL from the clock module must go to analog pin 5. Finally, we need to connect the interrupt pin from the clock module to digital pin 2.

Figure 3-14. Close-up of the clock build, minus backup battery circuitry

Software

I will present an example of how you can integrate the RTC and alarm interrupt into a project so it will shut down the Arduino and go to sleep. After the specified time has elapsed, the RTC will wake the Arduino by changing that state of the clock interrupt output. This output is tied to the Arduino digital input pin 2, which is configured as a wake up interrupt.

Because this is only an example, your code might vary somewhat—it mostly depends on the actual RTC module in question. However, if you follow the preceding guide when selecting your clock (I2C, interrupt output, and so on), you can easily modify the library for the RTC8564 to suit the module you purchased. These clocks all work roughly the same way, as constrained by the I2C bus communication requirements. It is simply a matter of copying the library, renaming it, and then editing the files. In particular, you need to adjust the addresses for the various time elements, as well as a possible modification to some byte data used in configuring the clock. Any further discussion is beyond the scope of this book, but I wrote an article (`http://diy-scib.org/2011/05/using-the-rtc8564-on-arduino/`) in which I modify the DS1307RTC library that accompanies the Time library to exercise the RTC8564. Note that this library does not provide for alarm and interrupt functionality, so it should only be considered an example of how to mod libraries for similar devices.

After the Arduino wakes up, it reads four analog inputs. It then reports the time as well as the analog data over the USB serial port to the serial monitor. The USB cable will be powering the Arduino in this case, negating all the hard work we did building the solar power and battery system. This is only a test to verify that we can get the clock working and integrate it with our own project. We have a lot of functional blocks to verify and we need to take it one step at a time. The next chapter will follow up on this project, adding radio transmission and SD card backup of the data.

Libraries

Because the modified DS1307 library does not allow for alarms and interrupts, I had to either do a more aggressive search for an appropriate library or start building my own. Luckily, I was able to turn up a Japanese website that featured the RTC8564 (it is more popular in Japan than the DS1307RTC). Don't worry; I won't force you to learn Japanese just to use this clock module! You can download Daisuke Sonoda's RTC8564AttachInterrupts library here:
`http://projectsbiotope.blogspot.com/2011/03/arduino-3.html`.

Install the entire folder into the `Arduino/Libraries` folder. In addition, you should pick up the RTC8564AttachInterruptSleep sketch at the same URL. Finally, you will need the Sleep library from Arms22 installed in the library folder:

`http://code.google.com/p/arms22/downloads/detail?name=Sleep003.zip`.

Code

The code in Listing 3-1 is mostly Daisuke's work. The clock is set to wake the Arduino every 10 seconds by triggering an interrupt on digital pin 2. Upon waking up, the Arduino gets 4 analog values and prints them to the serial port. Most of it is dealing with setting the clock time and preparing the sleep and interrupt routines. If you started by loading his sketch, you need only to add a few lines of code. I only added a few lines of code to acquire the analog readings and print them to the serial port. I realize that slaving the Arduino to a serial cable defeats the purpose of building a solar and battery powered system. I only wanted to verify that the Arduino was in fact going to sleep, waking up to take measurements and reporting in. From here, you could easily send the date to an SD card, or move on to the next chapter, where we send the data over a radio connection.

Listing 3-1. Setting the RTC8564 Clock Time and Putting the Arduino to Sleep

```
/*
 * sketch name     : Rtc8564AttachInterruptSleep_Analogs
 * summary         : RTC8564で定周期タイマー割り込み & スリープ
 * releases        : 2011/3/15
 */

#include <Wire.h>
#include <Rtc8564AttachInterrupt.h>
#include <Sleep.h>

/* Project variables */
int A0raw, A1raw, A2raw, A3raw;


/* RTC */
#define RTC_SEC  0x00    // seconds
#define RTC_MIN  0x18    // minutes
#define RTC_HOUR 0x23    // hour in 24hr format
#define RTC_DAY  0x15    // day of the month
#define RTC_WEEK 0x02    // day of the week (00:Sunday - 06:Saturday)
#define RTC_MON  0x03    // month
#define RTC_YEAR 0x11    // year
byte date_time[7] = {
   RTC_SEC
  ,RTC_MIN
  ,RTC_HOUR
  ,RTC_DAY
  ,RTC_WEEK
  ,RTC_MON
  ,RTC_YEAR
};

/* Check the power reset flag - this will decide if we should reset the clock or not */
boolean init_flg = false;
/* Measurement interval - how long do we want the Arduino to sleep? */
#define RTC_INTERRUPT_TERM 10
/* What is the interval? 0:seconds, 1:minutes */
#define RTC_INTERRUPT_MODE 0

/* Which pin is the clock interrupt connected to? We only have a few options */
#define RTC_INTERRUPT_PIN  2
void setup() {
  Serial.begin(9600);
  // Date and Time initialization
  Rtc.initDatetime(date_time);
```

```
   // RTC start
   Rtc.begin();

   // Check periodic interrupt time
   if (!Rtc.isInterrupt()) {

     // if so, set interrupt
     Rtc.syncInterrupt(RTC_INTERRUPT_MODE, RTC_INTERRUPT_TERM);
   }

   // interrupt setting
   pinMode(RTC_INTERRUPT_PIN, INPUT);
   digitalWrite(RTC_INTERRUPT_PIN, HIGH);
}

void loop() {
   // Upon waking up, we should check to see if there was a power event if (init_flg)
ReadRTC(); init_flg = true;
   // stuff to do before sleep
   // read the pins
   A0raw = analogRead(0);
   A1raw = analogRead(1);
   A2raw = analogRead(2);
   A3raw = analogRead(3);
   // print it up
   Serial.print(A0raw);
   Serial.print(" : ");
   Serial.print(A1raw);
   Serial.print(" : ");
   Serial.print(A2raw);
   Serial.print(" : ");
   Serial.println(A3raw);
   Serial.println();


   // Sleep time! Dont put anything else in the main loop after this!
   // Delay required to assure wake cleanly
   delay(100);
   SleepClass::powerDownAndWakeupExternalEvent(0);
}

void ReadRTC()
{
   Rtc.available();
   Serial.print(0x2000 + Rtc.years(), HEX);
   Serial.print("/");
   Serial.print(Rtc.months(), HEX);
   Serial.print("/");
   Serial.print(Rtc.days(), HEX);
   Serial.print(" ");
   Serial.print(Rtc.hours(), HEX);
   Serial.print(":");
```

```
        Serial.print(Rtc.minutes(), HEX);
        Serial.print(":");
        Serial.print(Rtc.seconds(), HEX);
        Serial.print(" ");
        Serial.println((int)Rtc.weekdays());
}
```

As always, the first thing we need to do is include all the libraries needed later. The `Wire` library, which is responsible for the I2C interface, is installed when you install the Arduino IDE.

After including libraries, let's go ahead and define any variables we need for our end of the project. In the example, I simply wanted to read out the remaining four analog ports as raw data.

Next you see the block of RTC defines. This block of defines is where you will set the initial clock time and date. Although the digits are hex, they appear and read as normal digits. Thus, in the example code, the seconds are set to 0, the minutes to 18, the hour to 23 (ll p.m.), and so on. This block will set your clock to Tuesday March 15th, 2011 at 11:18 p.m. We then establish a 7 byte array, containing the date and time data.

After dealing with defining the time, we set up a few more variables and defines, including a flag that will tell us if the clock lost power and needs to be reset. We also define the period of time we want the Arduino to sleep. The `RTC_INTERRUPT_TERM` defines a count, while `RTC_INTERRUPT_MODE` defines what to count (minutes or seconds). With values of 10 and 0, the clock will wake the Arduino every 10 seconds. If the values were 15 and 1, the clock would wake the Arduino up every 15 minutes. Finally, we need to define which interrupt pin to use. Our only options for interrupts are D2 and D3 on a typical Arduino, with an additional 4 on the Mega (D18-D21).

Whenever the Arduino powers up for the first time, it always runs the `Setup` function one time. Here we establish communications. For the moment, we will continue to use the serial port for debugging, but in the next chapter we will convert it to a wireless radio. Next, because we know that the Arduino is fresh out of a powerup, we need to initialize the RTC, which will also prepare the I2C pins. Then we can establish a connection to it with `Rtc.Begin`.

With a connection established, the first thing we should do is ask the clock whether it has a periodic timer set. If it is not (by placing the ! in front of `Rtc.isInterrupt()`, which is an `Rtc` function defined in the Rtc library to check the clock settings), we sync the clock with the defines set previously. Finally, we can finish up by setting up the Arduino interrupt pin to prepare it for receiving interrupts.

Moving into the loop, the first thing we want to do is check whether the clock had been initialized and is running. Look back to the beginning of the code and you will see that the `init_flag` is defined and set to false. Thus, the first time through the loop, the `if` function will fail. We will not bother reading the clock the first time around. Instead, we set the flag to true, so that next time through the loop (and every time thereafter, so long as we don't lose power), we fetch the clock data using the `ReadRTC` function. Finally we get to our part of the code, in which we read the analog ports and print the data to the serial port. Before exiting the loop, we pause a moment, and finally put the Arduino to bed.

Testing It Out

For the first test, just run the serial monitor and verify that you are getting data and that it comes in every 10 seconds. You should see something like this:

```
2011/3/15 23:31:40 2

250 : 361 : 582 : 48


2011/3/15 23:31:50 2

248 : 358 : 582 : 48
```

If you have random information in the top line of each entry, there is something wrong with your clock circuit. It is likely something to do with the termination resistors. The second row prints out ADC values. Be sure that they are working properly by turning the variable resistors and observing the data. Alternately, you can tie the analog input pin high or low with a jumper. It should read either 0 or 1023.

Put It in a Case

Once you have verified that it all functions properly and have done some current testing to be sure you can predict the amount of uptime you can achieve, you should start thinking about mounting the system in a case. Before doing so, skim ahead to the next chapter. We will expand upon this chapter to add radio communications to the Arduino. You will want to be sure your case has room to fit your radio plan. In photos of the sample box seen in this chapter, I mounted the Arduino with the antenna inside the box. You can choose either/or.

The box I chose was a cheap box from a discount store (see Figure 3-15— obviously, I would not deploy a sensor like this; for a proper outdoor case, consider a Pelican or PacTec case. It was only meant to be a quick-and-dirty mockup of what I wanted to do, but turned out to be so handy for development that I now take it with me almost everywhere I go. It doubles as a AA battery charger when I am not using it for developing projects.

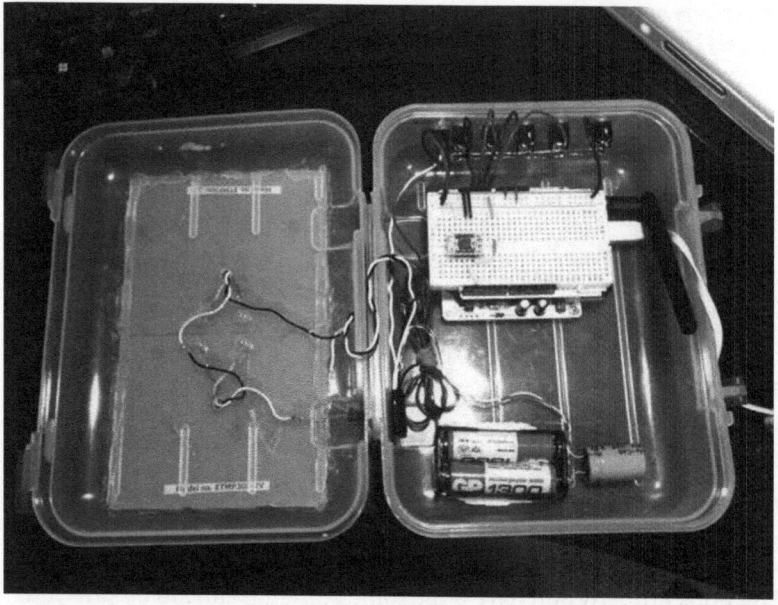

Figure 3-15. A $2 box makes a decent portable development kit.

Obviously, you will want to find a way around the USB tether for communicating data. You can check out the next chapter. Another option is to add an SD card and save data to it using one of the many Sdfat16/32 libraries available. Or you might have a project in mind that needs remote power, but does not need to record data. Remember that this chapter should serve as an assemblage of modular concepts that can be used individually or collected into a powerful monitoring device.

Resources

- A great link on how the Arduino sleep functions work:
  http://www.arduino.cc/playground/Learning/ArduinoSleepCode

- RTC8564AttachInterrupts library:
  http://projectsbiotope.blogspot.com/2011/03/arduino-3.html

- Arms22's Sleep library:
  http://code.google.com/p/arms22/downloads/detail?name=Sleep003.zip

- About Zener diodes: http://en.wikipedia.org/wiki/Zener_diode and
  http://knol.google.com/k/electronic-circuits-design-for-beginners-chapter-7#

- Charging NiCD and NiMH batteries: http://www.powerstream.com/NiCd.htm

- SparkFun
    - Boost converter/energy harvester: http://www.sparkfun.com/products/10255
    - LTC3588 energy harvester: http://www.sparkfun.com/products/9946
- AdaFruit
    - Solar LiPo charger: https://www.adafruit.com/products/390
    - MintyBoost: https://www.adafruit.com/products/14
- RTCs with interrupt support:
    - RTC8564
        - Akizuki module: http://akizukidenshi.com/catalog/g/gI-00233/
        - Library: http://code.google.com/p/arms22/downloads/detail?name=Sleep003.zip
    - Stalker 2
        - SeeedStudio Wiki: http://seeedstudio.com/wiki/index.php?title=Seeeduino_Stalker_v2.0
        - RTC RX8025 data sheet: http://www.spezial.com/commercio/dateien/produktbeitraege/RX-8025SA_NB.pdf
    - DS3234 breakout from SparkFun: http://www.sparkfun.com/products/10160
- Weatherproof cases:
    - Pac Tec: http://www.pactecenclosures.com/
    - Pelican 1020: http://www.pelican.com/cases_detail.php?Case=1020
    - Polycase: http://www.polycase.com/

CHAPTER 4

Telesensation

Wireless Communication for Long Distance Measurement

In the previous chapter, I introduced a remotely powered Arduino sensor platform that used batteries and solar panels. It included a real-time clock that allows the Arduino to go to sleep between measurement intervals in order to conserve as much power as possible.

I pointed out that while shopping around for Arduinos for the project that you should consider the future goal of transmitting the collected data over a wireless connection. Chances are, if you need batteries and solar power to keep your sensor running, you don't have wires to communicate. If you had, you could simply provide power and communications over the same cable. Therefore, I suggested several options, but one in particular stood out when considering building wireless sensor networks: the Freakduino-Chibi wireless Arduino clone.

This chapter will expand upon the previous project, adding the much needed wireless functionality. If you built the project using the Freakduino, you are ready to hit the ground running today. If not, skip back to the previous chapter and study it carefully before moving on.

The sensor node will read a collection of sensors at a remote site, transmit them to a receiving node attached to our computer, and then go to sleep for a predetermined time before waking up to do it all over again. Via solar charging, the node should last several days. The receiving node will hand the data off to a Processing application that will visualize and save the data to a file.

Getting the Lay of the Land

There is a bit of terminology you need to keep straight as you work through this project. There are several pieces of software and hardware that interrelate. Let's start with the hardware:

- A *wireless network* is an interconnection of *nodes* without the need for wires. Communication messages are transmitted "over the air." This describes everything from cell phones to televisions. In this chapter, we are referring to a network established utilizing the IEEE 802.15.4 protocol.

- There are many styles of network that can exist over the 802.15.4 protocol. For our purposes, we are concerned with Personal Area Networks (PANs). The most common PANs are these:

    - **Point-to-point**: two nodes exclusively communicating with each other.

- **Point-to-multipoint**: a Hub/Star network. A coordinator node acts as the controlling authority on the network. Communication from node to node is via rigidly defined paths.

- **Mesh**: Nodes are interconnected, and pathways are dynamic. The network "self organizes." In the case of Xbee, mesh networking is only available on Series 2 devices.

- A *protocol* is a series of rules that determine how the network functions. The 802.15.4 protocol specifies the physical layer (transmission hardware) as well as the media access layer (the method by which your software can talk and listen to the transmission hardware).

- A *node* is a device capable of communicating over the wireless network. In this case, each Arduino is considered a node. A node contains a radio transceiver. The node in charge of the network is called the *coordinator* (sometimes called a master). Other nodes on the network are either *routers* or *end devices* (sometimes referred to as slave devices). Every node has a unique node ID. A Mesh network might have no coordinators. All nodes can act as routers.

- A *radio transceiver* is a radio device that can transmit as well as receive data on the wireless network.

- A *data sink* is a collection point for data sources. It is usually a node with an attached storage device, connected to the Internet, or connected to a computer (or any combination of all three). On large networks, the coordinating node usually doubles as the data sink.

- A *channel* can be thought of as a television or radio channel. It is a specific portion of radio frequency on which we are transmitting or receiving. Only one wireless network can exist on each channel without risking constant data collisions.

- A *node ID* is a unique identifier associated with each node and is used to identify messages to and from the node. The node ID of the coordinator node and data sink nodes are of particular importance, as they are used to control message flow across the network.

Planning the Message Flow and Hardware

To clarify these points, we could take a detour into brainstorming a network topology and how we would like the message flow to operate. The following is not necessary to get a simple two-node network up and running (the goal of this project), so you can skip ahead if you so desire. However, if you have plans for multiple nodes, you might consider glancing through this section to get an overview of one method for network control.

In the following sections, I have outlined just one set of strategies out of many for dealing with the problem of managing message traffic on a wireless channel. It is decidedly complex, yet less so than some. Only the simple network strategy will be implemented here because the complex network strategy is beyond the scope this book.

A Simple Network

Network one contains only a single data source and a single data sink. In such a case, the simplest method of communication is to utilize a point-to-point topology. We instruct the data source to transmit data at will. It will transmit without ever concerning itself about the readiness of the data sink to receive data. Assuming that we are the only two devices on the network, it is pretty safe to assume that the data sink will always be ready and listening for new data. Our only problem is when the data sink needs to send something back to the data source. If the remote sensor (the data source) goes into a sleep mode between transmissions, there is no guarantee that it will be listening for this transmission. Thus the data source is acting like the coordinator while the data sink acts as an end node.

This method is not without flaws, but is incredibly easy to implement. There really is no coordinator *per se*. It is up to us to be sure that we account for message flow between the nodes. If we intend to put nodes to sleep, we need to be sure that we have a mechanism within the code to inquire about waiting messages before powering down.

In this chapter, we will build a simple point-to-point network, in which the source node will go to sleep. It will not wait for return messages. It will be strictly one way communication.

A Complex Network

The second example network includes several different data sources and sinks on network. Let's imagine a weather station up on the roof and a garden monitoring system. Perhaps we would like to share our weather data with the world via Pachube (see Chapter 5) while recording garden data history on a PC.

Imagine that our network is made up of four nodes. There are two outdoor data sources (the weather station and the garden monitor). There is another Arduino permanently attached to the Internet via an Ethernet shield. It acts as the data sink for the weather station and reports data directly to Pachube. Finally, we have a fourth node attached to our PC, which acts as the data sink for the garden monitor.

Which device should act as the master to coordinate communications among the four devices? At first, you might think the logical choice is the data sink attached to the PC. But consider how often your PC is turned off (you *do* save power when you are not home, don't you?). What would happen to the communication structure when you reboot or shut down? A better choice might be the other sink device. It is always on and online, even when your PC is off.

Now let's consider the message flow. First we need to identify nodes on the network. Imagine the following two scenarios:

- A slave powers up for the first time. It needs to announce itself to the master without disturbing communications. Because slave devices must be careful about communicating while other devices are using the channel, we must devise a simple method (protocol) to announce the devices on the network after they power up without adversely affecting existing and scheduled message traffic.

- In another scenario, the master node has a power interruption and falls out of communication. The slaves are patiently awaiting messages from the master, and are not going to announce themselves again and risk causing a communication error. They are in effect assuming the master is still online and is aware of them. We need a simple way to allow the master to query all the devices on the network when its power is restored.

Node IDs are very helpful to us in both cases. Let's start with the second situation first. The master node comes alive. Its first task is to see if any other nodes are already awake and waiting for it. It can send out a broadcast message to *all* nodes, asking them to check in. Because each node has a unique number, they can listen in, waiting for their turn to check in. The lowest-numbered node responds first, essentially saying "Yep, I'm here." All other nodes listen in, noting the last node ID to check in. They then calculate the difference between their own node ID and the last one that checked in.

Next, they multiply that value by x milliseconds (let's say $x = 100$). Now they start a countdown timer. If no other node checks in by the time the timer expires, it will go ahead and sound off to the master node. This system creates a sort of queuing window, in which each ID is given a 100–millisecond time slot. It ensures that each node checks in sequence with a reasonable allowance of time before skipping a node ID.

Unfortunately, on a sensor network, it is likely that most sensors are going to go to sleep to conserve power. The master node must give the sensor a specific time to check in. Something like "Hey, wake up in 15 seconds and check in. I will then query you for data." So we have a situation in which the sensor is sleeping, waiting for the 15 seconds to elapse. When the master node resets from a power failure, this plan might not be in memory. Therefore, the sensor node wakes up and announces itself, even if there are other nodes trying to check in. We have to plan a course of action when such a situation occurs.

One solution involves a two-pronged attack. First, we make certain that the sensor first listens to the channel, waiting for it to be clear of traffic. Second, it announces itself on the network. Finally, the master must send an acknowledgment to the sensor before it can assume itself to be a reliable node on the network.

In the event that another node was scheduled to transmit at precisely the same time as the new node sent its announcement, there will be a data collision. To handle this situation, we instruct the sensor to wait for a response from the master before sending any further data. If the response does not come back before a countdown timer expires, we can generate a random number and use it to calculate a new countdown timer. After this second timer expires, we send another announcement.

By solving the announcement-collision issue, we also subsequently solved the first scenario: a lone slave resetting from a power failure and attaching to a preexisting network.

The preceding model, while complex, is not impossible to implement in the Arduino. Depending on the radio hardware you are using, some or all the functions mentioned may be implemented already. Before settling on any particular radio hardware, you should carefully consider what the future needs of your network will be, how you intend to handle message traffic, and what features the radio implements natively to handle these situations. Preferably, you should choose the technology that implements a complete strategy rather than offloading it to the Arduino, and thus to you. The Arduino should be focused on handling the sensors and high-level tasks.

For our simple two-node project, we won't need to concern ourselves with most of the previous issues. I felt it was important to mention it though, in case you decide to venture fourth, building ever more complex networks. It always helps to have a good plan before you start.

A Look at Available Radio Options

You have a number of communication options to choose from. Some of them are not specifically Arduino shields, but are designed for general electronics hobbyists as well.

Serial AM/FM Radio

The oldest trick in the book for wireless radio communications is to use serial radios. They are either AM- or FM-band radios that accept a TTL serial input. It is still a very functional and valid choice today. The modules are cheap and available at enough frequencies that you can usually find one that will conform to your local laws. There are three forms of radio: transmitter, receiver, and transceiver (for bidirectional communication).

These radio modules are not specifically Arduino shields. However, they usually fit into a breadboard quite easily and have only a few pins to connect (generally only 5 volts, ground, and data lines). An example module is the FM breakout module from SparkFun: `http://www.sparkfun.com/products/8482`.

Most of these modules function as either a serial port or a similarly simple connection. In fact, you could use two transceiver radios to remotely upload a new sketch to your device! Simply attach one transceiver to a USB-to-serial device and the matched transceiver to the Arduino Tx and Rx pins. To be precise, you still need to hit the reset button on the Arduino at just the right moment to force the bootloader to prepare for a new sketch. However, there are modified bootloaders that get around this limitation for true remote wireless uploading.

Serial radios are a great option for adding simple point-to-point network functionality to existing Arduino hardware. They are very simple to operate (think serial print commands) and require no special configurations. The only major disadvantage is that they operate very close to commercial signals and can be hard to tune when near other radio stations. It may not be an issue for many projects (it would work quite well for this chapter's project). Also, very little in the way of flow control is implemented over the radio channel, offloading much of that to the coder. At first this may not sound like an issue, but when you consider that these radios generally operate in the AM and FM bands, there could be all sorts of interference from garage door openers, old radio telephones, and a host of other devices.

Bluetooth UART/Serial Modems

Another easy (and relatively cheap) option is to build your network on Bluetooth. Easy-to-interface serial adaptors are readily available, which act in much the same way as the serial FM radios. You simply make a few serial connections and you are ready to go. Again, you are limited to a two-node network (unless you are willing to create some complex firmware for the Arduino). You may also need to set some network IDs within the radios before establishing your connection, in order to avoid conflicts with other Bluetooth devices in the area.

A Google search for "Bluetooth uart module" will bring up more than a few options. The Robotstore carries multimode modules for under $20. You will need to find a USB module as well or use an FTDI adaptor with the Robotstore module in order to connect up to your PC.

Cutedigi carries a wide range of Bluetooth uart modules and supplies, including an Arduino with onboard Bluetooth, and a mini USB Bluetooth module for under $10.

Zigbee and Xbee

Zigbee is not hardware *per se*. Rather, it is a wireless stack specification. It defines how a wireless node should handle data transmission. The specification deals with most of the problems with wireless communications for us.

You could certainly pay a lot of money to the relevant organization and port the Zigbee specification directly into code to run on the Arduino. You would still need a radio. In the case of Zigbee, you usually use a radio that operates around either 900 Mhz (varies slightly with jurisdiction) or the 2.4 Ghz band. 2.4 Ghz is the same frequency as PC wireless routers. Regardless of operating frequency, The 802.15.4 specification assigns channels within the frequency band.

- Europe: 868-868.6 Mhz, 1 channel

- North America: 902-928 Mhz. 30 channels

- Worldwide: 2400-2483.5 Mhz, 16 channels

Rather than building your own radio modules, the simpler option is to buy a prepared module that includes an appropriate radio, as well as a purpose built microcontroller that implements the stack for you. You pay an added cost for the one-piece license of the stack, but you save a lot of hard work on your end.

The most common Zigbee radio used with Arduinos is the Xbee line of modules. These modules require an additional shield to mount them on an Arduino. It is not hard to imagine that as your Arduino gets stacked up with shields and modules, so does the cost of each node. Just about anyone selling Arduino hardware also sells Xbee modules and adaptor shields.

Zigbee is a complex beast. If you are going to dig in to the hardware, it is worth your time and effort to at least skim through the reference manuals available at digi.com. In addition, a few good books exist on the subject.

While searching for reference material online, virtually every user-rated experience I found reported difficulties getting things working well. I myself had trouble getting my series 2 radios to connect. Once I finally worked that issue out (lesson learned: forget about API modes and stick with 9600 bps unless you actually need more speed), the fact that I was initially sleeping the Arduino, but allowing the Xbee to manage its own sleep patterns caused all sorts of dropped data issues.

Given the troubles, why would you want to use Xbee instead of the other options presented? For one, Xbee is readily available to many people. For another, there is a lot of documentation available online. With due diligence, there is no Xbee problem that can't be solved with a bit of research. You might not be so lucky with other products made by other manufacturers.

In addition, Digi (and the Zigbee standards committee, as well as the greater Zigbee community) is keen on maintaining good relations with the various worldwide regulatory boards. Thus, you can be certain that if Wi-Fi is legal in your area that Zigbee would also be legal. When in doubt, you could always verify directly with Digi.

Using FM transmitters may not be legal in all jurisdictions. Assuming it is legal, your chosen module may be transmitting on an illegal frequency. If you are working outside the United States, you would be wise to verify the legality of transmitting on AM/FM frequencies before ordering parts.

But perhaps the most compelling reason to use Zigbee is the fact that series 2 Xbee radios handle mesh networks out of the box and with very little overhead on the Arduino. While the initial configuration is a bit of a pain to work out, adding new nodes to the network is simply a matter of copying the existing settings to new nodes. You can grow your network in a matter of minutes. What's more, individual nodes will be able to rely on each other to pass messages forward to the coordinator node. This form of indirect contact is critical in a mesh and incredibly useful in a multinode network strewn across a large space, such as a farm or industrial site.

Which Series?

Xbee modules are divided into series 1 and series 2 modules. Series one modules are lower level 802.15.4 radios, and operate in the lower frequency band. Setting up a two point communication system is easier than utilizing series 2 radios.

Series 2 radios add a whole lot of features to the radio stack. In particular, you now have mesh networking and multi-hop routing at your fingertips. The added complexity certainly makes configuration more difficult. However, if you plan on having more than two nodes, the increased configuration headaches will be well worth the effort once your network is ready to deploy. Series 2 radios operate in the upper frequency band, alongside Wi-Fi networks. This has the added benefit of making any Wi-Fi antenna hardware compatible with Xbee.

A lot more can be said about the differences between series 1 and 2. The point to remember is that like the Freakduino-Chibi, the series 1 radio is a minimal protocol stack, whereas series 2 adds all the bells and whistles. For more a more complete comparison, the Digi site has a lot of easy to access documentation.

Freakduino

An alternative to the Zigbee specification is the Freakduino-Chibi radio stack. Chibi, which means "midget" in Japanese, is a very tiny 802.15.4 stack. It is meant to be as small as possible because instead of being built into the radio module, the software stack goes into your Arduino CPU instead. This means you take a small hit on CPU performance, but Akiba, the designer of the stack and Freakduino, has made the software as tight as possible.

The stack has two goals:

- To provide a free wireless radio stack. That's right. Free. The stack is totally open source and available online (and not just for the Arduino). This fits in nicely with the open source nature of the Arduino itself.

- To make the stack incredibly simple to operate. There are only three primary commands required to establish communications between two nodes. Don't let that simplicity fool you; there are a lot of additional options and commands under the hood (check out the user guide, and if you are really twisted, the `chibiUsrCfg.h` file in the Chibi library folder).

Compared with the Zigbee stack, the Chibi stack truly is a midget. A lot of the complex network features have been omitted in favor of speed, performance, and user simplicity. This could be a disadvantage, especially on networks with a large number of nodes or considerable traffic flow. The question you should ask yourself is "Yes, but do I really *need* all that extra functionality?" Zigbee is incredibly flexible and complete. It is a professional stack. With that professionalism comes a whole lot of overhead that the coder must be aware of. It can be difficult just to establish communications and send your first message. With the Chibi stack, you only incur the overhead and performance hits (and associated coding nightmares) if and when you decide you need the extra features.

Under the hood, the Freakduino radio section is very similar to an Xbee module. They both operate on the same frequency band and use similar transmitter chips. The only difference is that while the Xbee has an additional microcontroller acting as a go between the Arduino and radio, the Freakduino does not.

In my opinion, the biggest advantage of the Freakduino and Chibi stack is the price! If you chose Zigbee, you would need an Arduino, adaptor shield, and Xbee module for each node. This will get expensive quickly. The Freakduino includes everything you need on one board. It is an Arduino with a radio module built in. It also happens to be about the same price as a standard Arduino!

Antenna Considerations

Once you decide between the Xbee and Freakduino, you will want to start thinking antennas. Fortunately, in both cases, the radio operates in either 800Mhz or the 2.4 Ghz band. Thus, a range of inexpensive antennas is available for almost any situation. Assuming you stick with 2.4Ghz, any antenna hardware that works with your Wi-Fi network will also work for your sensor nodes.

Xbee modules often come with a stiff wire antenna, but some sort of external antenna connection is usually an option. If possible, try to get modules with the external connector. The Freakduino-Chibi comes with a an external jack on the board and comes with a screw-on antenna. These are dipole antennas. The radiated power could be visualized as a large doughnut or pincushion. Directly above or below the antenna (on the same axis) the signal won't be that great. But just about anywhere else, signal strength is generally good.

If you want to be more selective about where your signal goes, you can try an assortment of antennas. Each style is designed to in some way shape the radiation pattern. In so doing, there is usually at least some small gain in range:

- A patch antenna will radiate outward from one direction. Think "forward, but not backward."

- A corner antenna is very similar to a patch antenna, except that its radiation pattern is even more limited. It's very close to 90 degrees.

- A dish-type grid antenna will have a very narrow radiation beam. Range is increased dramatically (think kilometers). However, both nodes must be carefully aligned. This type is only ideal for semipermanent installations.

Building the Two-Node Sensor Network

If you have not already done so, go back and read through the previous chapter. This project builds upon that project, adding the wireless functionality to the sensor node as well as preparing the data sink node attached to your computer.

Assuming you build the previous project with the Freakduino, you will only need one additional Freakduino to act as the data sink. I present the Freakduino version first.

If you intend to build your sensor nodes using Xbee, you will need to skip ahead a bit. The system I used is the StalkerV2 board from SeeedStudios/Dangerous Prototypes. It utilizes an R8025 RTC from Epson. I had to do a lot of library hacking to get the alarms working. Even if you are using the Freakduino, I suggest you take a look at the Clock section. As for Xbee modules, I am using Series 2 modules. In this case, I am not using a second Arduino to communicate with the PC. Instead, an Xbee module is mounted in a USB adaptor, which I connect directly to the PC.

Freakduino-Chibi Version Hardware

This Freakduino version of the project will not have much new hardware for you to acquire, assuming you built the previous project. You will need a second Freakduino board to act as a data sink, your choice of radio antennas, and it might be nice to mount the data sink Freakduino in a project box—but not absolutely necessary.

In addition to the hardware, you will also need some new software tools:

- Download and install Processing from www.Processing.org.

- Download and install the Chibi Arduino in the Arduino Libraries folder from http://freaklabs.org/index.php/chibiArduino.html. Don't confuse it with the standard Chibi stack, which is meant for other processors.

- You will also want a proper terminal program:

  - I use Termite on the PC: http://www.compuphase.com/software_termite.htm

  - And CoolTerm on the Mac: http://freeware.the-meiers.org/

The Build Process

Reading through this chapter and keeping the information straight in your head is going to be especially challenging because we are dealing with three complete applications, running on three different devices, which are being developed simultaneously to function together. Complicating the matter is that we will step through several revisions to the final product.

So, to be clear, I will try to use the same naming conventions throughout the chapter:

- The *sensor node* or *source node* is the node that will be remotely located and was built in the previous chapter. When referring to code, I will say something like *sensor node code*, or *sensor sketch*.

- The sink node or host node is attached to the computer and receives data from the sensor node. I will refer to its sketch as the *sink* or *host sketch*.

- Finally, running on the PC is a Processing application sketch. It collects the data from the host node, displays it, and saves it. It will always be referred to as the *Processing sketch*.

In addition to these separate pieces of software, we have a rather challenging problem juggling two Arduino sketches being developed in the same computer. Consider that while building up the project and debugging sketches, you are likely to have both the source and sink nodes attached to the same computer. Not only is it difficult to remember which code window goes to which Arduino node but you also need to keep straight in your head which serial ports on your computer the nodes are attached to.

It is important to adopt a convention early on. Thankfully, the Processing and Arduino windows are different color schemes, making that situation quite simple to deal with. As for handling two Arduino windows, I always put the source node's sketch on the left side of the screen, with the sink node sketch on the right. It follows this simple concept: "data flows from left to right."

We need to get into the habit of always checking which serial port has the check mark in the serial list of the Arduino IDE before uploading code. We want to ensure that we don't overwrite the source node's code with the sink node's code. This will leave you scratching your head trying to figure out what's wrong with your system. "It was communicating before! All I did was change this one little variable!"

Before getting started, it is a good idea to attach a tag to each Arduino board, indicating the serial port information. On the PC it will be "COMx," where x is a number. On the Mac, it will be something like "usbserial-Axxxxxxx." Luckily for us, these names will remain consistent on this computer, regardless of which USB port you actually plug it into. Tagging each Arduino you own will be of great assistance moving forward.

At this point, I suggest that you go ahead and plug in both Freakduino boards, load up two simple Arduino sketches (such as examples/blink), set up your desktop, and practice with juggling the two nodes. Even though we are not transmitting any data, go ahead and save the left sketch as something like **blink_source**, and the right sketch as **blink_sink**. Get sharp on dealing with these two sketches independently before moving forward. Set two different blink rates and upload them again. Did the appropriate sketch go to the correct node?

A Simple Application to Get Your Feet Wet

Let's start out simply and gradually scale up the project. For this first step, all you do is verify that the radio connection is functional and you gain a basic understanding of its operation through a sample project.

To get started, load the chibi_ex2_hello_world2 sketch. This sketch demonstrates both sending and receiving of the classic "hello world" message. Connect two Freakduino boards to your computer, and upload the sketch to *both* nodes. Then choose one node by selecting its serial port and launch the serial monitor. You should see the yellow LEDs (pin 13) flash as they send each other the message. Also, the board you are connected to will print it each time it is received.

The two boards are sending the same message to each other. This serves to verify that the hardware is in order and transmitting. Let's take a look at the code in Listing 4-1 to understand what is happening:

Listing 4-1. Freakduino-Chibi communication example 2

```
/* Chibi for Arduino, Example 2
This is the same Hello World example except that both
transmit and receive handling is included.
*/

#include <chibi.h>

byte msg[] = "Hello World";

void setup()
{
  Serial.begin(57600);
  chibiInit();
}

void loop()
{
  // We're going to add 1 to the message length to handle the
  // terminating character '/0'. We're also sending a broadcast so
  // any node in listening range will hear the message.
  chibiTx(BROADCAST_ADDR, msg, 12);

  // if any data is received, then print it to the terminal
  if (chibiDataRcvd() == true)
  {
    byte buf[CHB_MAX_PAYLOAD];  // store the received data in here

    chibiGetData(buf);

    // The data consists of ASCII characters in byte (unsigned char) format. The print
    // function requires ASCII characters be in char format so we need to inform the function
    // that its okay to convert the format from unsigned char to char.
    Serial.print((char *)buf);
  }

  // delay half a second between transmission
  delay(500);
}
```

As always, we start by importing any necessary libraries. In this case, the Chibi library is needed to run the radio.

Then any required variables are prepared. We create an array of bytes to hold a string called msg. When no number is specified between the square brackets, the compiler will automatically count the number of characters in the quotes after the assignment operator and add one additional character for a string terminator.

We are now ready to start up the application. For the moment, we only need to start the serial monitor and initialize the Chibi stack and radio.

Each time through the main loop, we will perform two primary tasks: first we transmit our message; then we receive and print anything we hear.

The Chibi stack accepts a message to be transmitted using the `chibiTX` function. You need to give it three pieces of information: the address you wish to send to, the variable or placeholder of the message, and the expected message length. Note that the stack will always finish up after receiving a string termination character, even if the number of bytes transmitted is less than the specified expected message length.

■ **Note** While it is perfectly acceptable to overestimate the expected message length, you are likely to flood the radio buffer. It is best to specify the maximum message the code is likely to generate. Also, specifying a length too small will cause problems.

Once transmission is complete, we then start listening for new data. To be clear, the radio has been listening the whole time and has already collected a small buffer of data received from the other node. So really, we are asking the radio "Is there anything in the receive buffer?" If the radio responds with "Yes," we can begin to process the data.

First, a buffer of bytes is created, equal to the number specified by the constant `CHB_MAX_PAYLOAD` (because we really don't know what to expect). This constant is defined in the `ChibiUsrCfg.h` file, and is set at 100. If you suspect that your project will transmit more than 99 characters at a time, you can specify a specific value (up to 150). Just be sure to add one for the string termination character.

With a buffer defined, all that remains is to get the characters from the radio's receiver buffer and copy them to the buffer we created by using `chibiGetData(copy destination)`.

With the data in hand, we can print it quite easily using the usual `serial.print` command. However, because we are dealing with a buffer, we have to feed the pointers to each character in the buffer to the `serial.print` command by using `Serial.print((char *)buf)`.

Looking at Other Chibi Radio Stack Commands

We have already seen four Freakduino-Chibi commands. Before going further, it would be a good idea to read through the Chibi wireless guide book available on FreakLabs.org (and in the library folder). I will summarize some of the more important commands, but you should familiarize yourself with the possible options.

- `chibiInit()`: initializes the Chibi radio stack. Required.

- `chibiSetShortAddr(0x1234)`: sets the node address.

- `chibiGetShortAddr()`: gets the node address.

- `chibiSetChannel(byte channel)`: sets the radio channel 11–26.

- `chibiTx(unsigned int address, byte data[], byte len)`: transmits.

- `chibiDataRcvd()`: returns true if the radio has data waiting.

- `chibiGetData(destination)`: not only gets the data from the radio and drops it in the destination but also returns the length of the data.

- `chibiSleepRadio()`: non-zero will wake the radio; zero will put it to sleep. This particular function is very important for battery-powered sensors.

What's My Address?

In the previous two examples, we did not care about the node ID when sending and receiving messages. We simply sent the same message to all nodes. If you were to turn on 3, 5, or 100 nodes, they would all receive and process the same message.

Actually, this is a fine enough solution for a two-node network. However, as the number of nodes increases, we will quickly run into a lot of problems if we continue to use the broadcast ID for every message we send. It is much better if the source node keeps the sink node's ID on file and sends messages with that ID. This way, other source nodes will simply ignore those messages, rather than attempt to decipher their meaning. Likewise, on a large network it is absolutely critical that the source node maintains a list of source nodes and communicates in a direct fashion.

Consider the following example. You have implemented a command code structure in all your nodes, so the sink node may command a source node to take a measurement now or go to sleep for a specified period. Now imagine the sink node is communicating with one of the source nodes and instructs it to transmit a reading. If the source node uses the broadcast ID, every node on the network will take a reading and attempt to send data. It is unlikely much of the data will arrive because it is attempting to grab a single channel. The data will simply collide in the air. Then the sink node instructs the node to sleep, except that every node on the network receives the message and goes to bed!

Even if you decide to keep to a simple two-node network and use the broadcast ID for simplicity, you should still set unique ID numbers and mark them on the tag you attached to the node.

Fortunately, it is an easy process. Load the Freakduino-Chibi cmdline sketch. Compile and upload the sketch to both Freakduinos. The cmdline sketch gives the Freakduino a terminal-like command line. There are three built-in functions, and you can easily add your own. Notice that the terminal command name is slightly different than the actual Chibi stack command it issues:

- `getsaddr`: gets the short address of the node from the radio eeprom.

- `setsaddr`: sets the short address; "setsaddr 0x200" would set it to hexadecimal 200.

- `send`: sends a message to another node; "send 200 Here is my message" would send "Here is my message" to node 200.

Note that address 0xFFFF is the broadcast address. You should not try to set the node ID to 0xFFFF. Likewise, you should avoid address 0x0000.

To access the command line, you should use a proper terminal program. The serial monitor does not handle user input very well. Load the terminal application, and set the settings as follows:

- Data/Baud rate = 57600

- Data Bits:8, Parity:none, Stop Bits:1

- Append CR, Local echo OFF

Now that you are configured, hit Connect in the terminal application. In the terminal window, you may need to press the Enter button on your keyboard a few times to get the cmdline's attention.

```
CHIBI: Command not recognized.

************** CHIBI ******************
CHIBI >> setsaddr 0x0001

************** CHIBI ******************
CHIBI >> getsaddr
Short Address: 1

************** CHIBI ******************
CHIBI >>
```

Type **getsaddr** into the cmdline, and you should receive a response back from the Freakduino with its address. Now type **setsaddr**, followed by the address in hex you wish to assign to this node. Just to be sure it took, retry the **getsaddr** command.

Sketch Blender: Getting the JunglePower Sketch to Send Data

We were able to verify that the radios were communicating by loading the same sketch into both Freakduino nodes. In order to tailor our wireless sensor system to our needs, we need to create two separate sketches: one for the sensor node and one for the data sink node.

We will be juggling several code windows on the screen, so it is critical that we comment our code as we work. Also, we need to get into the habit of checking the menu bar of each code window before we start editing to be sure we are editing the correct code.

We will be referencing past sketches, as well as Chibi stack sample sketches to build two new sketches (one for the source node and one for the sink node).

Writing the First Source Sketch

We will start with the source sketch. Open the JunglePower sketch from the previous chapter. Save the sketch as something like **JunglePower_Transmitter** and close the old JunglePower sketch so that you do not accidentally overwrite it.

We will be converting this new sketch into a transmitter. Arrange the sketch window so it is about half the width of the screen and is sitting on the right side. Now open the Chibi stack example "chibi_ex2_hello_world2." Place this sketch on the left side of the screen. We will use it as a reference while building our sketch. We will then convert the example sketch into our receiver sketch.

Looking at the sample transmitter sketch, the first thing we need to do is add the Chibi include line to the modified JunglePower sketch. We should also go ahead and create a transmitter buffer.

Before moving on to the setup function, we want to define any project variables. Remember that we are using I2C lines for the RTC. These pins are on analog 4 and 5, which makes them not usable for analog input.

■ **Note** One point not entirely clear in the Chibi stack documentation is that the radio is attached to analog pins 2 and 3, making them unable to perform ADC functions!

Because analog 2 through 6 are occupied, we can take ADC readings only on A0 and A1. With that in mind, let's define variables to hold the data from the ADC. The remainder of the variables and define section of the new transmitter sketch remains as it was in the JunglePower sketch.

The Chibi stack needs very little in the setup function to get going. Simply start the stack with `ChibiInit();`.

We will be doing several modifications to the main loop, so study both sketches carefully. Before copying radio code into the old JunglePower sketch, first eliminate any references to analog inputs 2 through 5. If we attempt to read those analog inputs while the radio is running, there could be damage to the Freakduino. If your sketch does not read A0 and A1, go ahead and add the typical code to do so: `A0raw = analogRead(A0);`. You may also want to print the data to the serial port for debugging purposes.

■ **Note**   The Chibi radio stack expects that your message will be a string of characters. The sketch must compose all data into a string of characters in the transmit buffer.

We can prepare our message using several methods. For example, typecasting will help in converting data from one type to another, so it is easier to pack into the message. Pointers are also very helpful because they eliminate the need for complex `for` next loops to shuffle data into the buffer. For our first experiment, let's keep it simple and use `memcpy` to copy the data to the buffer. It does not care about the data type; It will take the binary value from the source address and copy it to the destination.

Looking at the code `memcpy(XmitBuf, &A0raw, 2)`, it is easy to see that we are taking the `A0raw` value and dumping it into `XmitBuf`, but what is the `&` and the value `2` about? `&` indicates that we are actually asking for the address of `A0raw`. An ADC value is 12 bits, and thus must occupy two bytes in memory. Thus we declare the storage variable to be an integer, which allows for more than one byte of data. So, by using the address, we can point `memcpy` to the memory location and let it do the rest. The number indicates how many bytes to copy.

After preparing the buffer, we can wake up the radio; send our transmission; then put both the radio and the Arduino to sleep. Listing 4-2 serves as a complete sleeping Arduino transmitter.

Listing 4-2. Simple Sleeping Transmitter

```
#include <Wire.h>
#include <Rtc8564AttachInterrupt.h>
#include <Sleep.h>
#include <chibi.h>

// Project variables
int A0raw, A1raw;
const int bufSize = 5;
byte XmitBuf[bufSize];

/* RTC preset clock*/
#define RTC_SEC  0x00  // seconds
#define RTC_MIN  0x18  // minutes
#define RTC_HOUR 0x23  // hours
#define RTC_DAY  0x15  // day
#define RTC_WEEK 0x02  // weekday(00:sunday . 06:saturday)
```

```
#define RTC_MON   0x03  // month
#define RTC_YEAR  0x11  // year
byte date_time[7] = {
   RTC_SEC
  ,RTC_MIN
  ,RTC_HOUR
  ,RTC_DAY
  ,RTC_WEEK
  ,RTC_MON
  ,RTC_YEAR
};

/* clock reset flag */
boolean init_flg = false;

/* countdown timer period */
#define RTC_INTERRUPT_TERM 10

/* Arduino wake interupt pin */
#define RTC_INTERRUPT_PIN  2

/* countdowntimer mode 0:seconds/1:minutes */
#define RTC_INTERRUPT_MODE 0

void setup() {
  Serial.begin(9600);
  chibiInit();

  // set the clock
  Rtc.initDatetime(date_time);

  // RTC start
  Rtc.begin();

  // check for interrupt
  if (!Rtc.isInterrupt()) {

    // set the interrupt
    Rtc.syncInterrupt(RTC_INTERRUPT_MODE, RTC_INTERRUPT_TERM);
  }

  // prepare the interrupt pin
  pinMode(RTC_INTERRUPT_PIN, INPUT);
  digitalWrite(RTC_INTERRUPT_PIN, HIGH);
}

void loop() {

  // check the flag and read the clock data
  if (init_flg) ReadRTC();
  init_flg = true;
```

```
  // stuff to do before sleep
  // read the pins
AOraw = analogRead(AO);
A1raw = analogRead(A1);
Serial.print(AOraw);
Serial.print(" ");
Serial.println(A1raw);

memcpy(XmitBuf, &AOraw, 2);

chibiSleepRadio(O);  // wake up the radio
delay(100);
chibiTx(BROADCAST_ADDR, XmitBuf, bufSize);
chibiSleepRadio(1);  // go back to sleep

  // Arduino Sleep time! Dont put anything else in the main loop after this!
  delay(100);
  SleepClass::powerDownAndWakeupExternalEvent(0);
}

void ReadRTC()
{
  Rtc.available();
  Serial.print(0x2000 + Rtc.years(), HEX);
  Serial.print("/");
  Serial.print(Rtc.months(), HEX);
  Serial.print("/");
  Serial.print(Rtc.days(), HEX);
  Serial.print(" ");
  Serial.print(Rtc.hours(), HEX);
  Serial.print(":");
  Serial.print(Rtc.minutes(), HEX);
  Serial.print(":");
  Serial.print(Rtc.seconds(), HEX);
  Serial.print(" ");
  Serial.println((int)Rtc.weekdays());
}
```

by modifying an existing sketch and importing new bits of code from the examples provided for the Chibi stack, we were able to quite easily build a functional radio transmitter.

If you load this sketch into the source node and run the **serial monitor**, you should see something similar to the following output:

```
439 395
2011/3/15 23:22:30 2
402 407
2011/3/15 23:22:40 2
399 406
2011/3/15 23:22:50 2
413 415
```

```
2011/3/15 23:23:0 2
408 412
2011/3/15 23:23:10 2
411 414
```

This lets you know that we are fetching the time from the clock and properly reading both ADC values. What you can't see from the serial monitor is what we are transmitting over the radio. For that, we need to set this node aside, plug in another node, and upload a sketch to read display the radio transmission.

Writing the Sink sketch

The receiver sketch is relatively simple in comparison. You could open one of the sample sketches from the Chibi stack and modify it. Take a look at the listing:

Listing 4-3. Chibi Receiver Demo Sketch

```
#include <chibi.h>
byte buf[CHB_MAX_PAYLOAD];

void setup()
{
  Serial.begin(57600);
  chibiInit();
}

void loop()
{
  if (chibiDataRcvd() == true)
  {
    unsigned int rcv_data;
    chibiGetData(buf);
    Serial.println((char *)buf);
  }
}
```

Save the sketch with a similar name as the transmitter sketch. Walking through the sketch, it should be pretty familiar by now. In assigning the size of the buffer, I went with the maximum setting defined by the stack, which is 100 bytes. The radio buffer actually has a limit of 120, but we should try to keep all our messages at 100 bytes or less.

I want to draw attention to the `Serial.println` function. The data sitting in the buffer is of the byte type. It is unreadable to us (although the computer can deal with it just fine). If we want to be able to understand the data printed to the screen without the need for a scientific calculator to convert it to something we understand, we need to change it from byte to integer. Remember that in the transmitter sketch, we converted it from integer to byte using the `memcpy` command. Here we are simply converting it back. We could use `memcpy` as well, but typecasting on the fly is quite simple from within the `print` command. We do so by calling the `char typecast` function, and hand it a pointer to the temporary buffer.

Remember that in this first baby step, we are only transmitting one of the two ADC values, and that it is simply the raw value from the ADC. Load this sketch into the sink node and run the serial monitor once more. Be sure you have selected the appropriate port and baud rate settings. Turn the source node on and you should start seeing the ADC number print in the monitor every 10 seconds. Keep an eye on the RTC module on the source node. When the LED blinks, you should receive the value shortly thereafter.

Congratulations! You have just set up your first wireless sensor network! We have a lot more work to do, but at this stage, you have a functional single data-point transmitter. You can do any data conversion on the sink node before outputting it to the terminal and have a quite serviceable project. However, we would like to add the second data point, transmitting the timestamp as well as the data, the ability to change the clock time and period, and finally logging.

Transmitting and Receiving More than Just One Data Point

It would be nice to read more than just the one analog input. Also, having the timestamp might be nice. Sure, we could timestamp the data from the PC when we save it, but we may want the source node to work in a standalone mode as well. For that, accurate timestamping can be important.

From this point on, you can leave the data sink node and its sketch alone. It will serve well by simply listening in and printing what it hears. Later, you can always add transmission features if you need to talk back to the source nodes.

I am going to modify the source node sketch once more (see Listing 4-4). This time, I want to compile all the various bits of data together into one single line of radio output. If I separate each data point by a comma, it will be very easy for me to pick up the data on the PC, using a simple application. Also, the data will be compatible with a spreadsheet application. The message output is more easily parsed by the PC application.

Listing 4-4. Formatted Data Transmitter Sketch

```
#include <Wire.h>
#include <Rtc8564AttachInterrupt.h>
#include <Sleep.h>
#include <chibi.h>

/* Project variables */
const int bufSize = 30;
byte XmitBuf[bufSize];

/* RTC preset clock*/
#define RTC_SEC   0x00  // seconds
#define RTC_MIN   0x18  // minutes
#define RTC_HOUR  0x23  // hours
#define RTC_DAY   0x15  // day
#define RTC_WEEK  0x02  // weekday(00:sunday . 06:saturday)
#define RTC_MON   0x03  // month
#define RTC_YEAR  0x11  // year
byte date_time[7] = {
    RTC_SEC
   ,RTC_MIN
   ,RTC_HOUR
   ,RTC_DAY
   ,RTC_WEEK
```

```
       ,RTC_MON
       ,RTC_YEAR
};

/* clock reset flag */
boolean init_flg = false;

/* countdown timer period */
#define RTC_INTERRUPT_TERM 10

/* Arduino wake interupt pin */
#define RTC_INTERRUPT_PIN  2

/* countdowntimer mode 0:seconds/1:minutes */
#define RTC_INTERRUPT_MODE 0


void setup() {
  chibiInit();
  Rtc.initDatetime(date_time);  // set the clock
  Rtc.begin();  // RTC start
  if (!Rtc.isInterrupt()) {     // check for interrupt
    // set the interrupt
    Rtc.syncInterrupt(RTC_INTERRUPT_MODE, RTC_INTERRUPT_TERM);
  }
  // prepare the interrupt pin
  pinMode(RTC_INTERRUPT_PIN, INPUT);
  digitalWrite(RTC_INTERRUPT_PIN, HIGH);
}

void loop() {

 PrepMsg();
 WakeRadio();
 Transmit();
   // Arduino Sleep time! Dont put anything else in the main loop after this!
 GoToSleep();
}

void PrepMsg()
{
  Rtc.available();
  char temp[bufSize];
  sprintf(temp, "%x,%x,%x,%x,%x,%x,%d,%d",
   Rtc.months(), Rtc.days(), (0x2000 + Rtc.years()),
   Rtc.hours(), Rtc.minutes(), Rtc.seconds(),
   analogRead(A0), analogRead(A1));
  memcpy(XmitBuf, temp, bufSize);
}
```

```
void WakeRadio()
{
  // wake the radio, transmit, then put it back to sleep
 chibiSleepRadio(0);  // wake up the radio
 delay(100);                    // adjust min wakeup time before xmit
}

void Transmit()
{
  chibiTx(BROADCAST_ADDR, XmitBuf, bufSize);
}

void GoToSleep()
{
  chibiSleepRadio(1);  // Sleep the radio
  delay(100);                    // adjust min radio shutdown time
  SleepClass::powerDownAndWakeupExternalEvent(0);
}
```

Notice that I have cleaned up the code, arranging blocks into functions. This will make it much easier for you later if you decide to add new functions to your communication scheme.

Take a close look at the PrepMsg() function. That string of percent signs, commas, and letters is rather funny looking. It is our transmitted message, but takes the form of tokens. Each %x or %d represents the value type we want to place between the commas. An %x token means that we will insert a hexidecimal value (remember that the RTC talks in hex). The %d token indicates a decimal value.

The other thing you should notice is that this line does not terminate with the typical ; marker. In fact, the next three lines are part of the first line. After specifying the tokenized message we want to transmit, we need to give the sprintf() function the variables we wish it to replace the tokens with, in the proper order.

Take a moment to look at the token message and the data we will drop into place. Count how many characters we require. Don't forget that the comma counts as a character, and we also need a termination character, which is added automatically by the sprintf() function. By my count, we need about 30. Don't forget that the ADC values could be as high as 1024 (4 characters). Thus, the BufSize has been increased in the top portion of the code.

Load this code into the source node. For testing purposes, you can leave both nodes plugged into your computer or run the source node on batteries. Plug the sink node in, select its com port, and run the serial monitor or terminal if you prefer. You should see output like the following:

```
3,16,2011,0,15,50,443,441
3,16,2011,0,16,0,699,672
3,16,2011,0,16,10,659,647
3,16,2011,0,16,20,592,591
```

The first field is the month, followed by the day and the year. Next we have the hours, minutes, and seconds. (Wow, I did this at midnight; looks like my source node is not the only thing that needs to go to sleep!) The final two fields are analog 0 and 1.

From here, you could skip ahead to the Processing section. However, even if you built the Chibi version of the hardware, I still encourage you to delay jumping forward and instead continue reading. The following hardware version utilizes much more common Xbee modules. It is likely that you will eventually come across a need for them. In addition, we will be hacking another RTC library, this time adding several key functions.

Xbee version Hardware (Stalker version 2.0)

In this version of the design, I will utilize two series 2 Xbee modules. In addition, the Stalker version 2.0 board (see Figure 4-1) is well suited to low power sensor applications, given that it has the following items built in:

- It has an onboard lithium polymer battery management controller.

- It has a solar panel input for charging the battery.

- It has an onboard socket for the Xbee module, negating any need for an additional shield.

- The onboard RTC includes an external interrupt and periodic alarms.

So the parts count is quite low to get the systems set up. We need the Stalker board, lipo battery, and solar panel from Seeedstudios. While you are there, you should also pick up the programming adaptor. The Stalker does not have a built-in FTDI chip. The adaptor lets you upload new code to the Arduino. We also need two Digi Xbee modules (series 1 or 2; I am using series 2). We also need one USB-to-Xbee adaptor. Any device will do. I purchased mine from SparkFun. However, Seeedstudios has a board made for the Stalker that doubles as a USB-to-Xbee interface. You can save yourself some money there. Finally, we need a 10K ohm resistor. That's it!

Figure 4-1. SeeedStudios Stalker version 2.0

Stalker Board and Hardware

The Stalker has much of what we need built in. The RTC subsystem includes a super capacitor backup system to keep the clock ticking when the battery is too low. The battery management system automatically handles charging the battery via the solar panel. There is also a battery sensor that reports the charge level of the battery. The onboard Xbee socket is prewired. Finally, there is an onboard temperature sensor.

For a complete reference to the Stalker version 2.0 hardware, see the Seeed Studio wiki page here: `http://www.seeedstudio.com/wiki/Seeeduino_Stalker_v2.0`. While you are there, you should go ahead and download the base libraries and install them in the Arduino library folder. The base libraries are part of the demonstration sketch (`http://www.seeedstudio.com/wiki/File:Stlker_logger_AM06_Serial.zip`). You will need to copy them from the demo sketch folder into the Arduino libraries folder. However, we will be making copies from the Arduino/libraries folder into our own sketch, just as the demo sketch does. This way, we can modify them without affecting the original library.

You may also want to go ahead and grab the fat16 library for later use. The fat16 library provides access to the SD card. We won't be using it in our sketch, but you may want it for your own sensor projects later (`http://www.seeedstudio.com/wiki/File:Stalker_code_Fat16.zip`).

Rather than adding new sensors (you are absolutely encouraged to do so later), for demonstration purposes we will be reading and reporting the battery level and the temperature sensor data up to the Processing application presented later in the chapter.

But before we can do that, we still have a lot of work to do on the base hardware and libraries. Let's get started.

Stalker RTC

My Stalker is version 2.0. The RTC is made by Epson Toyocom. The part number is RX8025SA, and the datasheet is available here: `http://www.epsontoyocom.co.jp/english/product/RTC/set03/rx8025sa_nb/index.html`. (See `http://www.seeedstudio.com/wiki/index.php?title=Seeeduino_Stalker` for variations among each Stalker generation).

You should study the data sheets carefully because you need to create library tools to access each clock function.

Before we continue, we need to mod the Stalker board because the board is ready for the RTC interrupt pin, but it has not been enabled. To do so, we need to solder a jumper on the bottom of the board. Referring to the image of the bottom of the board, solder the two pads labeled "INTA_RTC" together (see Figure 4-2). This will route the RTC interrupt pin to Arduino pin D2, which also happens to be interrupt 0 in the Arduino sketch.

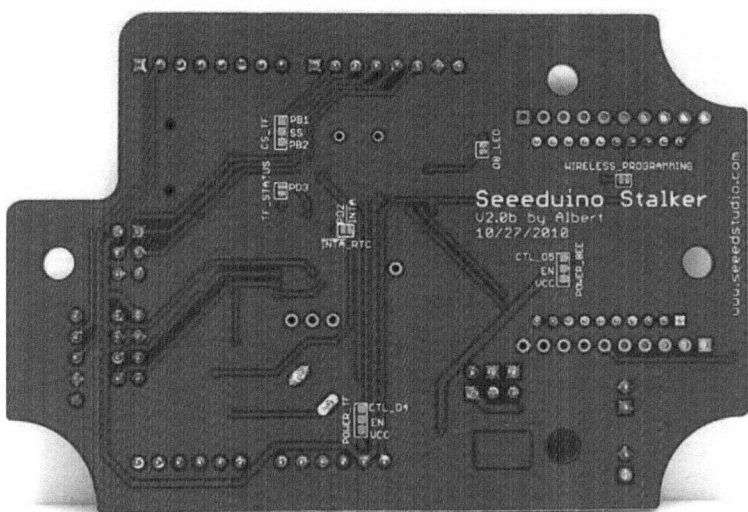

Figure 4-2. *The Stalker version 2.0 bottom side. Solder the two pads marked INTA_RTC (near the center of the board) together to connect the clock interrupt pin to the Arduino.*

The final bit of RTC hardware we need to address is the pull up resistor on the interrupt pin. If you consult the RX8025 manual, you will find that the interrupt pin works in the following way:

- When the interrupt fires, the clock pulls the pin to ground.

- When the interrupt is in the waiting state, the pin is in a high impedance state. Essentially, it won't allow current pass. *This does not mean that it is sourcing current.*

So in order to present a high state to digital pin 2, we need to provide our own current. The clock simply blocks this current from entering the clock.

Find a medium value resistor (say, about 10K ohms) with sufficiently long legs so you can connect it to both pin 2 and the 3V3 pin. Bend the ends of the legs down and insert them into both pins. The resistor will just fit, spanning the width of the board. Once you finalize your sensor project, you can incorporate this resistor into the shield. You could also extend the resistor legs with some clippings from other components and a bit of solder.

This simple pullup resistor will supply current to pin 2 from the 3.3 volt supply. A higher resistance will lower the current, extending the battery and protecting the Arduino input circuitry. We don't need much current to keep the pin high, so anything up to 1 megohm (possibly higher) should work fine.

When the clock wishes to fire an interrupt, it pulls its interrupt A in low. This has the effect of temporarily shorting Arduino pin 2 to ground through the clock. We will use the interrupt falling-edge detection to see this transition, wake up, and perform the sensor tasks.

Library Hacking

The Stalker RTC library is very minimal. Our first order of business is to get this up to snuff. We will hack the library to add new the new features required of our project.

To get going, load up the Arduino IDE. Now open the Stlker_logger_AM06_Serial demonstration sketch. Notice that the project not only opens the main sketch but also several `.h` and `.cpp` files as well. These files are the various log files we need for this application.

Go ahead and compile and run this application, just to verify that all the hardware works. You will need to upload to the Stalker using an interface cable. Don't worry if you don't have a blank SD card installed. The Stalker will simply report an absent card in the terminal window. If all is well, you should see a time, date, temperature, and battery voltage printed in the terminal.

■ **Note** Whenever working on new libraries, or modifying existing ones, it is wise to copy the `.cpp` and `.h` files for the library directly into the project sketch folder. The compiler will use these files instead of the original library. This way, you can play around with the files without overwriting the original library.

Prepare a Working Directory

Close the Arduino IDE. Now locate the Stalker demonstration sketch. Make a copy of the whole folder, and rename it something like **Stalker_RTC_hacking**. Rename the sketch file (`.pde` file) as well. We can also rename the RX8025.h and `.cpp` files to myRX8025.h and `.cpp`. Finally, delete all the other `.cpp` and `.h` files. We don't need them for the moment and they only get in our way. We now have a clean work folder, in which to play around with the RTC without destroying our original files.

Reconnecting Libraries

Our first order of business is to repoint our application to the myRX8025 files, and to eliminate references to the other libraries.

At the top of the sketch, delete the includes that reference anything other than RX8025.h and avr/sleep.h. Also, rename the RX8025 include to point to myRX8025.h.

Similarly, scour the sketch for any mention of the other libraries. For example, delete the print functions related to the Temperature and battery voltage. Eliminate those variables as well. For now, we are only concerned with the time aspect of the sketch. We will go back and add the other functions later, but for now, they are only in our way.

Finally, we need to modify the myRX8025.h and .cpp files so that they can "see" each other. Click on the myRX8025.cpp tab. Again, we need to rename the include, so that it now reads "myRX8025.h". Now click on the myRX8025.h tab and rename the two defines at the very top of the code. It should read:

```
#ifndef myRX8025_h
#define myRX8025_h
```

At this point, we should save our work and check that everything compiles. We don't need to upload it yet. Just verify that you can compile without errors. If you get any, inspect and clean up the sketch and libraries so you have a clean compilation.

myMR8025.h File

Click the myRD8025.h tab. This header file acts sort of like a table of contents to the library. It lets our sketch know what functions and variables are available.

The first block of the file simply defines the header file. Immediately after that, we see a bunch of definitions for the RX8025, such as `#define RX8025_SEC` 0. This section defines the address numbers within the clock. Consulting page 6 of the RX8025 manual, you see the same listing. These registers contain clock settings, as well as the clock data. Note that the datasheet refers to address 10 as A, and so on. We need to remember that the data sheet works with hexadecimal. At any rate, these definitions were set up by the original library author, but never implemented in code. You are welcome to use them, but doing so only adds to typing time. (Which is easier to type, "RX8025_AD_MIN" or "0xB0"?) Another important point to note is that the addresses use the high byte in hex values. It is common to assume the address sequence would be 0x01, 0x02 etc. Instead, it is the high byte that is incremented. So the addresses in hex are 0x10, 0x20, through 0xF0.

We next see groupings of external variables. These are the variables provided by the library to our application. So long as the header file is linked in our sketch, we can use these variables the same as any others in our program. These are all defined the same way: "extern unsigned char". There is also an 7 element array, that holds the time.

The remainder of the header file defines the functions available to the sketch.

Adding What We Need

Looking through the myRX8025.h file, you will notice that only a few variables are defined to hold the status of clock registers. Also, the only functions available are to initialize the clock, set the time, and get it (read). There are no alarm functions, and very little access to the control registers, which we need in order to enable alarms and interrupts.

While adding all the new requirements, I also cleaned up the presentation a bit. In addition, I changed the name of two variables, which we will need to be aware of.

It seemed odd to call the day of the month "date," because date implies knowing not just the day of the month, but also the month and year. Thus, I called it simply "day". Likewise, what was termed "week" is not really the week of the month (1st week, 2nd week etc). Rather, it is the day of the week, such as Monday, Tuesday, etc. Therefore, I changed this to "weekday."

Here is my version of the library header file:

Listing 4-5. *myRX8025.h*

```
#ifndef myRX8025_h
#define myRX8025_h


//=================================================
#define RX8025_SEC        0
#define RX8025_MIN        1
#define RX8025_HR         2
#define RX8025_WEEK       3
#define RX8025_DATE       4
#define RX8025_MTH        5
#define RX8025_YR         6
#define RX8025_Doffset    7
#define RX8025_AW_MIN     8
#define RX8025_AW_HR      9
#define RX8025_AW_WEEK    10   // A
#define RX8025_AD_MIN     11   // B
#define RX8025_AD_HR      12   // C
#define RX8025_AD_RES     13   // D Reserved! DONT OVERWRITE!
```

```
#define RX8025_CTL1    14  // E
#define RX8025_CTL2    15  // F


//==================================================
extern unsigned char second;          // 0
extern unsigned char minute;          // 1
extern unsigned char hour;            // 2
extern unsigned char weekday;           // 3
extern unsigned char day;           // 4
extern unsigned char month;          // 5
extern unsigned char year;           // 6
extern unsigned char Doffset;          // 7
extern unsigned char alarmW_minute;   // 8
extern unsigned char alarmW_hour;     // 9
extern unsigned char alarmW_weekday;  // 10 A
extern unsigned char alarmD_minute;   // 11 B
extern unsigned char alarmD_hour;     // 12 C
extern unsigned char RX8025_Reserved; // 13 D Leave it alone!
extern unsigned char RX8025_control_1;// 14 E
extern unsigned char RX8025_control_2;// 15 F


//==================================================
extern unsigned char RX8025_all[16];
extern unsigned char RX8025_time[7];
extern unsigned char RX8025_alarmW[3];
extern unsigned char RX8025_alarmD[2];
extern unsigned char RX8025_Control[2];


//==================================================
void RX8025_init(void);
void setRtcTime(void);
void getRtcTime(void);
void getRtcAll(void);
void setRtcAlarmW(void);
void setRtcAlarmD(void);
void setRtcCtrl(void);
void RtcClearFlags(void);


//==================================================
#endif
```

myRX8025.cpp File

This file contains the actual code for the library. It is mostly comprised of the individual functions called out at the bottom of the header file.

The first thing the .cpp file does is assures that an instance of the wire library is linked to our application. The wire library handles I2C communication. Obviously, it is essential. We also assure that the myRX8025.h file is here as well. With that out of the way, we get into dealing with the RX8025 itself.

The original library kicks everything off by defining the address of the RX8025. This is the address we use to talk to the chip over the I2C bus. The address is not mentioned in the datasheet until page 26. You can be forgiven for scratching your head on this one. It would save a lot of time if it were on page one!

The next step is to define the settings for control registers. This works fine in theory, but what if you want to initialize the clock with a control register setting other than the one coded into the library? We will cut that out and provide the option to initialize with any settings you like via the setRtcCtrl function called out in the modified header file.

The original library then goes on to all the functions for the library. Curiously, the order is a bit strange. We have the setRtcTime function, followed by two internal functions that are used for converting the returned values from the clock into readable text. After which, we go back to the get and init functions. At any rate, let's take a look at the setRtcTime function.

We begin the transaction by sending the address of the device we want to talk to (in this case, the RX8025 address). After which, we send the register we want to begin from. Now we simply need to send the values we wish to write to the device, in order. Notice that the section of registers that make up the time are from 0 to 6, consisting of 7 registers total. The for loop in the setRtcTime function goes from 1=0 to 1<7. In other words, it goes from 0 to 6, consisting of 7 total values. When we are finished programming the clock, we end the transmission.

Receiving from the clock works in a similar manner, except that after sending the start register, we end the transmission, then receive from the clock the group of register values we want. We receive the values into an array, and then later assign the array values to individual variables, that we can use in our sketch.

My modified myRX8025.cpp file is this:

Listing 4-6. myRX8025.cpp

```
#include <Wire.h>
#include "myRX8025.h"

//===============================================
#define  RX8025_address  0x32

//===============================================
uint8_t bcd2bin (uint8_t val)
{
    return val - 6 * (val >> 4);
}

uint8_t bin2bcd (uint8_t val)
{
    return val + 6 * (val / 10);
}

//===============================================
void RX8025_init(void)
{
    setRtcCtrl();
    setRtcTime();
}

//===============================================
void setRtcTime(void)
{
    Wire.beginTransmission(RX8025_address);
    Wire.send(0x00);
```

```
  for(unsigned char i=0; i<7; i++)
  {
    Wire.send(RX8025_time[i]);
  }
  Wire.endTransmission();
}

//===============================================
void getRtcTime(void)
{
  unsigned char i=0;
  Wire.beginTransmission(RX8025_address);
  Wire.send(0x00);
  Wire.endTransmission();//
  Wire.requestFrom(RX8025_address,8);
  RX8025_time[i]= Wire.receive();//not use
  while(Wire.available())
  {
    RX8025_time[i]= Wire.receive();
    i++;
  }
  Wire.endTransmission();//

  year    = bcd2bin(RX8025_time[6]&0xff);
  month   = bcd2bin(RX8025_time[5]&0x1f);
  day     = bcd2bin(RX8025_time[4]&0x3f);
  weekday    = bcd2bin(RX8025_time[3]&0x07);
  hour    = bcd2bin(RX8025_time[2]&0x3f);
  minute = bcd2bin(RX8025_time[1]&0x7f);
  second = bcd2bin(RX8025_time[0]&0x7f);
}

//===============================================
void getRtcAll(void)
{
  unsigned char i=0;
  unsigned char RX8025_all[16];
  Wire.beginTransmission(RX8025_address);
  Wire.send(0x00);
  Wire.endTransmission();//
  Wire.requestFrom(RX8025_address,16);
  RX8025_all[i]= Wire.receive();//not use
  while(Wire.available())
  {
    RX8025_all[i]= Wire.receive();
    i++;
  }
  Wire.endTransmission();
  RX8025_control_2 = bcd2bin(RX8025_all[15]);
  RX8025_control_1 = bcd2bin(RX8025_all[14]);
  RX8025_Reserved  = bcd2bin(RX8025_all[13]);
  alarmD_hour      = bcd2bin(RX8025_all[12]&0x3f);
```

```
  alarmD_minute    = bcd2bin(RX8025_all[11]&0x7f);
  alarmW_weekday   = bcd2bin(RX8025_all[10]&0x07);
  alarmW_hour      = bcd2bin(RX8025_all[9]&0x3f);
  alarmW_minute    = bcd2bin(RX8025_all[8]&0x7f);
  Doffset          = bcd2bin(RX8025_all[7]);
  year             = bcd2bin(RX8025_all[6]&0xff);
  month            = bcd2bin(RX8025_all[5]&0x1f);
  day              = bcd2bin(RX8025_all[4]&0x3f);
  weekday          = bcd2bin(RX8025_all[3]&0x07);
  hour             = bcd2bin(RX8025_all[2]&0x3f);
  minute           = bcd2bin(RX8025_all[1]&0x7f);
  second           = bcd2bin(RX8025_all[0]&0x7f);
}

//==============================================
void setRtcAlarmD(void)
{
  Wire.beginTransmission(RX8025_address);
  Wire.send(0xB0);
  for(unsigned char i=0; i<2; i++)
  {
    Wire.send(RX8025_alarmD[i]);
  }
  Wire.endTransmission();
}

//==============================================
void setRtcAlarmW(void)
{
  Wire.beginTransmission(RX8025_address);
  Wire.send(0x80);
  for(unsigned char i=0; i<3; i++)
  {
    Wire.send(RX8025_alarmW[i]);
  }
  Wire.endTransmission();
}

//==============================================
void setRtcCtrl(void)
{
Wire.beginTransmission(RX8025_address);
  Wire.send(0xE0);
  for(unsigned char i=0; i<2; i++)
  {
    Wire.send(RX8025_Control[i]);
  }
  Wire.endTransmission();
}
```

```
//=================================================
void RtcClearFlags(void)
{
  Wire.beginTransmission(RX8025_address);
  Wie.send(0xF0);
  Wire.send(RX8025_Control[1]);
  Wire.endTransmission();
}
```

A Test Sketch

With our library files modified, let's take the clock for a test drive. This sketch (listing 4-7) will set the clock, initializing it with a one minute interrupt. When the interrupt fires, the Arduino will wake up, read the time and then print out the time, alarm settings, and the raw reading of all registers in the clock.

This is severely modified version of the original Stalker demonstration sketch. The temperature, compact flash storage, and battery monitoring functions have been removed. I wanted to concentrate solely on proving out the RTC and sleep functions before moving on.

Listing 4-7. RX8025 Demonstration Sketch

```
#include <avr/sleep.h>
#include "myRX8025.h"
#include <Wire.h>

//***********************************
// RX8025 stuff
unsigned char second = 0;
unsigned char minute = 0;
unsigned char hour = 0;
unsigned char weekday = 0;
unsigned char day = 0;
unsigned char month = 0;
unsigned char year = 0;
unsigned char Doffset = 0;
unsigned char alarmD_hour = 0;
unsigned char alarmD_minute = 0;
unsigned char alarmW_weekday = 0;
unsigned char alarmW_hour = 0;
unsigned char alarmW_minute = 0;
unsigned char RX8025_control_1 = 0;
unsigned char RX8025_control_2 = 0;
unsigned char RX8025_Reserved;

unsigned char RX8025_time[7]=
{
//second, minute, hour, week, date, month, year, BCD format
  0x00,0x45,0x14,0x03,0x28,0x05,0x11
};
```

```
unsigned char RX8025_alarmD[2]=  // daily alarm
{
  0x15,0x12  // minute, hour
};

unsigned char RX8025_alarmW[3]=
{
  0x45,0x07,0x06     // minute, hour, weekday
};

unsigned char RX8025_Control[2]=
{
  0x25,0x00  // E - Set 24 hour clock, 1-minute interrupts
             // F - clear all flags
};  // end RX8025 stuff

//======================================
// Sleep stuff
int wakePin = 2;                  // pin used for waking up
int sleepStatus = 0;              // variable to store a request for sleep
int count = 0;                    // counter
// end sleep stuff

//======================================
// program stuff
int LEDpin = 8;

//======================================
//======================================
void wakeUpNow()          // here the interrupt is handled after wakeup
{
  // execute code here after wake-up before returning to the loop() function
  digitalWrite(LEDpin, HIGH);
}

//======================================
void setup(void)
{
  Wire.begin();
  Serial.begin(9600);
  RX8025_init();
//  setRtcAlarmD();    // this is where you would set these
//  setRtcAlarmW();    // if you were going to use specific time alarms

  pinMode(LEDpin, OUTPUT);//LED pin set to OUTPUT
  pinMode(wakePin, INPUT);  // setup interrupt pin
  attachInterrupt(0, wakeUpNow, LOW); // use interrupt 0 (pin 2) and run function
                                      // wakeUpNow when pin 2 gets LOW
  digitalWrite(LEDpin, HIGH);
}
```

```
//======================================
void loop(void)
{
  delay(500);
  RtcClearFlags();
  getRtcTime();
  print_RX8025_time();
  print_AlarmD();
  print_AlarmW();
  getRtcAll();
  print_RX8025_all();
  Serial.println("--------------next--data--------------");
  Serial_Command();
  Serial.println();
  sleepNow();
}

//======================================
void print_RX8025_all(void)
{
  Serial.print(second,DEC);
  Serial.print(" ");
  Serial.print(minute,DEC);
  Serial.print(" ");
  Serial.print(hour,DEC);
  Serial.print(" ");
  Serial.print(weekday,DEC);
  Serial.print(" ");
  Serial.print(day,DEC);
  Serial.print(" ");
  Serial.print(month,DEC);
  Serial.print(" ");
  Serial.print(year,DEC);
  Serial.print(" ");
  Serial.print(Doffset,DEC);
  Serial.print(" ");
  Serial.print(alarmW_minute,DEC);
  Serial.print(" ");
  Serial.print(alarmW_hour,DEC);
  Serial.print(" ");
  Serial.print(alarmW_weekday,DEC);
  Serial.print(" ");
  Serial.print(alarmD_minute,DEC);
  Serial.print(" ");
  Serial.print(alarmD_hour,DEC);
  Serial.print(" ");
  Serial.print(RX8025_Reserved,DEC);
  Serial.print(" ");
  Serial.print(RX8025_control_1,DEC);
  Serial.print(" ");
  Serial.println(RX8025_control_2,DEC);
}
```

```
//======================================
void print_RX8025_time(void)
{
  Serial.print(year,DEC);
  Serial.print("/");
  Serial.print(month,DEC);
  Serial.print("/");
  Serial.print(day,DEC);
  switch(weekday)
  {
  case 0x00:
    {
      Serial.print("/Sunday   ");
      break;
    }
  case 0x01:
    {
      Serial.print("/Monday   ");
      break;
    }
  case 0x02:
    {
      Serial.print("/Tuesday  ");
      break;
    }
  case 0x03:
    {
      Serial.print("/Wednesday  ");
      break;
    }
  case 0x04:
    {
      Serial.print("/Thursday  ");
      break;
    }
  case 0x05:
    {
      Serial.print("/Friday  ");
      break;
    }
  case 0x06:
    {
      Serial.print("/Saturday   ");
      break;
    }
  }
  Serial.print(hour,DEC);
  Serial.print(":");
  Serial.print(minute,DEC);
  Serial.print(":");
  Serial.println(second,DEC);
}
```

```
//=====================================
void print_AlarmD(void)
{
 Serial.print("Daily Alarm = ");
 Serial.print(alarmD_hour,DEC);
 Serial.print(":");
 Serial.println(alarmD_minute,DEC);
}

//=====================================
void print_AlarmW(void)
{
  Serial.print("Weekly Alarm = ");
  Serial.print(alarmW_hour,DEC);
  Serial.print(":");
  Serial.print(alarmW_minute,DEC);
  Serial.print(" ");
  Serial.println(alarmW_weekday,DEC);
}

//=====================================
void Serial_Command(void)
{
  if(Serial.available()==3)
  {
    if(Serial.read()=='c')
    {
      if(Serial.read()=='c')
      {
        if(Serial.read()=='c')
        {
          Serial.println("Got Serial data");
        }
      }
    }
  }
  else
  {
    Serial.flush();
  }
}

//=====================================
void sleepNow()            // here we put the arduino to sleep

{
  digitalWrite(LEDpin, LOW);
    /* Now is the time to set the sleep mode. In the Atmega8 datasheet
     * http://www.atmel.com/dyn/resources/prod_documents/doc2486.pdf on page 35
     * there is a list of sleep modes which explains which clocks and
     * wake up sources are available in which sleep mode.
     *
```

```
 * In the avr/sleep.h file, the call names of these sleep modes are to be found:
 *
 * The 5 different modes are:
 *     SLEEP_MODE_IDLE          -the least power savings
 *     SLEEP_MODE_ADC
 *     SLEEP_MODE_PWR_SAVE
 *     SLEEP_MODE_STANDBY
 *     SLEEP_MODE_PWR_DOWN      -the most power savings
 *
 * For now, we want as much power savings as possible, so we
 * choose the according
 * sleep mode: SLEEP_MODE_PWR_DOWN
 *
 */
set_sleep_mode(SLEEP_MODE_PWR_DOWN);   // sleep mode is set here
sleep_enable();             // enables the sleep bit in the mcucr register
                            // so sleep is possible. just a safety pin
/* Now it is time to enable an interrupt. We do it here so an
 * accidentally pushed interrupt button doesn't interrupt
 * our running program. if you want to be able to run
 * interrupt code besides the sleep function, place it in
 * setup() for example.
 *
 * In the function call attachInterrupt(A, B, C)
 * A   can be either 0 or 1 for interrupts on pin 2 or 3.
 *
 * B   Name of a function you want to execute at interrupt for A.
 *
 * C   Trigger mode of the interrupt pin. can be:
 *             LOW       a low level triggers
 *             CHANGE    a change in level triggers
 *             RISING    a rising edge of a level triggers
 *             FALLING   a falling edge of a level triggers
 *
 * In all but the IDLE sleep modes only LOW can be used.
 */
attachInterrupt(0,wakeUpNow, LOW); // use interrupt 0 (pin 2) and run function
                                   // wakeUpNow when pin 2 gets LOW
delay(500);                 // keeps serial output clean after waking up.
sleep_mode();               // here the device is actually put to sleep!!
                            // THE PROGRAM CONTINUES FROM HERE AFTER WAKING UP
sleep_disable();            // first thing after waking from sleep:
                            // disable sleep...
detachInterrupt(0);         // disables interrupt 0 on pin 2 so the
                            // wakeUpNow code will not be executed
                            // during normal running time.

}
```

This code is a blend of the original demonstration, the Sleep demonstration available on the Arduino playground, and my own bit of code here and there. Upload and run the sketch. Open a the serial monitor and set it to 9600bps. You should see the following output:

```
11/5/28/Wednesday  14:45:0
Daily Alarm = 0:0
Weekly Alarm = 0:0 0
0 45 14 3 28 5 11 0 0 0 0 0 0 0 25 95
--------------next--data---------------
```

The message should repeat every minute, on the minute. In addition, the LED should light when the Arduino wakes up, and extinguish before going back to sleep.

Zigbee Setup

In order to prepare the Xbee radios, we will need to perform several tasks. First, we need to modify the Stalker board once more, in order to support sleep options on the Xbee module we will mount on the board.

The other task is to configure each Xbee radio, utilizing Digi's configuration tool. Getting the settings correct can be a headache, but fortunately the default settings are usually right on the money.

Modifying the Stalker to Support Xbee Sleep

To complete the modification to the Stalker board, we need to add two wires to the Xbee connector. These wires will plug into two digital pins. One wire acts as the sleep enable pin. With the Arduino digital pin configured as an output, we can set this pin high to force the Xbee radio to sleep. The radio will complete any message transactions before shutting down, so we don't need to worry about cutting off our message. When this pin is pulled low, the Xbee radio will wake up and prepare for transmission. We need only be sure to give it about 13 milliseconds to fully wake up.

The second wire acts as a report back from the Xbee concerning its sleep state. With the Arduino pin set as an input, reading a high on this wire indicates that the Xbee radio is awake. Reading a low here indicates it is sleeping.

The Sleep control input is on Xbee pin 9, while the Sleep status output is on Xbee pin 13. The Stalker board provides a set of solder holes on either side of the Xbee socket for each pin on the Xbee. We can simply solder a length of wire directly into the hole and insert the other end of the wire into the Arduino digital pin.

Looking at the Stalker board with the Xbee socket at the top, pin 9 (Sleep mode input) is on the left, second from the bottom. Solder a length of wire into this hole and connect it to Arduino digital pin 4. Xbee pin 13 (Sleep status output) is on the right side of the Xbee module. It is third from the bottom. Solder another wire here and connect it to Arduino digital pin 5.

■ **Note** You might be tempted to cut and solder the "POWER_BEE" jumper on the bottom of the Stalker according to the wiki so the Xbee module will be powered by Arduino pin D5. *Don't*. I have found that the digital output is not strong enough to keep the Xbee series 2 module powered up. This causes the whole Arduino to continuously reset. Your results may vary. The Xbee module includes plenty of low power and sleep options available, anyway. The better option, presented here, is to assert the sleep pin on the radio.

Configuring the Radios

Setting up Xbee modules begins by downloading the X-CTU application from the Digi web site. The application runs on windows only. If you are unfortunate enough to be running Mac or Linux, you will need to find a Windows machine or run an emulator. You could also research the use of Xbee serial AT commands. Much of the configuration could be accomplished via the serial terminal by manually typing a series of commands. The listing is in the Xbee manual. However, uploading new firmware may be a bit of a hassle using this method. I will stick to using the X-CTU software.

A Look at X-CTU

After downloading and installing X-CTU, running it will present the window in Figure 4-3. Your first task is to figure out what your Xbee to USB dongle's com port number is. The quick and easy way to do it is to be sure the device is *not* plugged in; then run X-CTU. Take note of the listed ports. Next, close X-CTU, plug in your Xbee USB dongle, and then restart X-CTU. Select the com port that was not on the list the first time. Be sure the settings are 9600 bps, no flow control, 8 data bits, one stop bit, and no parity. Also, be sure enable API is unchecked.

If you already have an Xbee radio module installed, you can go ahead and hit the Test/Query button. If all is well, you will get a small box reporting that communication with the radio modem was okay. It also reports the modem type, firmware version, and serial number. If you got a large box with a bunch of instructions, the PC could not connect to the radio. The best option is to try resetting the modem. If your dongle has a reset button, it could not be easier. If your dongle is like mine, you will need to momentarily touch a wire to both the ground pin and the reset pin on the dongle.

If you did not install a modem before you plugged in the dongle, unfortunately you will need to close X-CTU once more, remove the dongle, insert the modem, and then restart the process. X-CTU tends to have a problem recognizing the USB dongle being reinserted. It *looks* fine, but the software will no longer find a radio, no matter what you do.

Once you have confirmed communications, we can begin setting up the radios.

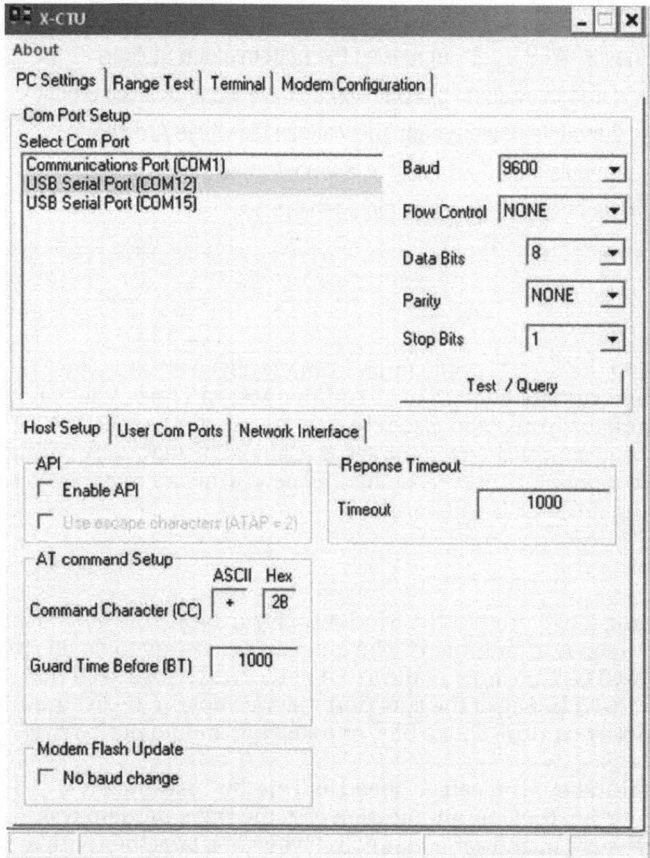

Figure 4-3. X-CTU com port settings and Xbee radio connections

Configuring the PC Radio (the Coordinator)

Before moving forward, it might help to somehow mark one of the radios, which radio will be the coordinator. It serves as the controller of the network and will be inserted into the PC. Maybe you want to tie a little flag onto the antenna or draw a smiley face on the board with a marker. Whatever makes you smile. Anyway, the point is not to confuse your radios because if things do not go as planned, you will be swapping radios back and forth as you try new settings.

Assuming you are using Xbee series 2 radios, we want to configure the radios in AT mode. In AT mode, the radios emulate a standard serial connection. Any bytes coming in on the radio's serial port goes out the antenna and vice versa.

API mode requires a lot of additional overhead and is much more difficult to debug. However, it offers many new robust network features and is the preferred method of building mesh networks. For now, we just want to establish a simple two-node network, so AT mode is perfect.

With your coordinator node radio installed in the USB dongle, plug it in and run X-CTU. Click the Test/Query button and be sure you are connected. Now, hit the Modem Configuration tab. Here is where all the action is (see Figure 4-4).

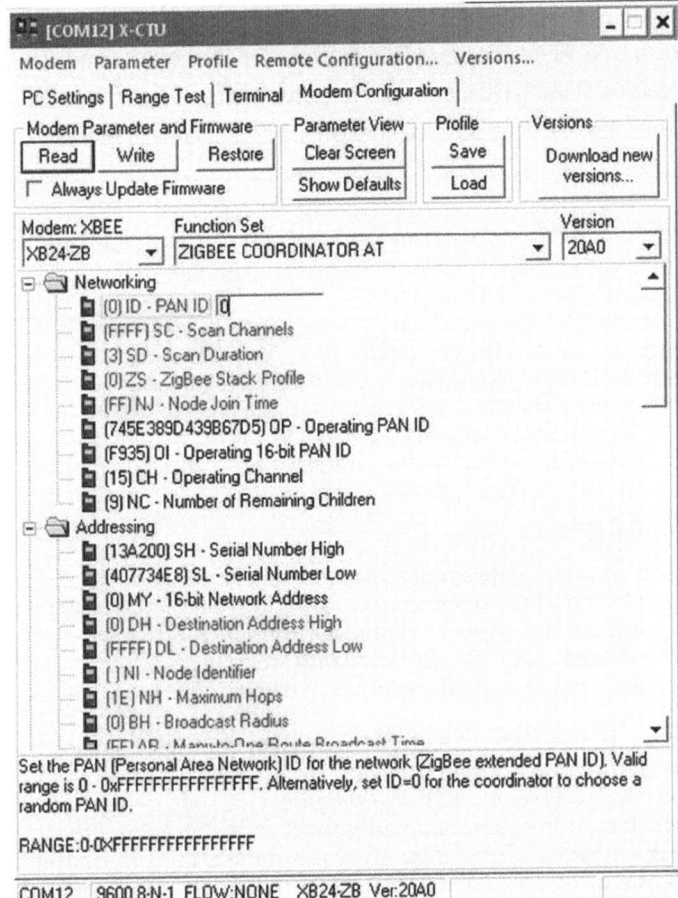

Figure 4-4. X-CTU Xbee modem configuration tab lots of options to play with

Initially the options table will be blank. You first need to hit the Read button, which will query the Xbee for its current firmware, function sex, version, and all the device settings. Hit the button, and after a few moments you will see the firmware settings table, as shown in Figure 4-2.

Note that the likely fresh-out-of-the box function set is as a router. We want to change the function set to Zigbee Coordinator AT mode. Simply pull the tab down and change it to the appropriate setting, and click the Write button. This will upload the new function set firmware to the radio. This process usually takes much longer than changing settings. The progress bar at the bottom will let you know how long you have to wait.

■ **Note**   I recommend against altering the modem type. Attempting to upload firmware for another modem type could damage your Xbee. Likewise, there is little value in using older firmware versions. You can be certain to be using the latest firmwares by clicking the Download new versions button before writing new function sets.

Once the new function set has been written to the radio, you can go ahead and play with the options table. You can always recall the factory defaults with the Show Defaults button. If you make a big mistake, simply click it and then rewrite the factory defaults to the radio.

To be honest, all the factory settings are perfect for the coordinator. In fact, messing with them too much may prevent us from establishing a connection with the end device later. The only setting we really need to be concerned with here is the PAN ID. The default is 0, which is fine. However, everyone else is likely to be using the same ID. If you want to be sure you don't have message collisions with other networks, you can change the ID. I used 2323. Just be sure that you jot it down because you will need to make sure both radios have the same PAN ID. Go ahead and write the configuration to the radio.

Configuring the Sensor Node Radio (the End Device)

Remove the USB dongle and swap your Xbees. With the node's radio installed, reinsert the dongle and restart X-CTU. Again, do a Test/Query in the PC settings tab to be sure you are connected. In the Modem Configuration tab, read the current modem configuration order to get the appropriate modem type. Now change the function set to Zigbee End Device AT and write the new firmware to the modem.

With the new firmware installed, we can begin configuring the settings. We have a few more to change than in the coordinator.

First, set the PAN ID to the same ID you wrote to the coordinator. Without this, they will be talking on different networks. Next, check that both Destination Address High and Destination Address Low are set to zero. Sometimes the low portion of the address is set to FFFF. We want the end node to be directing its messages to the coordinator, which is address zero. Low address FFFF is a broadcast to all nodes on the network. In this case, because the message is meant for everyone, there is no confirmation that the message is received. By setting the low address to zero, we ensure that the message is meant only for the coordinator, and that it will respond back with a confirmation to the end node radio. We don't have to worry about handling the response because it is all handled by the Zigbee stack.

Scroll down to the RF interfacing group of settings. It's not important for now, but you may want to play with the power levels in the future. If your node will be a short distance from the coordinator, you can lower the transmitter power and thus save battery life. The highest power level will give you maximum range.

Our final stop is the Sleep modes group. Normally, the sleep mode of the radio is set to a cyclical system, in which the radio wakes up on a predetermined interval. This is a problem for application. Like two college roommates, they never seem to have the same sleep schedule. It's rare for both the Arduino and the Xbee to wake up at the same time. This has the result of sending partial messages or simply garbage.

We really want to let the Arduino tell the Xbee when to wake up and get to work. When transmission is done, the Xbee can go back to sleep on its own. Set the sleep mode to 1- Pin Hibernate. This makes the Xbee's sleep condition dependent on the state of the pin 9 input. Now we simply need to instruct the Arduino to set the pin low when we want the Xbee to wake up and then set it back to high when the radio can go back to sleep (at the same time we sleep the Arduino).

Write the settings to the radio.

Confirming Xbee Communication

Unplug the dongle, remove the radio, and reinsert the coordinator. Place the end node radio in the Stalker board.

Reconnect the dongle and restart X-CTU. Once more, test the connection before proceeding. Click the Terminal tab. You will see a window much like the one in Figure 4-5.

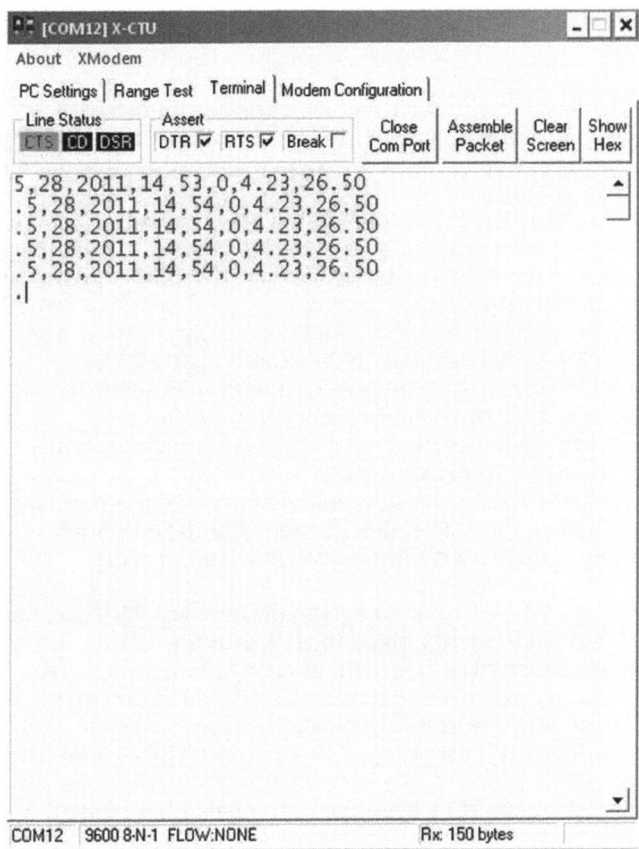

Figure 4-5. The X-CTU terminal window with data streaming from the end node

Connect the USB programming adaptor to the Stalker and attach it to your computer. Start the Arduino IDE, set the serial settings to the programming dongle, and start the serial monitor. This will serve as a confirmation that messages are being sent out of the serial connection. If your radio configuration is incorrect, you will see data in the serial monitor, but not in the X-CTU terminal.

Any sketch that sends text to the serial device will work for our purposes. You need only add the appropriate code to set the Arduino pin connected to the Xbee's sleep mode pin low. Alternately, you could plug the wire directly into a ground pin on the shield socket. You should see the same message in the X-CTU terminal as you do in the serial monitor. The only difference is that X-CTU reports a line feed any time you send `Serial.println()` with a period at the beginning of the new line.

If you do not get the message in the terminal, or get part of the message or garbage, you will need to inspect everything carefully. First check that the wiring is correct. I made a mistake initially because I was looking at a reference photo of the Xbee that had the metal RF shield on the top, whereas mine are on the bottom. Thus, I swapped the relationship of pin 9 and I soldered the wires. In other words, I soldered to pins 8 and 12 rather than 9 and 13!

If your solder skills prove good, next check the Xbee settings of the coordinator because it is already installed and running. If they check out, the end node is the only other culprit.

Final Code

By now, most of the code in the final sketch (see Listing 4-7) should be familiar. The output message has been reformatted so it is easier for the Processing application to parse. On the Freakduino-Chibi, the radio output and serial monitor output were treated separately. We were able to output additional debug information to the serial monitor and format it to be more easily read.

In the case of the Xbee, the interface is tied directly to the RX/TX lines of the Arduino, which are normally used for debugging and the serial monitor. We are essentially piggybacking the serial monitor. Therefore, we don't have the advantage of a "radio message" and a "debug message." With that in mind, the code actually becomes a bit smaller than the Chibi version.

This has one minor implication for our Processing sketch: the Xbee radios are configured to run at 9600 bps. Therefore, we will need to remember to change the data rate in the Processing sketch to match. We could certainly reconfigure the Xbee radios to run at higher speeds, but from experience, this can cause minor yet irritating issues attempting to use X-CTU. It was my feeling that we don't really need a high-speed communication link in this case, anyway, so rather than forego the constant frustrations, I simply changed the Processing sketch to match. It is a one-time fix.

To demonstrate the Stalker board, I added the temperature, battery, and memory card libraries back into the sketch. These are the same libraries that came in the Stalker files download from SeeedStudios. The Arduino will report the date and time, followed by the battery voltage, and finish up with the temperature.

In the sketch, I did not activate flash card storage. To back up your data to the onboard flash card, all you need to do is uncomment the call to `TF_card_init` in the setup function, as well as the call to `write_data_to_TF` in the main loop. Be sure a blank formatted card is in the slot, or you will get an error message. Before running the Processing application, you will need to modify the TF card library, so it does not print any messages to the serial port. You could convert the TF messages to an error code, and attach it to the data message after the temperature. Then, in Processing, pick up that error code and generate a debug message in the processing window.

With the Stalker board configured, sleeping, and transmitting over Xbee, our final task is to build the Processing application and start logging data.

Listing 4-7. *Final Stalker Wireless Sensor Node Sketch*

```
#include <avr/sleep.h>
#include "myRX8025.h"
#include "tmp102.h"
#include "TF.h"
#include "Battery.h"
#include <Wire.h>
#include <Fat16.h>
#include <Fat16util.h>
```

```
//***********************************
// RX8025 stuff
unsigned char second = 0;
unsigned char minute = 0;
unsigned char hour = 0;
unsigned char weekday = 0;
unsigned char day = 0;
unsigned char month = 0;
unsigned char year = 0;
unsigned char Doffset = 0;
unsigned char alarmD_hour = 0;
unsigned char alarmD_minute = 0;
unsigned char alarmW_weekday = 0;
unsigned char alarmW_hour = 0;
unsigned char alarmW_minute = 0;
unsigned char RX8025_control_1 = 0;
unsigned char RX8025_control_2 = 0;
unsigned char RX8025_Reserved;

unsigned char RX8025_time[7]=
{
//second, minute, hour, week, date, month, year, BCD format
  0x00,0x45,0x14,0x03,0x28,0x05,0x11
};

unsigned char RX8025_alarmD[2]=  // daily alarm
{
  0x15,0x12  // minute, hour
};

unsigned char RX8025_alarmW[3]=
{
  0x45,0x07,0x06     // minute, hour, weekday
};

unsigned char RX8025_Control[2]=
{
  0x25,0x00  // E - Set 24 hour clock, 1-minute interrupts
             // F - clear all flags
};  // end RX8025 stuff

//======================================
// Sleep stuff
int wakePin = 2;                // pin used for waking up
int beeSleep = 4;               // set high to sleep, low to wake up
int beeSleepStatus = 5;         // gets the Bee sleep status
```

```
//========================================
// program stuff
int LEDpin = 8;
float convertedtemp; /* We then need to multiply our two bytes by
                               a scaling factor, mentioned in the datasheet. */
int tmp102_val; /* an int is capable of storing two bytes, this is
                          where we "chuck" the two bytes together. */
char name[] = "data.log";      // file name in TF card root dir
unsigned int bat_read;         //analog read battery voltage
float bat_voltage;             //battery voltage
unsigned char charge_status;   //battery charge status


//========================================
//========================================
void wakeUpNow()            // here the interrupt is handled after wakeup
{
  // execute code here after wake-up before returning to the loop() function
  digitalWrite(LEDpin, HIGH);
  digitalWrite(beeSleep, LOW); // wake the bee
}

//========================================
void setup(void)
{
  Wire.begin();
  Serial.begin(9600);
  RX8025_init();
  //  TF_card_init();
  tmp102_init();
  Battery_init();
  pinMode(LEDpin, OUTPUT);//LED pin set to OUTPUT
  pinMode(wakePin, INPUT);  // setup interrupt pin
  pinMode(beeSleep, OUTPUT);
  pinMode(beeSleepStatus, INPUT);
  attachInterrupt(0, wakeUpNow, LOW); // use interrupt 0 (pin 2) and run function
                                        // wakeUpNow when pin 2 gets LOW
  digitalWrite(LEDpin, HIGH);
  digitalWrite(beeSleep, LOW); // wake the bee
}

//========================================
void loop(void)
{
  while(digitalRead(beeSleepStatus) == LOW) {
    break;
  }

  RtcClearFlags();
  getRtcTime();
  getTemp102();
  Battery_charge_status();
```

```
  Battery_voltage_read();
  //  write_data_to_TF();

  //debug data
  print_data();
  Serial_Command();  // pending return commands?

  sleepNow();  // nighty night
}


//=====================================
void print_data(void)
{
  Serial.print(month,DEC);
  Serial.print(",");
  Serial.print(day,DEC);
  Serial.print(",");
  Serial.print(2000 + year,DEC);
  Serial.print(",");
  Serial.print(hour,DEC);
  Serial.print(",");
  Serial.print(minute,DEC);
  Serial.print(",");
  Serial.print(second,DEC);
  Serial.print(",");
  Serial.print(bat_voltage);
  Serial.print(",");
  Serial.print(convertedtemp);
  Serial.println("\0");
 }

//=====================================
void Serial_Command(void)
{
  if(Serial.available()==3)
  {
    if(Serial.read()=='c')
    {
      if(Serial.read()=='c')
      {
        if(Serial.read()=='c')
        {
          Serial.println("Got Serial data");
        }
      }
    }
  }
```

```
  else
  {
    Serial.flush();
  }
}

//======================================
void sleepNow()            // here we put the arduino to sleep

{
  digitalWrite(LEDpin, LOW);
  digitalWrite(beeSleep, HIGH);
    /* Now is the time to set the sleep mode. In the Atmega8 datasheet
     * http://www.atmel.com/dyn/resources/prod_documents/doc2486.pdf on page 35
     * there is a list of sleep modes which explains which clocks and
     * wake up sources are available in which sleep mode.
     *
     * In the avr/sleep.h file, the call names of these sleep modes are to be found:
     *
     * The 5 different modes are:
     *     SLEEP_MODE_IDLE          -the least power savings
     *     SLEEP_MODE_ADC
     *     SLEEP_MODE_PWR_SAVE
     *     SLEEP_MODE_STANDBY
     *     SLEEP_MODE_PWR_DOWN       -the most power savings
     *
     * For now, we want as much power savings as possible, so we
     * choose the according
     * sleep mode: SLEEP_MODE_PWR_DOWN
     *
     */
  set_sleep_mode(SLEEP_MODE_PWR_DOWN);   // sleep mode is set here
  sleep_enable();             // enables the sleep bit in the mcucr register
                              // so sleep is possible. just a safety pin
    /* Now it is time to enable an interrupt. We do it here so an
     * accidentally pushed interrupt button doesn't interrupt
     * our running program. if you want to be able to run
     * interrupt code besides the sleep function, place it in
     * setup() for example.
     *
     * In the function call attachInterrupt(A, B, C)
     * A   can be either 0 or 1 for interrupts on pin 2 or 3.
     *
     * B   Name of a function you want to execute at interrupt for A.
     *
     * C   Trigger mode of the interrupt pin. can be:
     *             LOW        a low level triggers
     *             CHANGE     a change in level triggers
     *             RISING     a rising edge of a level triggers
     *             FALLING    a falling edge of a level triggers
     *
```

```
  * In all but the IDLE sleep modes only LOW can be used.
  */
attachInterrupt(0,wakeUpNow, LOW); // use interrupt 0 (pin 2) and run function
                                   // wakeUpNow when pin 2 gets LOW
  delay(500);                    // keeps serial output clean after waking up.
  sleep_mode();                  // here the device is actually put to sleep!!
                                 // THE PROGRAM CONTINUES FROM HERE AFTER WAKING UP
  sleep_disable();               // first thing after waking from sleep:
                                 // disable sleep...
  detachInterrupt(0);            // disables interrupt 0 on pin 2 so the
                                 // wakeUpNow code will not be executed
                                 // during normal running time.
}
```

Processing umm… Processes!

Now that we have a basic two-channel transmitter up and running, we can consider pulling the data off the serial port and doing something useful. For example, we could convert the data and save it in a file that is easy to read with a spreadsheet application.

Processing is a programming environment much like the Arduino IDE. After installing it, start the application. You will notice it looks very similar to the Arduino IDE, except that it is gray. Type the following code into the Processing window and save it:

```
import processing.serial.*;
Serial SinkNode;
String Month, Day, Year, Hour, Minute, Second, NodeData0, NodeData1;

void setup (){
  //sets up a serial connection named SinkNode.
  //The value after Serial.list in the [] indicates the port
  SinkNode = new Serial(this, Serial.list()[1], 57600);
}

void draw() {
 int gotData = 0;
 while (gotData == 0){
  if (SinkNode.available() > 0) {
    String data = SinkNode.readStringUntil('\n');
    if (data != null){
      gotData = parseString(data);
      PrintData();
    }
  }
 }
}


int parseString (String serialString) {
  String items[] = split(serialString, ',');
  println("From SourceNode: " + serialString);
```

```
    Month = items[0];
    Day = items[1];
    Year = items[2];
    Hour = items[3];
    Minute = items[4];
    Second = items[5];
    NodeData0 = items[6];
    NodeData1 = items[7];

    if (items.length == 7) {
    return 1;
    } else {
      return 0;
    }
}

void PrintData() {
  print(Month);
  print("/");
  print(Day);
  print("/");
  print(Year);
  print(" ");
  print(Hour);
  print(":");
  print(Minute);
  print(":");
  print(Second);
  print("   ");
  print("A0 = ");
  print(NodeData0);
  print("   ");
  print("A1 = ");
  println(NodeData1);
}
```

This first application simply pulls the data from the port and prints it in a easy-to-read format. First we import the serial library and define several variables, including a list of variables to hold each field of data.

In the setup function, we need only prepare the a serial object. We have one small issue in that we need to somehow identify the serial port we want to use. Rather than com ports or device names, Processing uses just a number in an ordered list. This can be tricky, but you could simply start with 1 and move forward until you find the one that connects.

The draw function in Processing is the same as the loop function in Arduino. For the first sketch, the draw function is rather short. Essentially, we want to check the serial port for available data. So long as data is available, we will read the data. We keep reading the bytes and sending them to the parse function until we reach the string terminator ('\n').

The parseString function accepts the data from the serial port and prints the raw data to the output box in the bottom of the Processing window. It then starts splitting up the entire data string into several individual strings. It uses the comma as the split indicator and dumps each piece into item strings sequentially. All we need to do is count the item strings and set our field strings equal to the item string number. When the number of items parsed equals 7 (don't forget the zero), we return a 1 back to the gotData variable, which called the function back in the draw loop.

Once we return to the draw loop, we can go ahead and call the PrintData function. This simply cleans up the display, giving us something easy to read.

Run the sketch, and after trying several serial port numbers to locate your sink node, you should get output similar to this:

```
WARNING:  RXTX Version mismatch
        Jar version = RXTX-2.2pre1
        native lib Version = RXTX-2.2pre2
From SourceNode: 3,16,2011,0,39,40,341,370

3/16/2011 0:39:40  A0 = 341  A1 = 370

From SourceNode: 3,16,2011,0,39,50,306,325

3/16/2011 0:39:50  A0 = 306  A1 = 325

From SourceNode: 3,16,2011,0,40,0,683,661

3/16/2011 0:40:0  A0 = 683  A1 = 661
```

If you need to process the data further (such as converting the analog values to something like temperature), you could create a new function block to do so relatively easily. You would call this function from the mainline just after parsing the data and before calling the PrintData function.

Adding Logging Features

Adding data-logging features will complicate the sketch quite a bit, but it is well worth the effort. You can easily elect to keep the RTC data or replace it with the PC's time data. You can save both raw ADC values and the converted data. It is entirely up to you what you want to have available. You could even add visualization to the application. Take a look at the seismometer project for a method for doing so.

For this project, let's try to keep it simple and just record the data as given into a text file that we can later open in a spreadsheet application:

```
import processing.serial.*;
Serial SinkNode;
String Month, Day, Year, Hour, Minute, Second, NodeData0, NodeData1;

// log file variables
String dataFolder = "../data/";
String logfilename;       // log file name
PrintWriter logFile;

// State variable
boolean logging = false;
```

```
void setup (){
  SinkNode = new Serial(this, Serial.list()[1], 57600);

  // set tentative file name
  logfilename = dataFolder + "Save_the_World-" + nf(year(),4) + nf(month(),2) + nf(day(),2)
              + "-" + nf(hour(),2) + nf(minute(),2) + nf(second(),2) + ".log";

  startLogging();
}

void draw() {
 int gotData = 0;
 while (gotData == 0){
  if (SinkNode.available() > 0) {
    String data = SinkNode.readStringUntil('\n');
    if (data != null){
      gotData = parseString(data);
      writeLog();
    }
  }
 }
}


int parseString (String serialString) {
  String items[] = split(serialString, ',');
  println("From SourceNode: " + serialString);
  Month = items[0];
  Day = items[1];
  Year = items[2];
  Hour = items[3];
  Minute = items[4];
  Second = items[5];
  NodeData0 = items[6];
  NodeData1 = items[7];

  if (items.length == 7) {
  return 1;
  } else {
    return 0;
  }
}


String formatLogEntry()
{
  String log_entry =
    Month + "/" + Day + "/" + Year + "," +
    Hour + ":" + Minute + ":" + Second + "," +
    NodeData0 + "," + NodeData1;
  return log_entry;
}
```

```
void writeLog()
{
  if (logging)
  {
    String log_entry = formatLogEntry();
    logFile.println(log_entry);
  println(log_entry);
    logFile.flush();
  }
}

void startLogging()
{
  // open file
  openLogFile();
  // start running
  logging = true;
  println("Started logging to " + logfilename);
}

void stopLogging()
{
  logging = false;
  closeLogFile();
  println("Stopped Logging.");
}

void openLogFile()
{
 // logfilename = logfileTextField.getText();
  if (logfilename.equals(""))
  {
    // set tentative file name
    logfilename = dataFolder + "Save_the_World-" + nf(year(),4) + nf(month(),2) + nf(day(),2)
      + "-" + nf(hour(),2) + nf(minute(),2) + nf(second(),2) + ".log";
  }
  logFile = createWriter(logfilename);
}

void closeLogFile()
{
  logFile.flush();
  logFile.close();
  println("Log file close.");
  // set tentative file name
  logfilename = dataFolder + "Save_the_World-" + nf(year(),4) + nf(month(),2) + nf(day(),2)
    + "-" + nf(hour(),2) + nf(minute(),2) + nf(second(),2) + ".log";
}
```

We added some variables to the top of the code. The dataFolder string sets the storage location. "../data/" means the previous folder from the one in which the sketch resides in a folder named data.

In setup, we call startLogging, which opens a log file, sets the logging variable to true, and gives us a status message. To open the log file, we first set a tentative string for the file name. It starts with the folder location, then we assign a project name, append the date and time, and make it a .log file. Note that the date and time are fetched from the PC, This is kind of nice, as it allows you to correlate the data if the RTC clock happens to be set to the wrong time. Once the file name is decided, createWriter is the built in function that actually establishes the pipe between the Processing application and the file on the hard disk.

Returning from the startLogging function, we drop into the draw loop. Everything here is the same, except at the end of the loop we execute the writeLog function. Also, we no longer need the PrintData function because we will do that as part of the writeLog function.

The writeLog function first makes sure that we are logging. If not, it simply exits. If we are logging, it creates a string named log_entry, and sets it equal to the formatLogEntry. Doing so automatically calls the function to output a formatted entry for the log. It is in the formatLogEntry function that we define how we want our log to look. I converted the date and time into the standard mm/dd/yyyy and hr:mn:sc format. I then added the analog data. Be sure to place a comma between each field so our spreadsheet program can easily cut it up again. It then returns this complete string back to the log_entry string in the writeLog function. When it arrives back to the writeLog function, we print it to the display. Flushing the logFile will force the string to be written to the file automatically each time. We could elect to wait for several entries and then write them all at once. This would be useful if we had a fast stream of data. Constantly nailing the hard drive with single-entry writes would bog down the computer and make it unusable. It would also prematurely wear out the drive. However, in our case, we are only writing the single entry every 10 seconds, so it is perfectly acceptable to flush the data to the file each time.

There is a final function, but as yet unused. I leave it for you, in case you decide to expand the Processing application. The closeLogFile function will force a final flush of the data to the file, close it, and prepare the logfilename for a fresh new log.

One suggestion for this function is to set a daily timer, so you start a new log every day (say, at midnight). Imagine that you want to collect data for several weeks. Daily files may be easier for you to manage than one huge file.

When you hit the stop button in Processing, it will automatically flush the remaining data to the file and close it.

The Processing debug window should look something like this if all goes well:

```
WARNING:  RXTX Version mismatch
          Jar version = RXTX-2.2pre1
          native lib Version = RXTX-2.2pre2
Started logging to ../data/Save_the_World-20110616-012424.log
From SourceNode: 3,16,2011,1,28,40,620,608

3/16/2011,1:28:40,620,608

From SourceNode: 3,16,2011,1,28,50,686,666

3/16/2011,1:28:50,686,666

From SourceNode: 3,16,2011,1,29,0,689,664

3/16/2011,1:29:0,689,664
```

```
From SourceNode: 3,16,2011,1,29,10,649,616
```

```
3/16/2011,1:29:10,649,616
```

Reading Data into a Spreadsheet

Let the Processing app run for a while; then stop it. In your computer's file browser, navigate to the processing documents folder. You should find a new folder named `data`. Open the `data` folder, and you will find a file with a name something like `Save_the_World-20110616-012424`. You see that it is the Save the World project, followed by the date, followed by the time the log was started. By default, you can't open this file because it is a `.log`. However you can force your Notepad application to read it. It is a normal text file. If this is frustrating, you can always change the sketch to save the file as a `.txt` file instead. The log file looks like this:

```
3/16/2011,1:28:40,620,608
```

```
3/16/2011,1:28:50,686,666
```

```
3/16/2011,1:29:0,689,664
```

```
3/16/2011,1:29:10,649,616
```

You can now open this file using the `import` function of Excel or OpenOffice. In Excel, go to choose File/Open. Navigate to the `data` folder. Initially you will not see any files. You need to change the file types to All files. Select the log file and click Open. In the pop-up box, select Delimited and click Next. Click the Comma check box and click Next. Excel now breaks out each field into columns. You can now select the date column and instruct Excel to treat it as a date and select the month/day/year format. Click Finish and you are presented with a wonderful Excel sheet of all your data. Unleash your Excel hacking skills!

Conclusion

Adding radio functionality to a project is a bit complex, but if you break it down into steps, it is easier to manage. The hardest points are establishing your first communication link and then converting all the various data types into one compatible with the Chibi stack.

On the Xbee, the challenge is in getting the settings just right. The factory settings usually work great, but without a decent reference guide tweaking the settings can be a hair-pulling experience.

With those first baby steps out of the way, we were able to quickly build up the application, with each iteration becoming more functional.

The key to easily accessible data is to transmit our data as a single string message, with commas separating each field of data. In the Chibi stack, this is easily expandable up to a 120-character message.

Processing lets us grab the message, split it back up into individual bits of data, and log it to a file. From there, it is easy to post-process the data in an application such as Excel or we may write our own post-processing apps using the Processing language.

Perhaps the most challenging aspect of the project has been managing all the different functions. The use of libraries helps to keep the code manageable. As larger functions are proved out, you can go back and create new libraries to handle the major functional blocks.

Wireless radios take a lot of power while transmitting. Even while idle, their current requirements can be a major drain on a low-power sensor system. Utilizing the sleep function granted to us by the RTC to sleep not only the Arduino, but the radio as well, will allow us to extend the battery life considerably.

Finally, with wireless nodes in hand, we can set up longer-range networks using an appropriate antenna pair.

Resources

- FreakLabs

  - FreakLabs ChibiArduino:
    `http://freaklabs.org/index.php/chibiArduino.html`

  - FreakZ Zigbee stack: `http://freaklabs.org/index.php/FreakZ-Open-Source-Zigbee-Stack.html`

    (The FreakZ Zigbee stack is not required here. The ChibiArduino comes installed with a simplified 802.15.4 radio stack, called "Chibi" which is featured in this chapter.)

- SeeedStudio Stalker Arduino:

  - `http://seeedstudio.com/wiki/index.php?title=Seeeduino_Stalker_v2.0`

- Serial radios:

  - Serial radio library - `http://www.open.com.au/mikem/arduino/HopeRF/`

  - `http://www.radio-modules.com/products/telemods/rm001-b-detail.shtml`

  - `http://www.radio-modules.com/products/radiodatamods/radiodatamods.shtml`

  - `http://www.radio-modules.com/products/radiodatamods/tranceiver-modules.shtml`

  - `http://www.gridconnect.com/nlosmodule.html`

- 802.15.4:

  - `http://en.wikipedia.org/wiki/IEEE_802.15.4`

  - `http://en.wikipedia.org/wiki/Comparison_of_802.15.4_radio_modules`

  - 900 Mhz antenna products from L-com: `http://www.l-com.com/category.aspx?id=2071`

  - 2.4 Ghz antenna products from L-com: `http://www.l-com.com/category.aspx?id=2073`

- Bluetooth:
  - http://www.robotshop.com/bluetooth-uart-module.html
  - http://www.cutedigi.com/advanced_search_result.php?keywords=bluetooth
- Xbee:
  - X-CTU Xbee module firmware configuration tool:
  - http://www.digi.com/support/productdetl.jsp?pid=3352&osvid=57&s=316&tp=5&tp2=0
  - Arduino Xbee shield documentation: http://www.arduino.cc/en/Main/ArduinoXbeeShield
  - Official product site: http://www.digi.com/xbee/
  - Series 1 vs. Series 2: http://www.digi.com/support/kbase/kbaseresultdetl.jsp?id=2213
  - http://en.wikipedia.org/wiki/XBee
  - Product comparison chart: www.digi.com/pdf/chart_xbee_rf_features.pdf
  - xBee Library for Arduino by Andrew Rapp: http://code.google.com/p/xbee-arduino/
  - http://code.google.com/p/xbee-api/wiki/XBeeUseCases
  - A great primer on Arduino and Xbee Series 1: http://bildr.org/2011/04/arduino-xbee-wireless/
  - LadyAda's Xbee/Arduino tutorial: http://www.ladyada.net/make/xbee/arduino.html
  - Setting up Series 2 modems: https://sites.google.com/site/xbeetutorial/xbee-introduction/zigbee_setup
- I2C
  - http://www.arduino.cc/en/Reference/Wire
  - http://tronixstuff.wordpress.com/2010/10/20/tutorial-arduino-and-the-i2c-bus/
  - http://tronixstuff.wordpress.com/2010/10/29/tutorial-arduino-and-the-i2c-bus-part-two/
  - http://en.wikipedia.org/wiki/I%C2%B2C
- Arduino Sleep modes
  - http://www.arduino.cc/playground/Learning/ArduinoSleepCode

CHAPTER 5

Contributing to the Hive Mind

Submitting Your Data to Online Services

We all know the hubbub about how the Internet makes it easier than ever to share data, collaborate, and communicate over vast distances and across cultures and geo-political boundaries, so I won't bore you with the obliquely obvious.

I would, however, like to point out that enormous, groundbreaking (dare I say earth shattering?) discoveries have been made possible on the shoulders of the Internet. After all, the Internet was originally created to connect universities around the world so scientists could share data and discoveries. Scientists from every corner of the globe share resources, knowledge and information, and even virtual lab space over the Web. Every facet of research is aided by it.

All the while, these scientists have struggled with one bottleneck: while publishing spreadsheet files of collected data is rather easy, publishing live real-time data is actually quite difficult. More so is the work of indexing and visualizing that data, even as it is being generated.

Certainly, in days past, you could have set up your own server to collect data, as well as create client applications to send data to the server. But to do so, you would have had to know quite a bit about the server/client process, as well as be somewhat of an Internet guru to get it to all work together properly. All this assumes that you have built hardware capable of accessing and posting to the server over the Ethernet in the first place.

In the last five years or so, the idea of the "Internet of things" has cropped up, So many of our daily devices have embedded computers in them, yet they lack the ability to communicate. An Internet of things is an Internet in which all things have the ability to communicate. The stove in your kitchen may automatically alert you via text message when it is time to run the cleaning mode or alert the service contractor of a failed part.

Not long ago, this still seemed like fantasy. But in the last few years, it has become much more than just a simple buzz word. Many jurisdictions in Europe and a few in the United States already have smart utility meters reporting data directly to the utility company, without the need to send someone out to manually read the dials.

Soon, bathroom scales will remind you via your phone to come stand on them. Around lunchtime, they will send you an encouraging message about how best to enjoy the salad diet you are on. Later in the day, your coffeemaker will remind you to hit the Java Hut to pick up another bag of your favorite blend. That evening, your water heater will give you a weekly report of how much gas and water was used in the shower. After all, being environmentally *friendly* starts with being environmentally *conscious*.

Along with the Internet of things, the online services capable of easily collecting, storing, and visualizing all this data in real time have finally come of age as well. The real power of the Internet of things (in my opinion) is the chance to finally collect and analyze large data sets. For example, a weekly report from the water heater is nice, but without a long-term history, you can't really get a sense of your progress. Even if the machine records a year's worth of data, in order to present you with your own history, it still fails in one key area: the ability to benchmark your usage against other users in similar conditions.

Let's look at a bigger picture example. After the Tohoku earthquake in northern Japan in March of 2011, the Fukushima Dai-ichi nuclear power plant was severely damaged by the resultant tsunami. Several reactors went into partial or complete meltdown. The radiation released threw Japan into panic.

SafeCast is a grassroots project that sprang up in response to the situation. It is a citizen lead open source data network, charged with collecting as much radiation data over the long term in Japan as possible.

Data aggregation sites like Pachube made it possible. These sorts of services provide a place to upload and store large data sets, visualize them, and manipulate them. Anyone can easily search for sensor nodes and data sets. They provide a public forum for sharing and digesting data.

Introduction to Online Data Aggregation Services

There are several services currently available for posting your own sensor data and environmental projects. Each has pros and cons. Unfortunately at the time of this writing, only a few services have matured beyond the beta testing phase.

Pachube.com

Pachube (pronounced *patch bay*) is the clear frontrunner. A well-documented application programming interface (API) with several examples, it makes publishing data quite straightforward. It has created several libraries for various languages and environments, all easily found on the site. To round out the support package, a member forum is provided, in which many common questions have already been answered.

This chapter will outlay a framework and a demonstration project for one method of posting data from the Arduino so that you have a clear understanding of how to integrate the service into any project you can dream up.

Before pushing forward, however, I would like to provide a lay of the land of other data aggregation services available (as of early 2011).

Google.com/powermeter

Google Powermeter is another service that is highly mature. It has been built with the primary focus of utility services (the electrical grid in particular). If your project is all about electrical generation (be it solar, wind, geothermal, whatever) and usage, it is a great online service. However, be advised that it strongly pushes commercial hardware, such as utility meters installed by your service providers. This makes using Google Powermeter for non-electrical grid-related projects virtually impossible. I would recommend looking into it only if you already have a smart meter or plan on having one installed in the future.

Power monitoring can be a bit tricky and dangerous if not done carefully. There is a project later in this book to accomplish the task, but opening your breaker panel on your own to install homemade utility monitors is not recommended unless you have the training to do it safely.

Sensorpedia.com

Sensorpedia should be out of beta by the time this book goes to print. The Oak Ridge National Laboratory in the United States funds the project. Because it is partially government-funded, the service will likely be free. Sensorpedia will be as "open source" as possible, which will make it easy to develop applications for.

One interesting aspect of the Sensorpedia philosophy is leveraging social media to enable interpersonal networking based on sensor interest. This is the first site that will focus on matching researchers with voluntary data collectors.

Water contamination specialists need only to enter a few tags into their profile or the site's search system, and they will see not only a list of users with similar interest but also a list of water contamination sensors around the world (or in any local of interest). Collecting data for comparative quality analysis is now simply a matter of following a selected list of sensors.

Open.Sen.se

Finally, there is OpenSense (`http://www.Open.Sen.se`, a strange but wonderful URL). OpenSense intends to be the point-and-click site of data aggregation. Again, it is currently in limited beta, but the front end looks promising. It is very visual, with large icons representing the complete data flow process, from the real-world device through to final visualization. Installation usually involves nothing more than clicking an icon, followed by filling in a short form or clicking a few option buttons.

The user has access to a series of applications and modules to be installed in the dashboard that performs a variety of tasks such as interfacing to specific hardware, crunching numbers, or outputting data in many visual formats (unlike Pachube's single "chart strip" option). There are also several programming-like modules that allow you perform actions similar to If… Then… and Do while… statements.

OpenSense already works with a few home appliances, such as smart bathroom scales. Data could be directly published to your other social media sites, such as Facebook and Twitter. If your morning weigh-in is tweeted to all your friends, are you more motivated to lose a few pounds?

Taking a Closer Look at Pachube

Swing your browser over to `http://www.Pachube.com` (see Figure 5-1), and right away you will see a world map, with loads of pins marking out sensor systems of various categories. Go ahead and click a few. You will be presented a card for the pin, with a URL ending in an `.xml` extension. This URL directly will feed raw text data to your browser. If you want to see the actual feed page on Pachube, you need to click the feed title. Notice that the URL is slightly different.

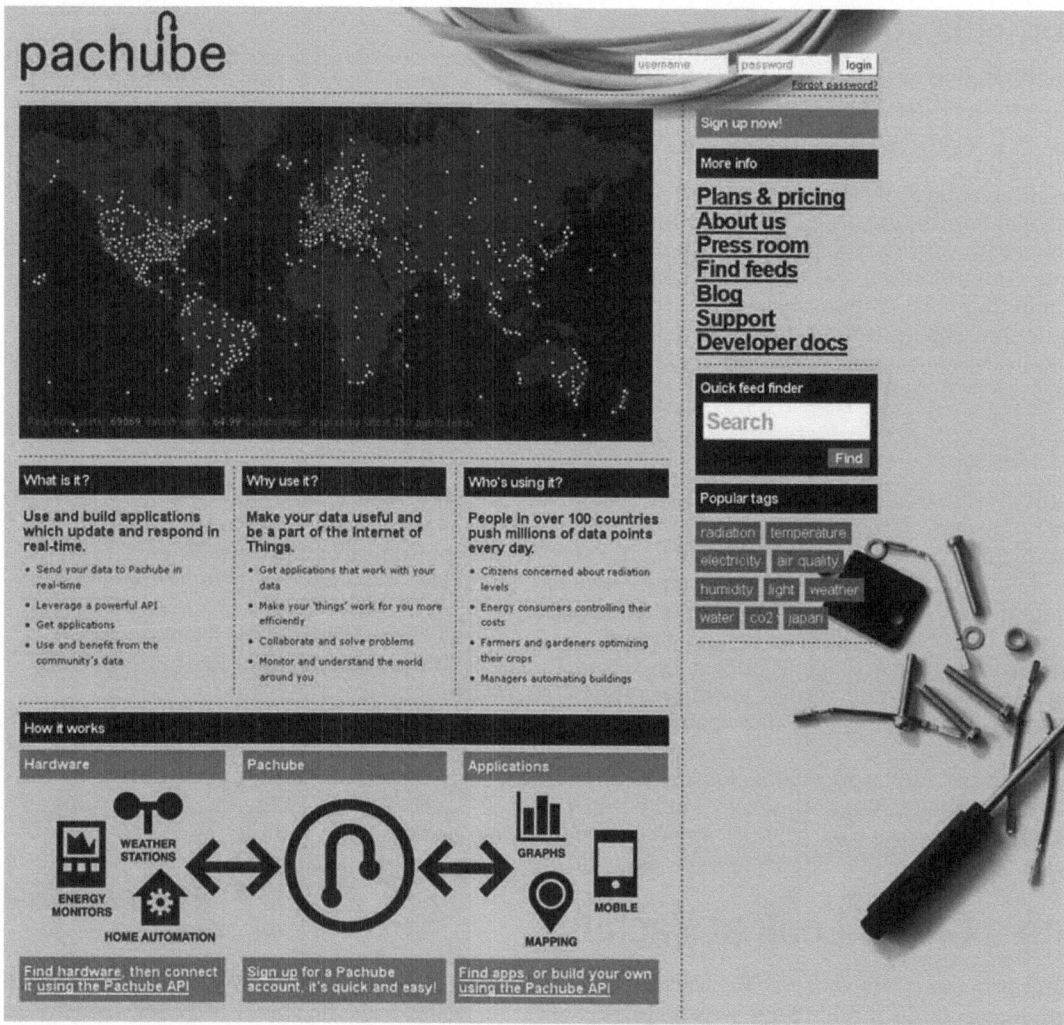

Figure 5-1. Pachube's home page

Type http://www.pachube.com/feeds/14263 into your browser. Notice that you see a feed description with a map location on the top section, while the bottom contains all the sensors (streams) for this feed. Currently, Pachube has only one visualization type: the chart recorder strip.

Take a few moments to explore the site. Much of what you need to know to get up and running on the site is right at your fingertips.

Terminology and Account Limitations

Shown in Figure 5-2 is a typical feed. This one is a SafeCast radiation test feed. A *feed* is a collection of streams, and a *stream* is an individual sensor, actuator, or indicator. So you can think of a feed as a project, with streams being all the hardware elements of that project. The feed in Figure 5-2 has only one stream: the Geiger counter measurement.

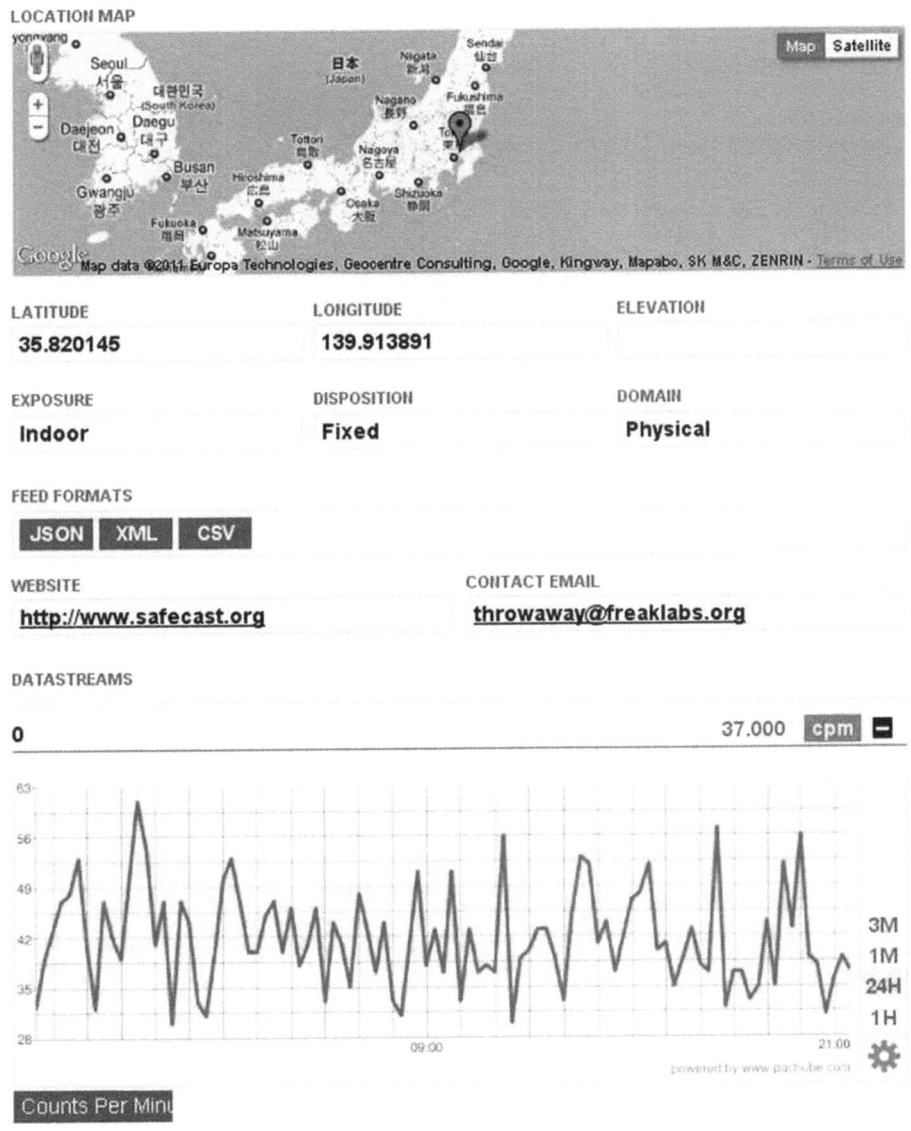

Figure 5-2. A typical Pachube feed display

When you are ready to get started with Pachube, click the orange "Sign up now!" button on the Pachube main page. You are presented with a breakdown of the various account options (see Figure 5-3). Take special note of the account limitations for the free account. This is the account type we will start with. We are limited to five streams per account, not five streams per feed. We could have one feed with five streams, five streams with one feed each, or any combination between. Another point to be aware of is the feed update rate limit. We are allowed five API requests per minute. Essentially, this means that our API (the Arduino via the feed) can only send data at most once every 12 seconds. (Note that Pachube is likely to change its site and plans, so your screen may be different—such is the nature of the Web.)

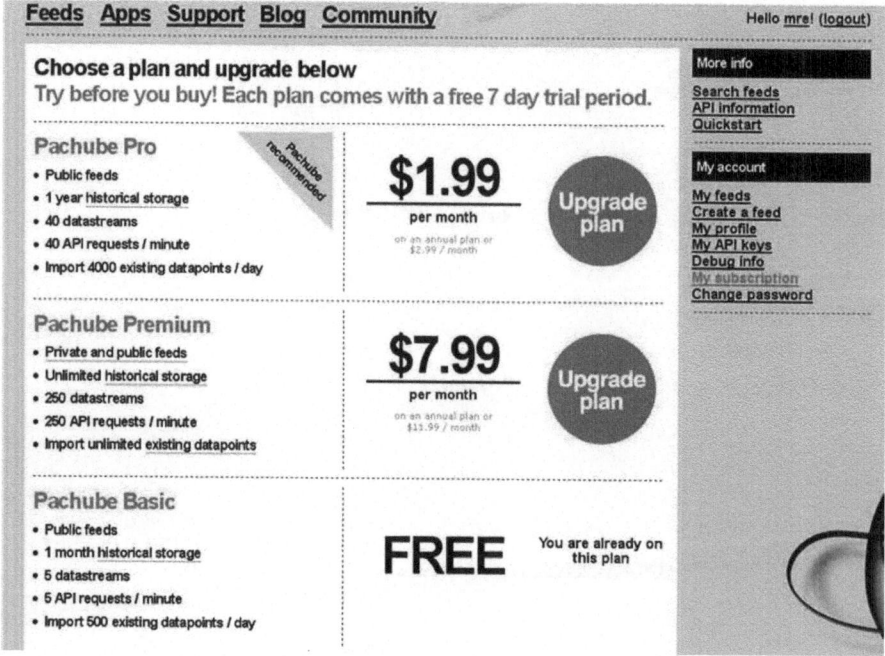

Figure 5-3. Pachube's service plans

■ **Note** It is especially important that we pay attention to our API request rate. If exceeded, Pachube will stop responding to our requests for a period of time. At the time of this writing, Pachube allows five API requests (postings of data) per minute on the free account. This means you cannot send data more than 5 times per minute, or roughly every 12 seconds.

Pachube, Meet Arduino

There are two primary methods that Pachube uses to collect data, as well as two additional methods to create the physical connection.

Data can either be posted to your feed via your hardware, or Pachube can be instructed to seek out your hardware and request the data. It is an important distinction. There are several examples of each in the Pachube documentation, and knowing the method of choice will greatly reduce frustrations. In particular, if instructed to locate your hardware to request it send data, Pachube must be able to pass your network firewalls. Thus, the method you choose to use will be dictated by ease of setup as well as your network design and permissions.

The method we will use in this book is to navigate our hardware to Pachube and manually post our data every 12 seconds.

The other primary decision we need to make is the physical connection to the network. The Arduino has two options here. First, we can purchase an Ethernet shield to act as the connection. This is a simple option because all the code required is contained within the Arduino. While this is the preferred method (as well as the simplest to code), it has a few drawbacks. First, several nodes require several Ethernet shields. This can get expensive very quickly. Second, you have no local visualization to verify data; it becomes hard to peek inside the machine. Finally, you may want to view data in real time, even while posting to Pachube only every 12 seconds.

The second method involves connecting the Arduino to a PC via the USB port. The PC serves as both your window into the Arduino and the connection to the network. You will be able to save data to the PC at a much higher granularity than you are allowed on Pachube, as well as maintain records for more than the data storage time that the site provides.

We add Processing, which is the Arduino's twin application for writing visually rich PC side applications. Processing will actually perform the function of reading data from the Arduino and posting it to Pachube. Throwing Processing into the mix gives us the added advantage of local data backup as well as visualization. In addition, we can wire in several Arduino's into one PC. We are limited only by the available USB ports.

Processing and the Arduino IDE have been developed by the same group of people, and thus work very well together. In fact, the IDEs for both applications look and function in the same manner (see Figure 5-4). You will quickly become quite comfortable in the Processing environment.

Figure 5-4. The Arduino IDE on the left, with the Processing IDE on the right

Getting Started

From the Pachube home page, click the red Signup button. You will then see Figure 5-3 on your screen. Choose your plan and fill in the form to sign up for an account. I suggest that you start with the basic free plan. You'll have a chance to try out the hardware and evaluate the site. You can always upgrade later.

After selecting the plan, you need to provide a username, e-mail address, and password. Be sure to confirm both the e-mail and password in the appropriate boxes. Finally, you need to properly fill out the CAPTCHA (that hard-to-read group of letters that checks whether you are human) words.

After submitting the form by clicking the Sign Up button, you will receive an e-mail from Pachube at the supplied e-mail address. Follow the instructions within the e-mail carefully to confirm your account and get started. If you do not receive the e-mail within 30 minutes, you should check the spam filter on your account.

After registering for an account, the first thing you will want to do is to find your API keys (see Figure 5-5). The API key is like a secret handshake between your hardware and the Pachube server. Without submitting a key, Pachube will deny access to your devices.

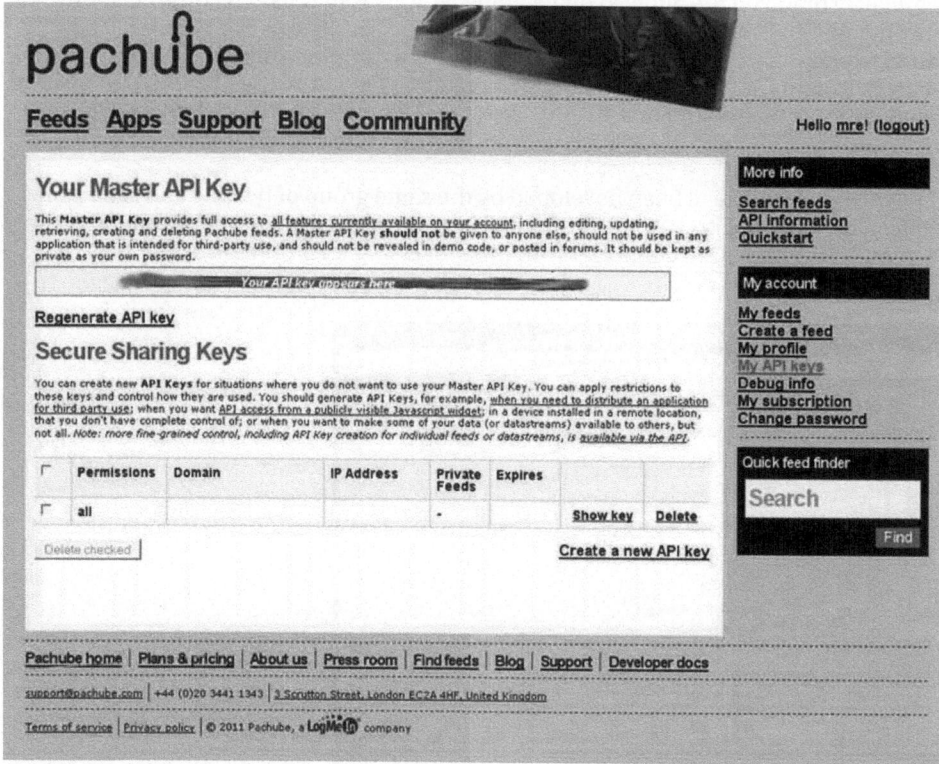

Figure 5-5. The API Keys panel

You can find the link to your keys in the "My account" block on the right side of any page.

Pachube now offers two forms of keys. The first is your Master API Key, which should be kept secret as if it were the pin code to your bank account. It is best not to utilize this key for any projects.

You can also create additional keys. You can apply restrictions to the keys, create and destroy them at will, and set them to automatically expire. It is recommended that you create a new key for each device you build and publish on Pachube.

▪ **Note** Remember the location of your keys. We will copy and paste them into Processing code later. Also, never click "Regenerate API Key." This will create a new set of keys, rendering your originals no longer valid. This has the effect of shutting down any hardware utilizing that key until you go back and reload the hardware's firmware with new keys.

Install Processing and Various Libraries

With our Pachube account set up, the next stop is http://processing.org/download/ to download and install the Processing IDE. You will be happy to know that the IDE looks and functions nearly identically (save for color scheme) to the Arduino IDE, so you will be quite familiar with it.

Back at the Pachube site, near the top of the page, click Libraries & Examples. You will be brought to the community site. Click Pachube + Processing/Java (alternatively, you can navigate directly to http://www.eeml.org/library/).

The Extended Environments Markup Language (EEML) is a protocol for sharing data. It defines a format and method for sending sensor data over the Internet to remote collection servers. The EEML library is a powerful library that allows Processing to manage connections and streams of data to and from Pachube. EEML does not simply enable Arduino. In fact, connecting an Arduino is just a small part of what the EEML and Processing combination can do. Any data your computer can collect, it can post to Pachube. Likewise, any data collected from Pachube can then be fed into virtually any application on your computer, including virtual data generated by your own applications. For example, you may want to turn the camera on the bottom of your mouse into a data device. You could write some application with Processing to read the raw data from the camera and turn it into a series of values. This data could then be picked up and transmitted to Pachube via the EEML library.

Download and install the library into the Processing/Libraries folder. Simply copy the EEML folder from the downloaded archive to the libraries folder in Processing.

We need one more library to get the whole system working. Thankfully, it is almost certainly to be installed on your computer already. Run the Arduino IDE, and click Sketch. Under Import Library, verify that you have the Firmata library installed. If not, visit http://firmata.org to download it.

This library allows us to create special functions to transmit data over the USB port. The data can be picked up by another application (in our case, Processing). With it, we will send data to Processing, which will then use the EEML library to pass that data on to Pachube.

The Build

We will be using a slightly modified sample sketch from the Firmata examples on the Arduino. This sketch will simply output all analog port values through the USB virtual serial device.

We will then pick up these values using Processing. In a sense, we offload all the work to Processing, which will convert values and make decisions about what to do with data. We can then send this information from Processing to Pachube over our PC's Internet connection.

You will need the following parts:

- Any Arduino
- Breadboard shield or a separate breadboard
- 5 x 1K ohm potentiometers with wires attached
- A PC attached to the Internet

In addition, you need the following software tools and libraries:

- Arduino IDE
- Processing IDE
- Firmata library installed in the Arduino IDE (usually preinstalled)
- EEML library installed in the Processing IDE
- Arduino library installed in the Processing IDE (usually preinstalled)

The physical build is rather simple (see Figure 5-6). All we want to do for this first project is to provide five knobs that we can turn, feeding that positional data into Pachube. (Alternatively, you could use the hardware presented in Chapter 2.)

Using the breadboard shield (or a separate breadboard and some longer wires), connect the 5 volt and ground pins from the Arduino to the power strips on the breadboard.

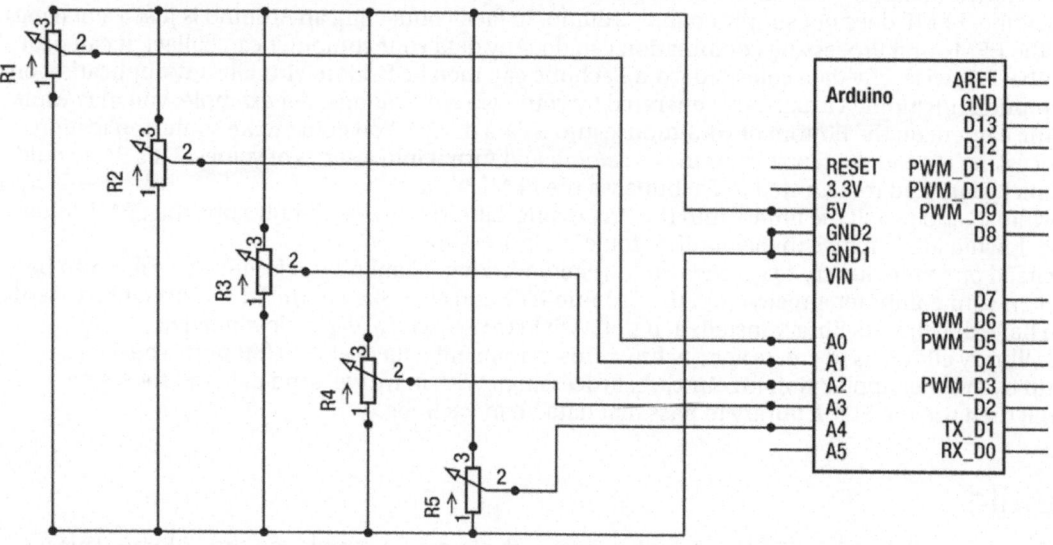

Figure 5-6. Connecting five variable resistors (1k ohm potentiometers) to the Arduino

Now solder wires to each leg of the potentiometers. Connect each potentiometer to the power strips, by connecting one outer leg of the potentiometer to the positive strip, and the other outer leg to the ground strip.

Finally, connect the center pin of each potentiometer to one of the analog inputs on the Arduino.

Setting Up a Feed on Pachube

Now is a good time to set up your feed. Remember that a feed is a collection of streams. Consider the feed as a piece of hardware (such as your Arduino), and streams are the individual sensors connected to it. So, we will set up one feed (Arduino) with five streams (knobs).

Log into your Pachube account and click the "Create a feed" button. You will be presented with a screen much like Figure 5-7.

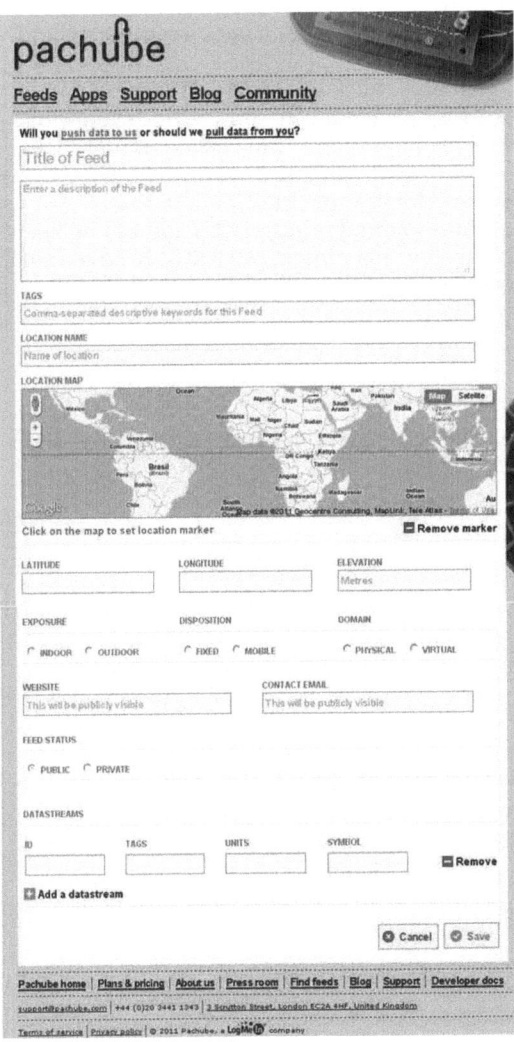

Figure 5-7. Registering a new feed

We will be manually logging data to Pachube. In other words, our hardware will contact the server and update data on a set schedule, rather than instructing the server to find and interrogate the hardware. We will "push" data to Pachube.

Think of a snappy name and enter it in the "Feed title" box. Add a description so that people browsing your feed will know about your hardware and the purpose of the feed. You can also add some tags to help others find your feed more easily. This could include information like *weather station*, *temperature*, *radiation*, and other useful tags. A nice tag to add for your first feed is *test* so that people can filter out your feed because at this stage, you are only testing out firmware and hardware. Finally, be sure to find your hardware location on the map and place a pin point, so we all know where the hardware is located. This is not important for test gear, but it is critical for environmental sensors.

The additional information about the feed, such as a web site URL, contact e-mail, and location name are not so important at this point. However, you may want to leave your feed private while you test your gear. You can always switch it to a public feed to share your data once you have everything up and running

The final step in setting up our feed is to fill it with data streams. Click the "Add a datastream" link at the bottom of the feed. The page will expand to expose an area for each data stream you add. You will need to add a stream for each knob. We could simply leave all the fields blank and click Save Feed. This is because we could force fill the information from our hardware's software later, as we build the Arduino and Processing sketches. However, we will go ahead and fill in some information now.

The ID for each stream must be a unique integer (0, 1, 2, and so on). For tags, enter something like **Knob 1** through **Knob 5**, but leave the units and symbols blank. For this project, we will only be sending raw ADC data. There are several stream types to choose from, but Basic SI tends to fill most needs.

■ **Note** Be sure to specify unique ID numbers from 0 to 5 for all your streams. Also, keep track of them. Later, when we build the Arduino and Processing code, we will match up the sensor data to the data stream using the ID number.

Arduino Sketch: Firmata

If your version of Firmata is previous to version 2.2, you may encounter an error or two attempting to compile most of the examples. For this reason, I recommend you get the latest version of the library. At the time I was building this application, however, I was using an earlier version. You may not need to make modifications to version 2.2, but for completeness, I will present my earlier versioned code.

We are migrating much of the hard work from the Arduino up to the Processing application. Therefore, we can get away with using a default Firmata sketch for our first application. We should always go over the sketch and make minor tweaks for each project, however.

In the Arduino IDE, load up the example Firmata sketch "AllInputsFirmata." Save the sketch with a new name, so that changes we make to the sketch will not alter the original.

Be sure you are now editing the new copy. Compare the sketch to the one in Listing 5-1 (this is a modified version of the Firmata example code as provided by the library):

Listing 5-1. Arduino Side Code

```
/*
 * This firmware reads all inputs and sends them as fast as it can.  It was
 * inspired by the ease-of-use of the Arduino2Max program.
 *
 * This example code is in the public domain.
 *
 * Note: one bug fix and changed sampling interval / com speed EWP
 */
#include <Firmata.h>

byte pin;

int analogValue;
int previousAnalogValues[TOTAL_ANALOG_PINS];

byte portStatus[TOTAL_PORTS];   // each bit: 1=pin is digital input, 0=other/ignore
byte previousPINs[TOTAL_PORTS];

/* timer variables */
unsigned long currentMillis;     // store the current value from millis()
unsigned long previousMillis;     // for comparison with currentMillis
/* make sure that the FTDI buffer doesn't go over 60 bytes, otherwise you
   get long, random delays.  So only read analogs every 20ms or so */
int samplingInterval = 1000;         // how often to run the main loop (in ms)

void sendPort(byte portNumber, byte portValue)
{
  portValue = portValue & portStatus[portNumber];
  if(previousPINs[portNumber] != portValue) {
    Firmata.sendDigitalPort(portNumber, portValue);
    previousPINs[portNumber] = portValue;
  }
}

void setup()
{
  byte i, port, status;

  Firmata.setFirmwareVersion(0, 1);

  for(pin = 0; pin < TOTAL_PINS; pin++) {
    if IS_PIN_DIGITAL(pin) pinMode(PIN_TO_DIGITAL(pin), INPUT);
  }
```

```
  for (port=0; port<TOTAL_PORTS; port++) {
    status = 0;
    for (i=0; i<8; i++) {
      if (IS_PIN_DIGITAL(port * 8 + i)) status |= (1 << i);
    }
    portStatus[port] = status;
  }

  Firmata.begin(28800);
  // your own additional setup stuff here
}

void loop()
{
  byte i;

  for (i=0; i<TOTAL_PORTS; i++) {
    sendPort(i, readPort(i, 255));  // bug fix this value specifies sending all port data
  }
  /* make sure that the FTDI buffer doesn't go over 60 bytes, otherwise you
     get long, random delays.  So only read analogs every 20ms or so */
  currentMillis = millis();
  if(currentMillis - previousMillis > samplingInterval) {
    previousMillis += samplingInterval;
    while(Firmata.available()) {
      Firmata.processInput();
    }
    for(pin = 0; pin < TOTAL_ANALOG_PINS; pin++) {
      analogValue = analogRead(pin);
      if(analogValue != previousAnalogValues[pin]) {
        Firmata.sendAnalog(pin, analogValue);
        previousAnalogValues[pin] = analogValue;
      }
    }
  }
}
```

Notice that I added a few notes to the top. You should do the same, with any sample sketch you modify. This way you can tell at a glance what changes you made and what the intent of the project is.

I have highlighted the three changes I made. They are as follows: First, I slowed down the sampling rate. Because we know that Pachube will only allow us to upload new data every 12 seconds, taking samples of the analog ports several times per second is just not necessary. I have reduced the sampling rate to once per second. This change will free up a lot of CPU time later if we decide to make extensive modifications to the Arduino sketch. We could reduce it even further, to match the post limit of Pachube, but we run the risk of repeating old data any time the next sample comes just after the post. Second, I slowed down the communication rate. Because we are now only sending data out to Processing once a second, we could slow the communication rate even more if we find that we have trouble (due to using older hardware or a very long USB cable). Finally (but most importantly), I edited a line of code that was missing a second value required by the ReadPort function. This value acts as a mask to tell the sketch which pins to read and transmit. It uses binary math to turn on or off specific pins. The value 255 translates to "all pins on."

For a preliminary check, go ahead and modify the code and upload it to the Arduino. Open the Serial Monitor and set it to 28800. When you press the reset button on the Arduino, you should see a short message from the Arduino, followed by a several bursts of apparently garbled data.

The Firmata library sends data to the PC in a nonreadable format. So if you get a bunch of junk in the serial monitor, you know it is working! If, however, you only see a short text message followed by the Arduino going silent, it is because we have not selected to transmit data. Go back and make sure the ReadPort function is correct.

PC Side: Processing and EEML

The Processing sketch is where all the action is. Instead of starting with a sample sketch, let's start fresh. I decided to blend in a bit of the code from the SpiderTemps project, to show you how you could do on the fly conversions of raw data from the Arduino in Processing before pushing that data up to Pachube. The fifth sensor (on Analog 4) will report temperature data, and in this example, I connected an MCP9700 temperature sensor.

Open Processing, and enter the sketch shown in Listing 5-2:

Listing 5-2. Processing Sketch to Read Analog Ports 0–4 and Transmit Them to Our Feed

```
import processing.serial.*;
import cc.arduino.*;
import eeml.*;

Arduino arduino1;
float lastUpdate;

int Analog0, Analog1, Analog2, Analog3, Analog4;

DataOut dOut1;


int TSensor = 4;        // temperature sensor ADC input pin
int TempADC = 0;            // variable to store ADC value read
int TempOffset = 500;   // value in mV when ambient is 0 degrees C
int TempCoef = 10;      // Temperature coefficient mV per Degree C
float ADCmV = 4.88;     // mV per ADC increment (5 volts / 1024 increments)
float TempCalc = 0;         // calculated temperature in C (accuraccy to two decimal places)



void setup()
{
  // establish connection to the Arduino
  println(Arduino.list());
  arduino1 = new Arduino(this, Arduino.list()[2], 28800);

  dOut1 = new DataOut(this, "http://www.pachube.com/api/[your feed number here].xml", "[ your
api key here ]");
```

```
// notify Pachube of the Stream ID and Stream TAGs
   dOut1.addData(0, "Analog 0, knob 1");         // add one line for each stream
   dOut1.addData(1, "Analog 1, knob 2");         // the Stream ID in the stream number plus tags
   dOut1.addData(2, "Analog 2, knob 3");
   dOut1.addData(3, "Analog 3, knob 4");
   dOut1.addData(4, "Analog 4, temperature sensor, MCP9700");
}

void draw()
{
    // update once every 12 seconds (could also be e.g. every mouseClick)
    if ((millis() - lastUpdate) > 12000){
        println("ready to POST: ");
        // Read Arduino1's analog ports:
        Analog0 = arduino1.analogRead(0);
        Analog1 = arduino1.analogRead(1);
        Analog2 = arduino1.analogRead(2);
        Analog3 = arduino1.analogRead(3);
        Analog4 = arduino1.analogRead(4);

        // Convert the temperature sensor:
        TempADC = arduino1.analogRead(TSensor);                      // read the input pin
        TempCalc = ((TempADC * ADCmV) - TempOffset) / TempCoef;    // the ADC to C equation

        // Display the data in the Processing debug window:
        println(Analog0);
        println(Analog1);
        println(Analog2);
        println(Analog3);
        println(TempCalc);

        // Send the data streams to Pachube:
        dOut1.update(0, Analog0);
        dOut1.update(1, Analog1);
        dOut1.update(2, Analog2);
        dOut1.update(3, Analog3);
        dOut1.update(4, TempCalc);

        // Check for a response from Pachube;
        int response = dOut1.updatePachube(); // updatePachube() updates by an authenticated
PUT HTTP request
        println(response); // should be 200 if successful; 401 if unauthorized; 404 if feed
doesn't exist
        lastUpdate = millis();
    }
}
```

We start by importing the Processing serial and cc.arduino libraries, followed by the EEML library. With libraries installed, the next task is to initiate variables, including a new variable type Arduino. I named this variable **arduino1**. You could connect as many Arduinos as you have USB ports for, so always give them logical names like "Arduino 1–6," "WeatherStation," "Geiger Counter," "Earthquake Sensor," and so on.

■ **Note** This project only reads analog values. You could also read digital pins on the Arduino. Consult the help guides in the Support and Community areas of the Pachube site for more information. Remember that while the Arduino contains six analog inputs, a free account on Pachube will only let you update five data streams.

Next, we set up a `DataOut` variable, in much the same way we set up the Arduino variable. DataOut is part of the EEML library and is the "pipe" through which we talk to Pachube. Our application uses the EEML library to properly format information in a way that Pachube will understand. Again, you can have multiple Pachube feeds in one application simply by adding more DataOut variables. You should name them accordingly, so they match up with the corresponding Arduino.

The final block of variables concerns the temperature sensor. If you were to review Chapter 2, you would see the same block of variables in that Arduino sketch. I go into much more detail there, but for now, I only want to demonstrate how you migrate much of the number-crunching work from the Arduino up to Processing.

In the setup portion of the sketch, we establish connections to both Arduino and Pachube. First, Processing will print out a list of available serial ports and display them in the lower debug window. When you first run the sketch, identify your Arduino's serial driver name (much like selecting the serial port in the Arduino IDE) and note the ID number associated with it. You will then have to stop the sketch, go back to the code, and correct it so that it now identifies the correct port.

We next establish a connection to Pachube with the `DataOut` command. Be sure to change the feed URL as well as copy your Pachube key. You will not need the square brackets in the feed URL or API key, but you *do* need to include the quotation marks.

Finally, we notify Pachube of the streams we want to update, as well as the tags associated with them. The code follows this format: `VariableName.addData(#, "tag 1, tag2, tag3…");` Where VariableName is the name given to the device, # is the stream ID number set in Pachube, with your tags to follow. In this way, Processing can actually fill the DataStream information rather than manually registering them yourself.

The draw() Function

`Draw()` is the same as the Arduino's `loop` function. It is the main line of code and does most of the actual work. The first thing it will do is check if it is time to do an update (every 12 seconds) using an `if` statement. Because we have no other tasks for the `draw()` function to do, it will simply wait around until 12 seconds have elapsed.

It then notifies us via the debug window that it is about to post data. It will now read arduino1's analog ports. Notice that we have full access to all the Arduino port control and read commands. However, we need to prepend the command with the name we have assigned to the Arduino in question, so that Processing knows which Arduino we want to talk to. In this case, that command looks like this:

```
Analog0 = arduino1.analogRead(0);
```

The Processing variable `Analog0` is receiving `analogRead(0)` data from the arduino1 device. Once we have the data in hand, we can calculate the temperature using data from the temperature sensor. Review Chapter 2 for more about how this block of code works.

After we read the ports and crunch some numbers, it is a good idea to print the data to the debug port, so we know what Processing is about to send to Pachube. We do that with the `println` command.

Finally, `dOut.update` takes care of actually posting to Pachube. It expects you to send first the stream ID number, followed by the variable holding the data you want to post. We do that with this:

```
dOut1.update(0, Analog0);
```

First, we specify the pipe we want to send, which in this case is `dOut1`. We then add the specific command to update some data. Finally, we specify the steam ID number, followed by the Processing variable that holds the data we want to post to the specified steam.

■ **Note** The EEML library provides several commands with which you can control Pachube, your feeds and streams. It is worth investigating the available sample sketches and documentation in more detail.

Our last task before clearing the timer is to check the response from Pachube and print it to the debug window. If we receive back a response of 200, everything went well. If not, we need to check our connections. The response number will print in the Processing debug window after the post data has been sent. We then set the `LastUpdate` variable to equal the current millisecond counter, which essentially resets the counter. When the `Draw` loop restarts, it will now wait until the current millisecond counter minus the last update variable exceeds 12 seconds, at which point it goes through the post process once again.

Putting it All Together

Connect the Arduino to your computer (if it is not connected already) and run the Processing sketch. After checking the serial ports listed by Processing in the bottom window, verifying your Arduino's serial port and correcting the code, rerun the Processing sketch.

If you received a 200 response from Pachube, you have successfully published data online! Congratulations. Navigate your browser to your feed page and refresh the chart strips. It takes several posts before the chart starts to appear meaningful, but you'll know things are working by comparing the raw numbers in Pachube to the printed output in Processing.

If you received a response other than 200, go back and double-check your code. Because the hardware is very simple, it is unlikely to be the culprit. There is a lot of code to go through, and the data takes several steps before ending up online. Therefore, you should divide the problem up, first verifying that you receive data from the Arduino in the Arduino IDE Serial Monitor. If you still have problems, you can strip out most of the Pachube code from the Processing sketch and just try to get data printing to the debug window.

With everything working, you should see an update every 12 seconds occurring in the debug window. Now you should visit the feed page and inspect the data. Notice that on the left, you have the integer values, and the right side shows a chart graph for each stream. The default view for this graph is usually too long to see anything noticeable. So, at first, you may want to view them in Last Hour mode.

Turn a few of the potentiometer knobs, and note the changed values in the Processing debug window. A few moments later, these changes should be viewable online. Simply refresh your browser to see new data.

Going Further

With this basic framework in place, you can now begin to expand upon your projects. Any sensor you can read via the analog input can be sent to Processing to be converted to usable data and finally posted online.

In addition, you can expand by pulling data from several Arduinos into one Processing sketch and publishing that data across several feeds. For example, you may have a weather station and an electric current usage monitor both plugged into one PC, sending data to their respective feeds via one Processing sketch.

You could even instruct Processing to take certain actions on one Arduino, based on data from another. Or mix data from two Arduinos into one feed.

Conclusion

Posting data online is useful not only to yourself but to others as well. Even if no one else looks at your feed, it is always comforting to know what's happening with a project when you are not around. Later chapters will continue to bring up Pachube and other data aggregation sites and how those projects can benefit from having their data online.

Where possible, I will provide both versions of code so you may choose which system you want to build. But in the absence of a Pachube version of a project, don't let that absence stop you from hacking it in. The purpose of this chapter was to get you comfortable with the process, so you can add Pachube functionality to any of your projects in the future.

References

- Pachube: `https://pachube.com/`

- EEML library: `http://www.eeml.org/library/`

- Pachube API documentation: `http://api.pachube.com/v2/`

- Arduino tutorials for Pachube: `http://community.pachube.com/tutorials#arduino`

- Get Processing: `http://processing.org/download/`

- Get Firmata for Arduino: `http://firmata.org`

- Internet of Things: `http://www.theInternetofthings.eu/`

CHAPTER 6

The Mass Effect

Measuring Earthquakes with a Digital Seismometer

March 11, 2011 is a day I will never forget. I had just arrived home to my Tokyo apartment and was searching the house for some documents I needed for an urgent errand. As I leafed through stacks of papers on my desk, I began feeling the all-too-common motion of an earthquake. Having lived in Tokyo for five years, the sensation had become commonplace in my mind, and I continued looking around. At first, I assumed it was just like all the other minor quakes I had experienced in the past.

After a few moments, the motion did not subside. Instead, it began to sort of swirl. The ground was not shaking in just one direction. It felt like I was bobbing in the ocean rather than standing on solid ground. As papers began to spill down from my table and onto the floor, I remember thinking, "GHAAA! This earthquake is going to be such an inconvenience! There's no way I'll make it to my appointment on time now!"

You have to understand that once something like an earthquake becomes so commonplace in your mind, what was once a nerve-wracking moment becomes just another inconvenience. Even when the sensation of motion exceeds that which you had experienced in the past. Your internal judgment of danger becomes optimistic. If a few papers shake off the desk, and a few knicknacks fall off the shelf, you still consider it relatively minor, even when the duration seems to go on forever. In the past I had experienced everything from a few quick sharp jolts to long rolling waves and ripples. "Nothing new here; just another delay to my busy day."

With a quick lurch, the quake became several orders of magnitude more violent. It was as if a monster truck started its engine inside my tiny apartment. As I watched everything within view begin to vibrate like tiny toys sitting on power speakers, I realized that I, too, was literally jumping up and down. My mind snapped from "Aww, this sucks!" to "RUN!" in an instant.

My neighbors all got the same idea at roughly the same time because we came pouring out of our houses and apartments all at once. Having escaped to the street (my apartment was on the ground floor), I felt much safer, even though my feet occasionally left the ground involuntarily.

Glancing up and watching the buildings sway, it dawned on me that the crowd I was in was standing directly under a massive tangle of overhead electrical cables, which was swinging and whipping around like jump ropes. We quickly moved to open ground, congregating in the middle of an intersection next to a small field.

After a few more tense moments, the quake ceased. We all had a few nervous jokes to pass around. We wished each other "Good luck cleaning up," and started filing back into our trashed homes. The calm was brief.

The first aftershock came shortly after I managed to push my way inside (so much random stuff blocked the doorway). It was clear that this aftershock would be nearly as potent as the original quake, and we all reconvened near the field to wait it out. By this point, we were all joking that it couldn't possibly get any worse. The damage is already done. (Oh, how I wish we had been right.)

About this time, my upstairs neighbor arrived by bike. She had been stuck in the train station, arriving there less than 10 minutes after me. She told us that a group of elderly women had huddled over a couple of toddlers, intent on shielding them from any falling debris.

That afternoon, I helped her clean up her apartment while we waited for news of her husband. Cell phone service was down, but Internet over 3G still managed to work if you were patient. Eventually we learned that he was walking home and would arrive about midnight. We watched the news while attempting to get in contact with all our friends and families (long live SKYPE!). Over the next week, we concurrently watched tsunami footage over and over, while keeping track of the unfolding Fukushima power plant disaster. All the while trying to mitigate the fears of our friends and families back in the USA.

I had a good friend living in Sendai, which received a lot of damage from the quake and is near the tsunami disaster zone. It was nearly two weeks before I was able to confirm that he and his family were safe.

During the first days of the disaster, we were all in severe shock. It was very similar in magnitude and emotional trauma to the September 11th attacks, except there was no one to blame. Also, at the time of the September 11th attacks, I was living in Arizona and had no personal connections to the victims. This time, I *was* a victim (albeit a minor one). Many of my friends *were* in danger, and one was actually missing. Some of my Japanese friends lost friends or family.

Everyone living in Japan (native Japanese and foreigners alike) has experienced various levels of post traumatic stress disorder. Even after six months, it remains difficult to talk and write about.

I am not a paranoid person. When I feel a tremor, I don't immediately jump up and run. But my internal threshold that dictates exactly when to run has certainly been calibrated at a lower setting than it used to be. More accurately, before the Tohoku quake, I really didn't know at what level of shaking I should start to be concerned. Now I have a pretty good clue.

I survived the Great Tohoku Earthquake in northern Japan on March 11, 2011. Even down in Tokyo, the force was incredible. It truly was akin to riding a wooden roller coaster. It was, and likely forever will be, the single scariest moment of my entire life. I should revise that because "moment" is not really the right word. The primary quake was several minutes long, with progressively increasing vibration plateaus. It was followed by hourly aftershocks and secondary quakes that lasted nearly a week.

In the hours and days that followed, we all lived in isolated shell shock. It took hours (and days) to reestablish telephone communications with the outside world. If not for the power of social media sites such as Facebook and the power of voice over IP phone technology such as Skype, my family back in the USA would have had to wait for days to find out I was safe. It was more than a week before my cellphone worked reliably, yet Internet was available in Tokyo the night of the quake.

All the while, watching and listening for news from the north was ever more depressing and heartbreaking. The earthquake was disruptive and caused considerable damage and a few casualties. But the resultant tsunami just about whipped entire towns and cities off the map. Thousands of people confirmed dead, and thousands more lost, possibly never to be found. The tragic personal stories were unfortunately overshadowed by the nuclear power plant meltdowns at Daiichi power plant, situated right on the beach, in the direct path of the tsunami.

Within hours of the quake, there was a press release about the magnitude. It was only a preliminary analysis. As each new bundle of data came in from seismometers all over Japan, the magnitude was adjusted. For several days, it seemed like the quake magnitude was much like that fish that got away:

Person 1 says: "It was a 7.5."

Person 2 says: "No no. More like an 8."

Person 3 says: "Actually, the latest data indicates a 9.0!"

After the initial shock and fear subsided, I immediately started thinking about the data. I wanted to know what the earthquake waveform looked like. Was it really a circular pattern or was it just my imagination? What was the amplitude of the up-and-down motion? I had a lot of geeky questions and no answers.

The Data

In the hours and days following the earthquake, the magnitude data was continually updated and revised. At first they said 7.5. By the next day, they were reporting that it was an 8. Only on the third day (at least, as far as I am aware) did they finalize on it being a magnitude 9 earthquake.

Why did it take so long to finalize the data? Japan has a world-renowned earthquake detection and analysis system. My best guess relates to the issue of storage and transmission of the data. Consider that a huge swath of the northern part of the Kanto region was without power and communications for several weeks after the quake and tsunami. It is very likely that seismometers in the region could not post their data before the lines were cut. So someone had to go out and manually collect the data for analysis. Having no personal experience with modern earthquake detection networks, I can only imagine that it is made up of sensors in which most are digital, storing earthquake data locally (on a hard drive?) as well as live streaming to a remote data collection system over the Internet. It is likely that at least a few strategically located sensors are also the old paper chart recorder type for redundancy and backup, in case the digital technology fails. During an earthquake, seismic researchers have little to do but fend for themselves while hoping the data comes in. The moment the quake ceases, their jobs become incredibly busy collecting data, reading data, and crunching numbers. It is understandable that their first guess as to the magnitude is only that: an educated guess.

To complicate matters, there are several scales on which an earthquake can be measured. The Richter Scale, for example, rates an earthquake on a logarithmic scale, and compares the energy released to an earthquake to that of a TNT or nuclear explosion. On the Richter Scale, each successive number represents a tenfold increase in measured amplitude. The difference between a level 2 and 3 is minor. A level 2 is often not felt; a level 3 is felt but causes little if any damage. The difference between an 8 and 9 is catastrophic. An 8 is severe damage in an area over several hundred kilometers. A level 9 quake is devastating for several thousand kilometers. We no longer actively use the Richter scale. Instead, the United States relies on the Moment Magnitude Scale (MMS). The MMS and Richter are very similar in resultant value, although the system of measurement differs. When Richter measurements are adjusted to the MMS, the difference in value is a few tenths (for example, Richter 6.2 = MMS 6.4). Thus, modern earthquakes measured in MMS are often misreported as Richter Scale numbers by the media or word of mouth. The U.S. Geological Service now strictly uses the MMS.

Here in Japan, we rely on an intensity scale instead of amplitude/magnitude. The Japan Meteorological Service Scale, Shindo, focuses more on human perception. For example, a Shindo 4 earthquake shakes the ground enough to wake most sleeping people. It is felt by most people, even when indoors. Dishes may rattle and electric wires swing slightly. Some people are frightened.

The Shindo scale relies on peak ground acceleration as the basis of measurement. A Shindo 4 earthquake has a PGA of about 0.25 to 0.8 meters per second (m/s^2). Because the Shindo Scale is concerned with the human factor and effects, it is a highly localized scale. An earthquake can have multiple Shindo ratings, depending on where you stand.

The Tohoku quake was a magnitude 9 on the MMS. Peak Ground Acceleration was recorded as 2.99 g, or 29.33 $m/3^2$. It released energy equivalent to 600 million times that of the Hiroshima bomb. In Tokyo, some older buildings showed signs of cracking. A suspended ceiling fell on a full auditorium. Supermarket shelves spilled their products onto the floors. This corresponds to a Shindo 5 to 6.

Farther north and closer to the epicenter, many older buildings were damaged beyond repair. Elderly people found it difficult or impossible to move without crawling. The ground split, and roads were rendered impassable to due to cracking. A 7, which is the maximum rating on the Shindo scale, represents catastrophe. At this point, infrastructure and community emergency services (such as ambulance and fire departments) cannot cope with the situation alone. A Shindo 7 represents the point at which casualties increase exponentially as a result of building and infrastructure damage.

I have the philosophy that when it comes to environmental data, the more data points you can collect, the more accurate your understanding of the phenomenon and its effects will be. Sadly, government agencies cannot manage nor afford to blanket the country with a comprehensive package of sensors every square kilometer.

For this reason, citizen data collection is not only important; it is vital. When citizens and volunteer organizations participate actively in environmental data collection, some very important things happen. For one, the cost of deploying sensors is distributed away from government agencies (and the large bureaucracy associated with spending tax money). Secondly, sensors are deployed much faster and in higher density than the government can do alone. This is due to the cost of professional grade sensors that the government insists on deploying and the low-cost DIY sensors that individuals build and deploy. Finally, data becomes public domain and open sourced.

I don't advocate blatant mistrust of the government, but there are occasions in which governments choose to actively suppress environmental data, thinking that it is in the best interest of the people not to spark panic. For more on this, take a look at the SafeCast (`www.safecast.org`) radiation measurement project, which seeks to blanket northern Japan with geiger counters in response to the Fukushima nuclear reactor meltdown caused by the tsunami that followed the Tohoku quake.

The Project

At some point in any investigation, your average data geek like me starts thinking, "More, more, MORE!" It is no longer enough to look at the past. I quickly became interested in having my own seismometer around. After all, Japan experienced hourly tremors and aftershocks in the month following the quake. The frequency has tapered down gradually to about one or two minor rumbles per week. This is still plenty of opportunity to catch one.

Seismograph Technology

There are a lot of options when it comes to building your own earthquake monitor : high tech, low tech, mechanical, or all digital. The main goal is to capture the motion of the ground in relation to a stationary object.

A mechanical system usually consists of a heavy weight with a pen attached that serves as the stationary object. Remember that Newton's laws of physics state that the heavy weight will have a tendency to remain motionless, even while the ground moves. This is true, provided the weight is mounted not in a fixed position, but allowed to move freely. Usually, a large heavy base is firmly anchored into the ground, so when the ground vibrates, so does the base. The weight is suspended either on a spring arm or on a chain, like a plumb level.

To create a time–lapsed motion recording, a long sheet of paper is dragged under the weight. The pen attached to the weight marks the paper. During an earthquake, the base (and thus the paper) remains fixed with respect to the ground, while the weight remains fixed in space. The waveform drawn on the paper by the pen is the difference between these two fixed points.

The device can be upgraded somewhat by adding electronic recording so the data can be transmitted or saved to a convenient disk file, saving the seismologist having to deal with long strips of paper and the inconvenience of needing to change drums periodically.

Modern electronic units contain the mechanical parts within a metal cylinder about the size of two soup cans stacked up. There is only a long cable coming out the end of the tube, and no paper drums and pens to deal with. They require a signal amplifier and computer to collect the data. The cylinder can be buried underground, while the electronics are easily accessible in a comfortable location such as a nearby shack.

I was looking for something a bit simpler, preferably all electronic. The first option that came to mind is the QuakeCatcher network. It is an online earthquake data-collection system, which deploys one of two sensors available on their site. I inquired about the possibility of building our own sensors using Arduino and modifying their software to accept the Arduino sensor. Unfortunately, they were very reluctant to do this, and rightly so: To accomplish their goals, they should only permit calibrated and certified sensors. The easiest way to do that is to simply regulate where the sensors come from. Sadly, this does not help us much. If you require professional-grade quake analysis software, they are still a good way to go, and their available sensor modules are not too expensive.

But the Arduino community is a do-it-yourself community. Half the fun of owning an earthquake sensor package will be the process of building it. Additionally, I suspected that you might have more uses in mind than earthquakes. For example, you might want to analyze traffic on a bridge in order to assess the stability of the structure. Or perhaps you want to count foot traffic or measure vehicle vibrations compared with engine RPM. There are lots of applications for a device that can conveniently measure motion and vibration in three axes at once.I needed a sensor that I could burry in my yard, which would measure the vibrations of the earth with a decent resolution. The sensor package would have to be small, resistant to the elements, and ridged. From the sensor, a long cable will need to bring data up into the house, where a computer could collect the data, log it, and display it in some meaningful manner. An accelerometer will measure ground motion in a similar way to the traditional seismometer. Even better, modern accelerometers utilize Micro Electro Mechanical Systems (MEMS) to make them incredibly compact.

How MEMS Accelerometers Work

The mechanical system fits inside a tiny package identical to a typical integrated circuit. Inside the plastic case of the three-axis accelerometer, you would find a similar mechanical system as a typical full-scale model, but built on a micrometer (and in some cases molecular) scale!

As the weight within the mechanical structure resists motion, it causes the connecting beams to bend, twist, and stretch. This motion causes a small capacitance (or current, depending on the manufacturing method) to be produced.

The MEMS chip not only contains the mechanical structure but also the signal amplifiers and other electronics required to read the changes in the structure and convert them to a usable signal. There is a host of MEMS accelerometers available, and in nearly all cases, they proved a 0- to 5- (or 3.3-) volt output for each axis. You can simply connect each one to an analog input on the Arduino, apply power and ground, and you are good to go! It is simply five wires.

Granted, interfacing the accelerometer to an Arduino is a very simple connection. However, the project itself, the entire system, is quite complex. We need to write two pieces of software, one within the Arduino sensor package buried in the ground; the other on the PC.

In addition, we have constraints on the sensor hardware package. After considering it for awhile, I decided that the simplest solution is use a glass jar, like the ones jams and jellies come in (mine was a peanut butter jar). I discarded the idea of using a metal soup can outright. It would eventually rust, and has no easily replaceable lid. Plastic would eventually degrade or collapse, and was not very rigid.

Glass is thick, very rigid, and not susceptible to the elements. The only concerns are that even though it is buried in packed earth, it might break due to extreme cold and heat cycles. The metal lid also poses some concerns, such as rust and water intrusion. These points can easily be dealt with, though. All in all, a ready-made jar is a better option than machining my own enclosure.

The biggest concern is that of actually fitting everything inside. An Arduino with a shield mounted on top might be quite difficult to wedge in. Also, we need to ensure that the sensor is absolutely firmly attached to the jar so when the jar moves, the sensor moves. Attaching to glass is very difficult. The best option is to affix it to the metal lid using bolts.

Finally, and perhaps most importantly, we need to consider the communication method. The USB cable we would normally use to read data from the Arduino is limited to just a few meters. If we are to run a cable up from a hole in the yard, around the house, through a window, and finally into our PC, we need a *long* cable. A USB connection won't be possible.

With these constraints in mind, I realized that for the hardware, using an actual Arduino would be impractical. The better solution is to obtain an ATMega chip preprogrammed with the Arduino bootloader (there is an excellent tutorial on the Arduino Playground showing how to program your own chips). We then build by hand the circuitry required on a set of small square boards, suitable for mounting to the can.

A simpler option is to use an Arduino clone designed to fit into tight spaces. An Arduino Pro Mini is a good choice for a complete ready-to-go Arduino with a compact design. It is similar in form to a wide IC package.

■ **Note** The hardware build for this project is rather complex. If you are unsure of your prototyping and soldering skills, I suggest you either seek out your local hacker space for assistance or wait for the kit to appear on the companion website.

I chose to demonstrate two options. The first is to scratch-build the circuit on square perf board. The stuff I use includes four mounting holes, and each circuit hole includes a copper "doughnut" we can solder to. The second option is using an Arduino Pro Mini on the same sort of perf board. In each case, I also chose a different sensor and resolution. After building both designs, the side-by-side comparison was very useful. My recommendation is to follow the second option and consider the first option a reference to one way to build an Arduino from scratch.

Building from scratch is quite cheap. Not counting the accelerometer and USB to TTL-serial adaptor, the parts' cost was under $5 USD.

So, with that in mind, you may still prototype the circuit on a breadboard, using a standard Arduino. In fact, I recommend you do so in order to develop and test the software. Once you decide on an application, you will need to decide on a mount. With the mount decided, you then need to build the hardware by hand. So gather your soldering tools and heat up your iron.

The Build

The initial prototype for the seismometer is incredibly simple. We need only an Arduino (any model will do), a mini breadboard, a few wires, and the MEMS sensor itself. I am using two sensors. The first is a KXM52 sensor mounted on a breakout module, with a 2 g resolution. It operates at 5 volts. The second is the MMA7361 from SparkFun, which operates at 3.3 volts. One very nice aspect of the MMA7361 is that it is a dual mode sensor. It can operate at 1.5 g or 6 g, simply by setting an additional pin on the board high or low. Figure 6-1 shows both modules.

You can also use an ADXL model from SparkFun or AdaFruit. Be sure to get the chip in module form, and be sure it provides all three analog outputs.

Some models may communicate using I2C only. For our purposes, we want to keep the code very simple, while reading the sensor as fast as possible. A higher sample-per-second ratio will give us a higher resolution. We will want to be able to balance this resolution against overall system performance. An I2C module may be too slow, create too much code overhead, or simply not allow us to adjust how fast we poll it for data. So be sure that whatever module you end up with, it at least has the option to output data as raw analog voltage on three pins. An I2C chip may still be a good option, even with the constraints mentioned previously. Of particular importance is the fact that the ADC is internal to the chip. There is very little stray signal coupling, so signal noise is much lower—meaning your data will be cleaner. Also, the internal ADC may be more than the 10-bit ADC built into the Arduino. This gives much higher resolution data, which is especially important for detecting minor tremors.

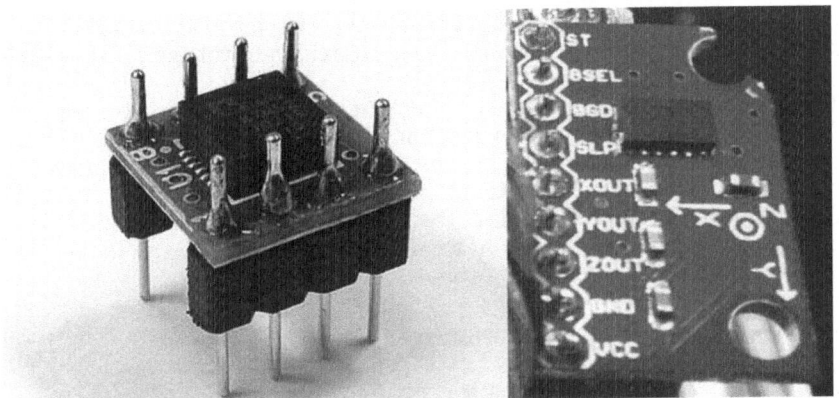

Figure 6-1. The KXM52 module by Akizuki Denshi and the MMA7361 board from SparkFun

Finally, the max G-force is really important. At first you may be tempted to go with the highest G-force sensor available. Don't. You should consider carefully before selecting the appropriate G-force. Consider it this way: the larger the max G-force range of the sensor, the larger the granularity is per G. Remember that regardless of the sensor range, we can only divide that range by 1024 slices. A +/- 5G sensor (a 10G span) would give us a granularity of about .01G per slice. As a point of comparison, the largest known earthquakes measure around 2Gs. Thus, a 5G sensor is not ideal. It has a broader span than we really need. The KXM52 sensor is a +-2G device, giving us a smaller granularity (about .004G). Initially, I thought this sensor would work out quite well. However, after completing the project and recording several earthquakes, I found that minor tremors rarely exceeded the noise floor of the sensor. Only a strong aftershock registered a spike on my recordings. Thus, I bought the SparkFun MMA7361 and am trying it again set to 1.5 g. Table 6-1 shows that the MMA7361 part is a bit more responsive than the KXM52.

Table 6-1. Comparison of KXM52 and MMA7361 Accelerometers

Product	V	G (+/-)	mV/g	Offset (0 g voltage)	Output range (V)	1 ADC count (mV)	ADC counts per G	G per ADC count
KXM52	3.3	2	660	1.65	0.33–2.97	3.2226	204.8	0.0048
KXM52	5	2	1000	2.5	0.5–4.5	4.8828	204.8	0.0048
MMA7361	3.3	1.5	800	1.65	0.45–2.85	3.2226	248.247	0.0040
MMA7361	3.3	6	206	1.65	0.414–2.886	3.2226	63.924	0.0156

Our seismometer will measure peak ground acceleration. As the ground shakes and vibrates, the sensor will detect the sudden changes in direction. The accuracy and resolution of our system determines at what force the sensor will detect motion.

Our sensor needs to be able to detect a G-force as low as 0.0017 in order to be useful. This is actually quite a challenge. There are a lot of factors that can cause problems for us. For instance, the ADC in the Arduino could be noisy, swamping the low end signal. I personally consider that a range of 5 ADC counts or less is mostly noise. From experience with my first attempt at a seismometer, the ADC bounced between 509 and 515 incessantly. This is just noise in the traces, the ADC reference voltage, and the ADC itself.

If you are serious about seismometers, you might also consider a standalone ADC, with a much higher resolution than 10 bits. Even a 12-bit converter will yield dramatic results. Consider that a sensor operating at 3.3 volts with the Arduino ADC (10 bits) has 3.2226 mV per ADC count (3.3/1024). That same sensor on a standalone 12-bit converter would have only 0.8 mV per ADC count (3.3/4096)!

When selecting your sensor, you should consider Table 6-2, which relates earthquake intensity, relative G-force, and two sensors. The table assumes that you are using the the Arduino ADC. In the table, sensor values are centered on 1.65 volts, which is ADC value of 512.

Table 6-2. *Peak Ground Acceleration Compared with Two Sensors*

Intensity	G-Force	Shake	KXM52 ADC Value 2 g, 3.3 Volt	MMA7361 ADC Value 1.5 g, 3.3 Volt	MMA7361 ADC Value 6 g, 3.3 Volt
1	0.0017	None	None	None	None
2–3	0.014	Weak	3	4	None
4	0.039	Light	8	10	3
5	0.092	Moderate	19	23	6
6	0.18	Strong	37	45	12
7	0.34	Very Strong	70	85	22
8	0.65	Severe	133	163	41
9	1.24	Violent	254	310	79
10	>1.24	Extreme	>255	>311	>79

Sadly, noise is a big issue with the Arduino ADC. Compounding the problem is the fact that it is only a 10-bit ADC. If I were to do this project again, I would definitely choose an I2C-based sensor with at least a 12-bit ADC. As is, I suspect that any earthquake less than an intensity 4 on the PGA scale will go undetected, even using the MMA7361. A deflection of just 10 ADC counts will be hard to reliably distinguish from noise. It may appear as a small peak.

Finally, we need to consider the rate at which we read the ADC. Body waves of an earthquake could oscillate as much as 20Hz (that's 20 waves per second). We need to be sure we sample the ADC at least 40 times per second in order to catch the wave. Sixty times per second would be better. A higher sampling frequency will also allow us to more reliably deduce what is noise and what is an earthquake. As the sampling frequency increases, the earthquake wave will go from just a single point out of line to a fully rendered undulation on the chart.

However, there is a trade-off. Higher sampling frequencies equals faster throughput required by the connection cable, as well as dramatically increased data files. The hourly log file could range from a few megabytes, to well over 50 megabytes, depending on the sampling frequency. The code presented is flexible enough for you to make your own decisions. Consider your storage capabilities and try to achieve the maximum sampling frequency possible. The general theory of code operation is to let the sensor package (the Arduino) sample and spit out data as fast as possible. The data-logging software on the desktop computer then selectively tosses data in order to compact the log files. As a rough example, sampling at 100Hz will yield a log file of about 8.5 megabytes per hour.

Building the Prototype Hardware

The prototype circuit is incredibly simple. All we need to do is put the accelerometer into the proto board, hook it to power and ground, and attach each of the three outputs to an analog input on the Arduino. The KXM module additionally needs some wires connected to 5 volts and ground.

- Carefully observe the module data sheet to know the pin names.

- Be sure you connect power and ground properly.

- Take note of which axis is connected to which Analog input.

In addition to power and ground, you may need to connect some other pins as well. For example, on the KXM52 module, I found that the power supply shutdown (PSD) pin needs to be connected to 5 volts to operate. Also, for accuracy, the Self Test pin must be tied to ground. On the KXM52, I chose to connect Output X to Analog 3, Output Y to Analog 4, and Output Z to Analog 5. Figure 6-2 illustrates the minimum connections for the KXM52.

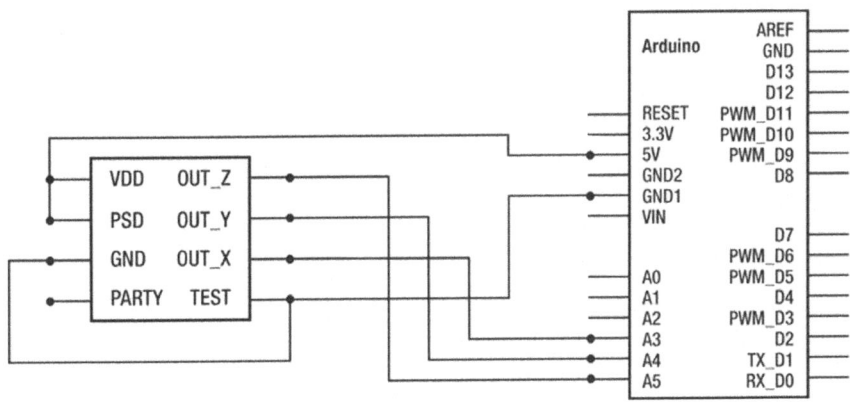

Figure 6-2. The prototype seismometer schematic utilizing the KXM52

The MMA7361 module has a few additional pins. I decided to connect all optional pins to digital outputs of the Arduino. Because I had built a new sensor board, I opted to switch to using an Arduino Pro Mini running at 3.3 volts rather than building an Arduino from scratch, like I did for the KXM52. So, I had a lot more board space to play with. It seemed prudent to go ahead and allow for future expansion of the Arduino code to take advantage of the additional control pins on the MMA7361. It also made setting pins such as the sleep/enable pin simple. I only had to set the pin on code, and not concern myself with miswiring it during the hardware build.

In particular, I connected the pins as follows: X-axis to A2, Y-axis to A1, Z-axis to A0. On the digital side, I connected Self Test to D6 on the Arduino, G-select to 7, 0g Detect to 8, and Sleep to 9.

Of particular interest to me for future expansion is the G-select pin. When it is set high, the module operates in 6 g mode. However, when set low, it operates at 1.5 g. At the moment, I am setting the pin low. However, I may want to implement some sort of high-g detection, and switch the pin dynamically to 6 g mode when a particularly strong quake occurs.

Software

While preparing the software for this project, I found I kept running into a major performance issue, even though I had been planning ahead to toss some incoming data, or in the worst possible case, slow down the data rate in the hardware. Yet no matter what I did, I still had excruciatingly slow drawing speeds.

Thankfully, I have access to a hackerspace and some talented programmers. A friend at the Tokyo HackerSpace, Taylan Ayken, was kind enough to take a look at my code and offer a solution. What I present here is an amalgamation of our code, which offers the best resolution to performance trade-offs we could come up with on short notice. I think you will find it quite functional, even in its primitive state.

The software will consist of two parts. First we have the software loaded into the Arduino. Its purpose is to simply read the three analog inputs, format them, and print it out to the serial port. We want the loop to be as fast as possible in order to gain the highest possible sampling rates. A high sampling rate equals more data to process, but gives us a chance to catch as much of the quake as possible. We can always filter noise later. In order to achieve high sampling rates, we should keep the code very short and simple.

The second piece of software resides on the PC. It is written in Processing, which is a software environment identical to the Arduino IDE, except that its purpose is to write software for the PC.

The Processing program will pick up the data from the transducer, split out the three axis values, log them to a file, and display them on the screen in a fashion similar to a traditional seismometer chart recorder. Because we are handling a lot of data, it is wise to implement some simple scheme of tossing unnecessary data. Thus, we will only be interested in the highest and lowest data point of each motion cycle on each axis, and will throw out any data between the highs and lows. This will help to keep the log file sizes more manageable.

When logging data, there are a few questions to ask:

- How fast will data be coming in? What data will it be?

- How should the data files be structured?

- How often should we flush (save) the data to the file?

- How big will the data files become?

- How often should we start fresh new log files?

Comparing the previous two-channel wireless transmitter project to the seismometer project is like comparing apples to oranges. More accurately, it's like comparing a bicycle to a sports car: the wireless project (bicycle) transmitted two data points with timestamps, but only did so once every 10 seconds. The seismometer transmits only three data points, but it does so several times per second (40–100 Hz). It is the sports car project, running incredibly fast.

This speed is necessary to have a decent resolution in our charts, but causes a nightmare of a problem in contending with the data. There are several issues we need to address in order to have a successful project. We need to attack on all fronts in order to minimize impact on system performance, while still maintaining accurate measurements.

The first thing we can do to help ourselves is to consider file structure. It is logical to assume that a long-term seismometer would have a huge log file, impractical and unwieldy when you retrieve it. Rather than one large file (which runs the increasing risk of being corrupted as it expands), let's plan to start a fresh log file periodically.

At first, while we are logging every sample, even a one-hour log file will have thousands of data points. We should think of a way to filter out the unnecessary data to reduce the size of the file. The simplest strategy is to simply throw out extra samples. We can set up a counter that simply ignores data until the predetermined count is reached, at which point we process only that one set of data points.

Why would we want to send data, only to toss it later? Each PC is different. You will need to spend some time fine-tuning yours to give you the quality of data you want, but balanced against system performance. Once you have determined the data rate that suits your setup, you can then alter the code in both the Arduino and the Processing application to send data at the rate you require. The method presented here, while not very efficient, is the most flexible for a wide variety of users.

Arduino Code

This is likely to be the shortest Arduino program of the book and should be mostly standard fare by now. Listings 6-1 and 6-2 are very similar. The only difference is in the pin assignments, and the MMA7361 has a bit of setup first in order to set the optional pins.

Listing 6-1. KXM52 Arduino Sampling and Transmission

```
/*
  Seismometer using Akizuki Denshi KXM52 sensor
  on scratch built Arduino 5Volt 8Mhz
*/

int Xaxis_pin = 3;
int Yaxis_pin = 4;
int Zaxis_pin = 5;

void setup()
{
  Serial.begin(57600);
}
```

```
void loop()
{
  char temp[15];
    sprintf(temp, "%d,%d,%d",
     analogRead(Xaxis_pin), analogRead(Yaxis_pin), analogRead(Zaxis_pin));
    Serial.println(temp);
   delay(50);
}
```

Listing 6-2. MMA7361 Arduino Sampling and Transmission

```
/*
  Seismometer using SparkFun MMA7361 sensor
  and Arduino Pro Mini 3.3Volt 8Mhz

  Setting GSEL
  0 = 1.5g, 800 mV/g
  1 = 6g, 206 mV/g
  Sleep: 0 = Sleep, 1 = Wake
  ZeroGD (output): logic high on this pin inidicates
  all three axis at zero G (freefall)

  */

// MMA7361 control pins
int ST = 6;          // Self Test
int GSEL = 7;        // G-mode
int ZeroGD = 8;      // Zero-g detect output
int SLP = 9;         // sleep pin
// Axis outputs
int Xaxis_pin = 2;
int Yaxis_pin = 1;
int Zaxis_pin = 0;

void setup()
{
  Serial.begin(57600);
  pinMode(13, OUTPUT);
  digitalWrite(13, HIGH);
  digitalWrite(SLP, HIGH);  //Awake
  digitalWrite(GSEL, LOW);  //1.5 G mode
}

void loop()
{
  char temp[15];
    sprintf(temp, "%d,%d,%d",
     analogRead(Xaxis_pin), analogRead(Yaxis_pin), analogRead(Zaxis_pin));
    Serial.println(temp);
    delay(5);
}
```

Load it into the Arduino, start the serial monitor select 57600, and watch as the data flies by on the screen. It is moving so fast that it is quite difficult to really comprehend the values. Shake the mini breadboard and you should see the length of the message expand and contract as one or more of the axis values shifts between 0 and 1024. We can confirm that everything is working properly by the fact that the value could span from one to four digits.

As is, you will quickly flood the Arduino serial monitor with data. It does not handle massive amounts of data like this so easily, so on a slower system you may notice it becomes impossible to do anything. Close the serial monitor window and you should get back to normal.

Processing

After confirming that the sensor and Arduino are in working order, we need to start working on the processing code. This will go through several iterations before arriving at a functional (albeit minimal) application. Let's review our roadmap before we get started:

1. Establish the connection between Processing and Arduino.

2. Adjust the values to zero.

3. Add timestamps to the data.

4. Prepare the logging function, saving the data to a file.

5. Visualize the waveforms on the screen.

Establish the Connection

Our first task is to get a Processing application up and running, reading in the data. If you worked your way through the previous two chapters on setting up a wireless sensor node, you will find that this code looks a bit different (see Listing 6-3).

Listing 6-3. Processing Serial Polling Event

```
void serialEvent(Serial port)
{
  String input = port.readStringUntil(linefeed);

  if(input != null)
  {
    input = trim(input);

    sensors = int(split(input,','));

    adjustSensors();
    printData();
    plotSensors();
    writeLog();
    count++;
  }
}
```

The `serialEvent` runs independently of the main loop. It waits for the serial port to signal that it has data in the buffer; at which time, the event springs into action.

It first parses the serial buffer into an input string. From there, it splits it up into fields using the comma as the indicator, and deposits the data into the sensors array.

It then calls a few functions successively. The first function adjusts the sensor values (ADC512 = 0). Then there is an optional `printData` function, followed by plotting and writing the log file. It then increments a counter before exiting. The counter helps us balance data flow versus performance by instructing the software to toss or ignore some data.

During testing, it is okay to utilize the printData `function`. In fact, you will need it to determine the baseline zero value for each axis. However, once you are up and running, you should comment out the call to the function. Data collection and printing is significantly slowed down by taking the time to print the text data to the screen.

To Convert or Not to Convert?

With the sensor mounted and in place, run the application with the `printData` function in place. You should see that the three axes are very stable. Observe the reported values and average them over time. Each axis will be somewhere around 512, but not dead on. For example, one axis may be about 498. Note these numbers, then comment out the `printData` function.

The value you recorded is the zero g state of the sensor. The `adjustSensors` function (see Listing 6-4) will subtract your noted values from the reported values, so that when the sensor is at rest, it reports 512, yet the Processing application sees zero. When the sensor reports 312, the application sees -200, and 712 reads as +200.

Listing 6-4. Sensor Adjustment Function

```
void adjustSensors()
{
  for(int i=0;i<sensors.length;i++)
  {
  sensors[i] = (sensors[i]*(upper-lower)/1023)+lower;
  }
  sensors[0] = sensors[0]-XAdjust;
  sensors[1] = sensors[1]-YAdjust;
  sensors[2] = sensors[2]-ZAdjust;
}
```

Add Timestamps

Adding timestamps is simple. We need only fetch the PC's time data and append it to the message. So, in this step, lets also start thinking ahead. For the log, it is much better for us to format a string message much like we did on the Arduino to transmit the data to begin with (see Listing 6-5). We can then quickly write the entire message to the log file; it is more efficient.

Listing 6-5. Formatting Each Log Entry with the Timestamp and Data, Separated by Commas

```
String formatLogEntry()
{
  String Hour, Minute, Second;
  Hour = nf(hour(),2);
  Minute = nf(minute(),2);
  Second = nf(second(),2);

  String log_entry =
    Hour + ":" + Minute + ":" + Second + "," +
    sensors[0] + "," + sensors[1] + "," + sensors[2];
  return log_entry;
}
```

Create the Log File Functions

Adding logging is greatly assisted by the PrintWriter functions of Processing. Essentially, PrintWriter creates a file stream to which, once configured, we can easily send data in the form of print commands we are familiar with. PrintWriter then buffers these print commands, and at periodic intervals, appends them to the file we specify. It handles all the file functions for us.

Some things we need to deal with on our own are the following:

- Setting the `dataFolder` where we want to store data
- Setting the file name
- Handling some flags to inform us of the logging status

There are a lot of functions involved in the logging process, but they are virtually unchanged from the functions as presented in the previous chapter, with the exception that we are now adding a daily folder path to the file name.

So rather than reiterate, I would like to draw attention to the `Draw` function, and the additional log-related code there.

`Draw` starts off with a simple comparison check: if the Day value in the log file name does not match the PC's current day, close the existing log, create a new folder with today's date (year, month, day) in the Data folder, and start a new log inside that folder.

In other words, every day at midnight the software will automatically create a new folder. At the end of a year's worth of logging, you will have 365 folders.

Assuming the program passes that check, it then does a similar check and action based on the hour. Thus, within the daily folder, you should find 24 files if you have been logging continuously, each file representing an hour.

This creates a very comfortable to navigate file structure, making it easy to locate seismic events by date and hour. Depending on the toss count you set, the files will start at about 1.2 megabytes per hour and rise steeply with smaller toss counts. Running full out (300 samples per second), a one-hour log file is around 500 MB. A toss count of 15 in Processing, with a 50 mS delay in the Arduino code gives an affective resolution of about 15–19 samples per second.

Visualize

Visualizing the data is arguably the most deceptive aspects of getting the application to work properly. We were initially attempting to plot at full speed and found it quite slow. We tried a lot of different tricks to try to coax more speed out of the plot, but at the end of the day, it was backing off the data speed that had the most effect.

The application also performs considerably faster once it has been compiled into a standalone application. You can do so by going to the file menu in Processing and exporting the application to native code.

The Draw method itself is quite simple. The stroke command sets the color. After that, we simply feed two sets of X,Y coordinates to the line function.

The first set of coordinates is the last known location. We simply take the current X-position counter and subtract one. Looking at the Y-position coordinate, it is important to note that we are maintaining two sets of data at any given time: the new incoming data as well as the previous set of data points. So the first Y-coordinate is simply the old data point. Also of note is the fact that the screen position is referenced to the top-left point (0, 0). So in order to center the data, we take the height of the screen, divide it in half, and then subtract the sensor value from it in order to actually plot it.

Once we finish plotting all three line segments, we copy the new data into the old sensor buffer and update the X-position counter. If the counter exceeds the width of the screen, we reset it to zero, clear the screen, and start again.

The function also divides the screen into three sections, drawing white lines between each section. Each axis is adjusted up or down in the plot, so it is drawn within its own "strip" on the screen. In addition, a center line down each strip indicates zero. See Listing 6-6.

Listing 6-6. Visualization Function

```
void plotSensors()
{
  stroke(255,0,0);
  line(xpos-1,(height*1/6)-((old_sensors[0]*200)/1024), xpos,(height*1/6)-
((sensors[0]*200)/1024));

  stroke(0,255,0);
  line(xpos-1,(height*3/6)-((old_sensors[1]*200)/1024), xpos,(height*3/6)-
((sensors[1]*200)/1024));

  stroke(0,0,255);
  line(xpos-1,(height*5/6)-((old_sensors[2]*200)/1024), xpos,(height*5/6)-
((sensors[2]*200)/1024));

  old_sensors = sensors;

  if(xpos >= width)
  {
    xpos = 0;
    background(0);
    stroke(255,255,255);
    line(0,height*1/6,width,height*1/6);
    line(0,height*2/6,width,height*2/6);
    line(0,height*3/6,width,height*3/6);
```

```
    line(0,height*4/6,width,height*4/6);
    line(0,height*5/6,width,height*5/6);
  }
  else
  {
    xpos++;
  }
}
```

You may be asking "Why not convert to g-force now?" I have a few justifications for not converting the data to g-forces. First, the sensors act in a linear manner. Thus, when the plot touches the top or bottom of its strip, that is the max g of the sensor. So, we can get a quick visual estimate quite easily. Second, adding g-force calculations adds yet more work for a system in which we are trying to balance data rates against processing power. A slower machine might be hindered by the additional functions. It's unlikely, but it could happen. More importantly, as a text file, the log file would increase considerably once the data is converted to g forces. Why? In raw mode, each data point adds no more than five characters to the log file. Each entry consists of the two digits for hour, minutes and seconds, separated by colons. This is followed by a comma and then each axis, separated by commas. Thus, the shortest entry is 13 characters, while the longest is 23 characters. The difference is due to the fact that an axis could be one character (a single digit positive integer) to 5 characters (3 digits, up to 512, plus negative sign, plus comma). The timestamp is a fixed width. An entry would appear like this: hh:mm:ss,-xxx,-yyy,-zzz.

Now consider what would happen if we converted to g-forces. In addition to the sign, g-forces will require several decimal places (refer to Table 6-2). A signal may six characters in the log file, not counting the sign. Some conversions could require considerably more decimal places to represent. In order to keep the log file nicely aligned and compact, we would need to introduce rounding to x decimal places. Rounding the data only compromises the accuracy of the data file. It is better to post-process the file to convert it to g-forces only when necessary. This can be done offline, long after the event was recorded. Thus, I opted to simply record raw data in the log file and use a simple visualization system to approximate the signal. The raw data can always be analyzed later.

Building the Final Transducer System

I have said many times that the prototype for this project is really simple, and it is. However, we really do not want to rely on a seismometer built on a breadboard and thrown in the ground.

Transducer Considerations

Our initial prototype should take you no more than a few moments to connect together. However, when we have worked out all our code and are happy with the software design, we should really build a purpose-built device. There are a few reasons for this:

- The Arduino board is too expensive to bury in the ground or strap to the side of a building for long duration monitoring.

- The Arduino board and a sensor mounted on a shield would be larger than desirable for the project. We want something compact that can fit into a small space. About 1 1/2 inches cubed.

- While we do plan to protect the device, building it on a breadboard is very unreliable. Consider that a magnitude 5 earthquake is likely to throw the sensor out of the board. We need a mechanically secure system.

So, once we are ready to put something in the ground, we will build from scratch a set of circuit boards. One is a transducer consisting of a custom purpose Arduino and associated circuitry. The other is the communications electronics to connect to the surface, as well as a simple power supply for the whole device. It will challenge your ability to build circuit boards by hand, but it is well worth the effort.

Cabling Considerations

Due to the fact that we want to mount the sensor outside, a few feet underground, we will need a long cable. Wireless transmission is not really practical in this case for two reasons:

- We still need to provide power. If we run a cable for power, we might as well run a cable for data. Not to mention the added cost of two wireless nodes.

- We want to transmit data as fast as possible, in order to have a high-resolution seismometer (about 200 samples per second). For this purpose, a wireless radio would be heavily taxed and consume a lot of power, making battery operation (or even solar charging) impractical.

Unfortunately, the maximum length of a USB connection is a few meters. To solve the problem, a flash from the past will come to the rescue. The RS232 serial port (for those of you too young to recognize it) is the predecessor to USB. The connector was made up of nine pins in a D-shaped shell. However, it only required three of the pins to communicate (transmit, receive, and ground).

RS232 is not nearly as fast as USB. Also, it does not handle multiple devices like USB does. RS232 only allows one device per serial port. Plainly, RS232 is inferior to USB in many ways.

However, in our case it offers one very critical advantage: cable length. We can use a cable length of 50 feet or more without too much trouble. Increased cable length is due to the fact that RS232 has a much higher voltage difference on the lines. You may recall that there is a dead band in digital logic between zero and 5 volts. Under .8 volts, we consider a *zero*, while over 2 volts is considered a *one*. USB has no problem distinguishing between the two. But as the cable becomes longer and longer, there is some signal attenuation. In other words, the signal gets weak. Eventually, a *one* has a voltage very close to 2 volts on the opposite end of the cable and is no longer detectable as a *one*.

RS232 solved this problem by adopting a bipolar scheme. Negative 3 to -12 volts with respect to the ground pin is considered a *zero*, while +3 to +12 is considered a *one*. Clearly, the signal is much stronger to begin with, and it is much harder to confuse the signal as it approaches the dead band in the middle. Between -3 and +3, the port reads nothing. Thus, much longer cables are possible. With typical cabling, 50 feet is the limit. However, the length limit depends largely on the capacity of the cable. Category 5 network cable has a capacity of about 17 picofarads per foot. With UTP CAT-5 cable (which we use in this book), we can run a cable as long as 147 feet. Additionally, lowering the data speed can increase cable length. If you were so inclined, you could run a cable as far as 3,000 feet! But your data rate would be limited to about 2,400 bits per second. For our project, we need to send data at 57,600 bits per second in order to get 3 channels of data at over 200 samples per second. Even so, we should be able to push data up a 75-foot long category 5 cable without much trouble.

There are many chips on the market to connect the Arduino up to an RS232 serial connection. The *de facto* standard is the MAX232 IC from Maxim (as well as many clones). It is known as a charge pump IC. It takes the lower-voltage TTL serial port signal from the ATMega chip and pumps it up to an RS232 serial port signal.

The communications link in our seismometer will consist of an RS232 charge pump IC inside the sensor canister, which takes the TTL serial signal from the ATMega chip and boosts to an RS232 signal, and sends it up category 5 Ethernet cable. The cable, which runs up inside the house is terminated with a second charge pump IC. This IC drops the signal back down to TTL-232. Finally, we put this signal into a serial to USB adaptor IC made by FTDI. The FTDI chip is identical to that installed on your Arduino board. If all goes well, you should even be able to reprogram the ATMega chip over the link, even as it is buried deep in your yard.

Finally we have to consider how we can power the device. I have already stated that we will send power down the cable. However, depending on the length of cable, we can't just send 5 volts down it. On the other end, we will have less than 5 volts. This is because all cabling has an internal resistance. If we want to be absolutely certain that the voltage supplying the circuitry and sensor is correct, it is best to built a voltage regulator directly within the sensor package. We then send a higher voltage down the cable, so we don't care how much is lost, as long as it arrives at the regulator above about 7 volts. The regulator then takes care of the rest, creating a nice clean 5-volt supply for our circuitry.

Parts List

As mentioned, we will first prototype the device with a normal Arduino; then transfer it to a custom device. As such, the parts list here may be a bit unusual. You can get the preprogrammed chip from several sources, or you can search the Arduino playground for a tutorial on how to program your own chip using the Arduino board as a host.

You will need the following parts:

- Arduino Pro Mini (many of the following parts can be eliminated by choosing this Arduino device rather than building from scratch)

- Sensor such as KXM53 or MMA7361

- 9-volt wall wart power supply (or battery pack)

- 5-volt regulator such as LM7805 or equivalent

- 1uF and 10uF capacitor for LM7805

- Breadboard (for prototyping only)

- Hook-up wire

- Small glass jar with painted metal lid (see text)

- 3 pcs. 2x2-inch square protoboard (see photos and text)

- 8 PCB standoffs and associated screws and nuts

- 2 x MAX232 or ADM2302 TTL-RS232 level shifting IC

- 8 x 1uF capacitors

- 8-Mhz crystal resonator

- 4 LEDs

- 4 1k ohm resistors

- 1 6 pin header, long legs

- 1 6 pin header socket

- 2 x 5 pin header

- Atmel ATMega168/328 IC preprogrammed with the Arduino bootloader

- Category 5 Ethernet cable length to be determined by PC and installation locations.

- FTDI-based USB TTL serial adaptor cable

- Anti-moisture desilicate packet

- Electric drill

- Toolkit consisting of solder, iron, nippers, pliers, screwdriver, and so on

- Lots of patience

Getting Prepared

While we can initially test the hardware using a standard Arduino and a mini breadboard, the final project needs to go in the ground.

In the first version, we will build a copy of the Arduino, stripping away parts we don't need and adding in the parts we do. We will have to cram this all onto two very tiny boards, because we want to install it all inside the lid of a jar. We can then run a long cable from the jar buried in the ground, up into our house and attach it to the computer.

In the second version, we will utilize the Pro Mini to reduce some of the work required. I highly suggest that you follow this version when building the Arduino/sensor board.

In order to accomplish this, our first task is to find a suitable enclosure. I chose a small glass peanut butter jar. I chose it for the following reasons:

- I can easily see through the glass when I bury it, so that it will be easy to align the accelerometer to face north.

- The glass will not decompose over time.

- The metal lid has a deep neck, such that the portion that screws over the glass is about 1/3 inch thick.

- The metal lid is also painted and contains a rubber gasket glued to the inside.

- It is quite small. The diameter is slightly larger than a coke can, and it is just over half the height of a coke can.

My only concern for the glass jar is the possibility of cracking in the freezing winter. However, the ground should act as a temperature buffer. You could also choose a plastic jar. Just be sure it addresses all of the previous points.

Our next task will be to test fit the prototyping boards inside the lid of the jar. Figure 6-3 shows a piece of perf board being test fit inside the lid. We can use standoffs to mount the board in the lid and drill holes in the lid to mount the standoffs. After assembly, cover the screws on the outside of the lid with generous helpings of silicon glue to prevent water leaking in through the holes. When mounting the board, be sure it is situated as close to the center as possible. If the corners overlap the rubber seal, you might need to nibble them down and round them with a pair of diagonal cutters.

Figure 6-3. *Square perf board mounted in the jar lid. Notice the cut corners of the board.*

A System of Three Systems

It is much easier to troubleshoot problems with a system when you can divide and conquer. Likewise, building a project in interconnecting pieces is much easier to do. By building a subsection of the project, testing it, and then moving on, you can verify from step to step. Finally, by separating a project into blocks, the individual block density is much less, making it far easier to construct, troubleshoot, and repair. For these reasons, I have divided the system into three circuit boards. Two reside within the sensor jar, while the third resides in a box near your PC. The system consists of the following three subsections:

- Arduino clone board with a 3-axis accelerometer
- Sensor's TTL to RS232 adaptor and 5-volt power supply board
- PC RS232-TTL-USB adaptor board, plus 9-volt wall wart supply

I recommend that you first build all three circuits on a large breadboard (or three small boards). This is a complex system, and you will need to poke around a bit to get it working.

Once you have everything going on the breadboard, migrate each subsection one at a time to the protoboard. Once one section is finished, reconnect it to the breadboard system. Verify that everything is functional and that you have documented the interconnections before moving on to the next subsystem. Eventually, you will have three boards all connected on the bench. If everything checks out, you can be confident about moving to the final assembly.

Arduino Board

The Arduino clone board is a stripped-down Arduino. It includes only the support components required to operate the ATMega CPU and connect the accelerometer. It also includes a connector to plug into the board below it within the sensor jar (the Sensor MAX232 board). The Arduino board receives 5-volt power from the MAX232 board and passes the communications and rest lines down through this connector. The schematic in Figure 6-4 illustrates a scratch-built Arduino.

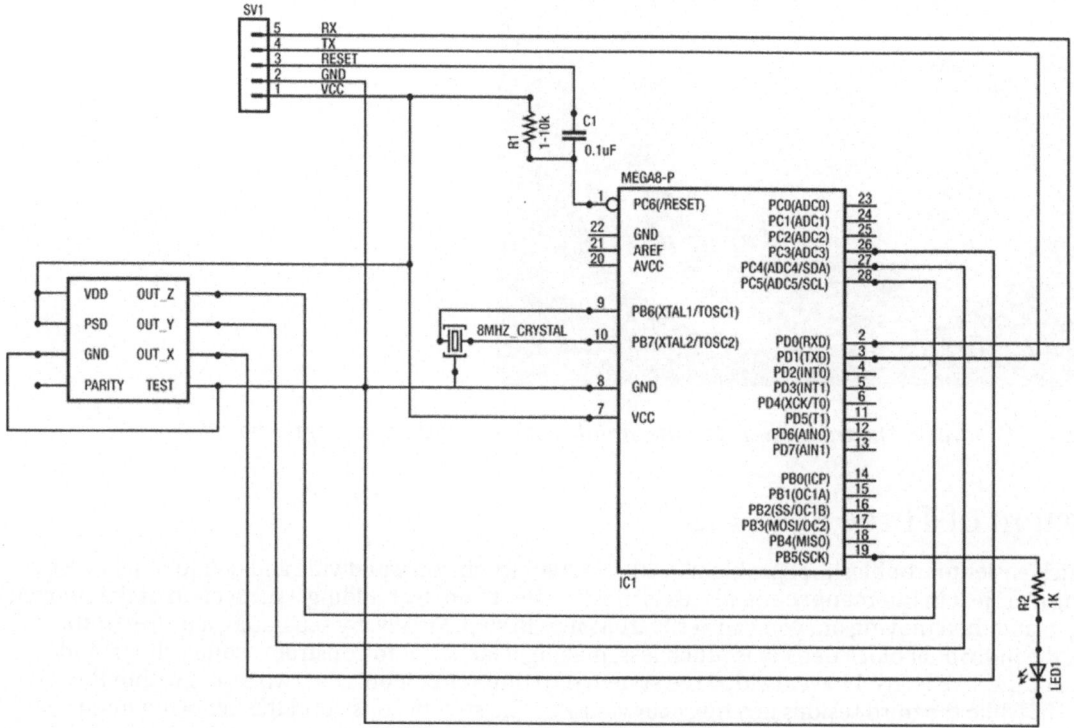

Figure 6-4. The primary components for the Arduino portion of the system. SV1 connects to the second board in the jar, which provides the RS232 adaptor and routes power.

Gather the Components

For the Arduino board, you will need an ATMega chip preprogrammed with the Arduino bootloader. These are available from a number of places, or you can opt to build a programming shield to program your own chips using another Arduino. I would definitely suggest this route, as you are likely to build a lot of hand-wired or one-piece Arduino clones. When you decide to make a project a permanent device, it is no longer economical to devote a full Arduino to them.

Gather the following parts:

- Square prototyping board that fits within the jar

- ATMega328 programmed with the Arduino bootloader

- 28-pin DIP socket to hold the ATMega328

- 2 x 1k ohm resistors

- LED

- 8 Mhz oscillator

- .1 uF capacitor

- 5- or 6-pin single row header, long pins

Plan the Layout

Gather your components and start thinking about how you will lay everything out on the board (see Figure 6-5). This is the most complex of the three boards, and careful planning now will save you headaches later. Not shown in the photo is the position of the header pins that drop to the board below.

Figure 6-5. A test fit of components for the Arduino board

Assembly

One of the challenges of this board (in addition to the normal prototyping headaches) is figuring out a way to have pin headers extending from the bottom instead of the top of the board. Notice there are no solder doughnuts on the top side of the board, so there is nothing to solder the headers to. I came up with a method of preparing the pins, as shown in Figures 6-6 and 6-7.

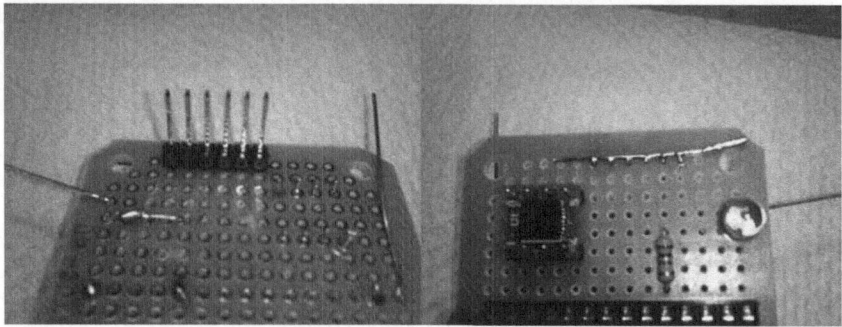

Figure 6-6. *A: placing the header pins on the bottom of the board. B: Soldering a length of wire across all of the pins, to temporarily hold the header in place. This wire is later removed.*

Place the header where you want it on the bottom of the board. Flip it over and solder a strip of stripped wire or a clipped-off component leg to the pins sticking through the top of the board (see Figure 6-7). Be careful to not apply too much heat, or you will detach the pins from the wire on the top side.

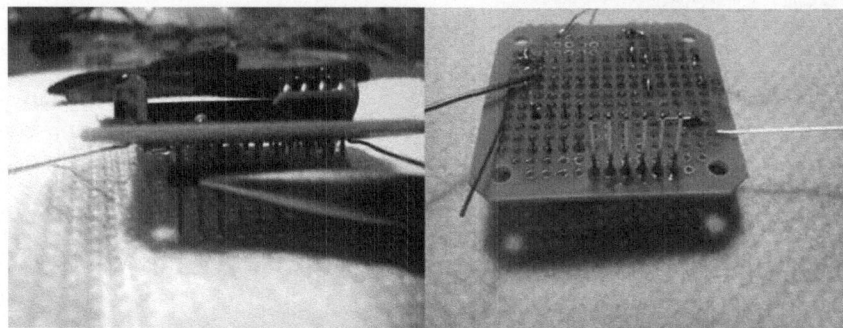

Figure 6-7. *A: Remove the plastic pin guide; set it aside and it can be replaced later. B: Solder the pins to the board.*

Flip the board back over and grab the plastic header frame with a pair of pliers. Carefully pull the frame down. You can place something hard under the pins and push down on the frame. Don't completely remove the frame.

Now solder the pins to the doughnut pads on the board. With the pins anchored in place, you can completely remove the frame. Finally, remove the wire from the top or simply clip between the pins. Be sure that you have a thick solder ball (or enough wire remaining) to act as an anchor for the pins. The doughnuts on the bottom side are only glued to the substrate and will not serve to secure the pins by themselves.

You will have to study the following pictures (Figures 6-8 through 6-10) carefully in order to figure out how it is all soldered together. I have tried to mark up the underside of the board as much as I can to provide some guideposts for you.

Figure 6-8. *Bottom side, with general locations of pins and parts. Some component legs are used to begin routing the circuitry.*

Figure 6-9. *Top side of the completed Arduino and sensor board, showing wires routing the circuitry*

Figure 6-10. Bottom side of the completed board; note that the orientation is rotated in relation to Figure 6-9.

Figure 6-11. The Arduino and sensor board inserted into a breadboard

Once the sensor board is complete, you should test it by breadboarding all the remaining circuits. The remaining circuits have been built on the breadboard for testing. In Figure 6-11 you see the Arduino/sensor board plugged into a breadboard. One by one, each subcircuit will be replaced with its associated completed board. Two wires provide power to the board, while three additional wires connect it to the MAX232 level shifter circuit. Unfortunately, there is an additional KXM52 sensor sitting dormant in the middle of the breadboard. I never thought I would have so many of them lying around! Anyway, the MAX232 level shifter circuit is on the far right end of the larger breadboard. It converts the TTL level serial signal up to an RS232 signal. This circuit will be built on to a second board and sit directly under the Arduino/sensor board within the jar.

Coming from the level shifter circuit is a set of twisted wires that connect up to the smaller bread board. Power cables also connect power to both breadboards. On the smaller board you will find yet another MAX232 level shifter circuit, which drops the RS232 signal back down to TTL serial. The signal then connects to an FTDI–based TTL serial–to–USB adaptor. In this photo, I am using a PCB device, but in the final project I use an FTDI cable with the circuitry built in. Everything on the smaller breadboard will eventually be built on to perf board and installed within a small project box, which resides near the computer.

By building the complete system on the breadboards and then replacing each subsection one by one with completed modules, I can easily keep track of the project, and diagnose and troubleshoot issues as they occur, rather than trying to track down an error somewhere deep in a completed project.

The Alternative Sensor Board Using the Pro Mini

You can save yourself a little bit of time by opting to use the Pro Mini rather than scratch-building the complete Arduino circuit. It also performs a bit better in the Analog section than my scratch-build device. Because the MMA7361 operates at 3.3 volts, I bought a Pro Mini that ran at 3.3 volts as well. This posed a small issue: the MAX232 needs 5 volts to operate (which is sent down the cable), but 5 volts would damage the Pro Mini and sensor. The solution is simple: I simply took the 5 volts from the header and passed it into a 3.3 volt regulator before powering the top board (see Figure 6-12). Figure 6-13 shows this modification, as well as the Pro Mini socket, while Figure 6-14 shows the completed board. (The analog connections are on the bottom side of the board, going straight from X, Y, and Z to Analog 2, 1, and 0 respectively. This keeps the connections as short as possible, to minimize noise.)

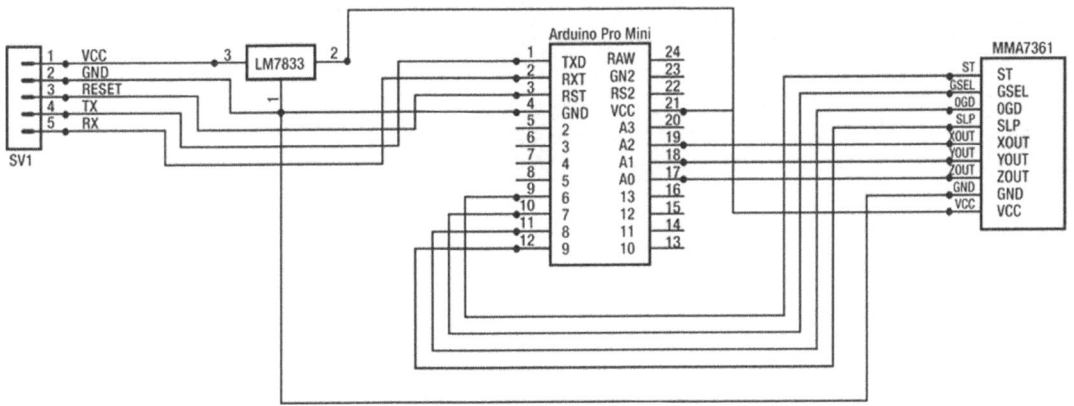

Figure 6-12. Schematic for Arduino Pro Mini board running at 3.3 volts, with MMA7361 sensor

Figure 6-13. *Socket for Pro Mini and 3.3 volt regulator; you can just make out the pins of the header that connects to the lower (MAX232) board*

Figure 6-14. *Completed Arduino Pro mini board with MMA7361 sensor T*

Sensor's MAX232 Board

The MAX232 interface board (see Figure 6-15) within the sensor package serves two purposes. First, it provides the higher-voltage interface for the ATMega to communicate over RS232. The RS232 cable can be much longer than a USB cable, allowing the sensor to be installed some distance from the computer tasked with collecting the data. In addition, it accepts a higher–voltage power supply from the cable and converts it to 5 volts to operate the MAX232 interface IC, as well as the ATMega and accelerometer.

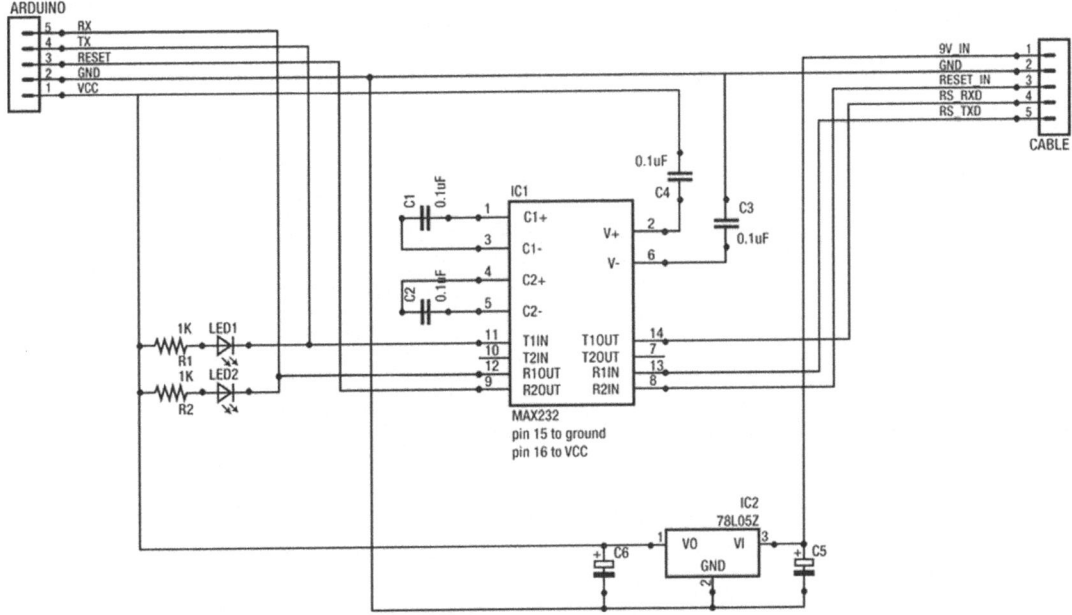

Figure 6-15. *RS232 interface schematic; this is the second circuit to be mounted within the jar*

Gather the Components

There are many devices that perform precisely the same as the MAX232, as well as sharing the same pin connections. I used an Analog Devices ADM3202.

Regarding capacitors to drive the IC, I have seen various ratings. Common choices include 0.1uF, 1uF, and 10uF. Often the IC will come with a set of capacitors. If you are using electrolytic capacitors, be sure to refer to the IC data sheet when connecting them because they are polarized and must be connected a certain way. The small blue .1uF capacitors that came with my ADM3202 chip were not polarized, so it did not matter which way I installed them.

Gather the following parts (shown in Figure 6-16):

- MAX232 or ADM3202 RS232/TTL interface IC

- 16–pin DIP socket for the IC

- 4 x .1uF–10uF capacitors

- 2 x LED

- 2 x 1k ohm resistors

- LM7805 5 volt regulator (choose the smallest package possible)

- 1 uF capacitor

- 10 uF capacitor

- 5– or 6–pin header female socket (match the connector used in the Arduino sensor board)

- 5-pin header

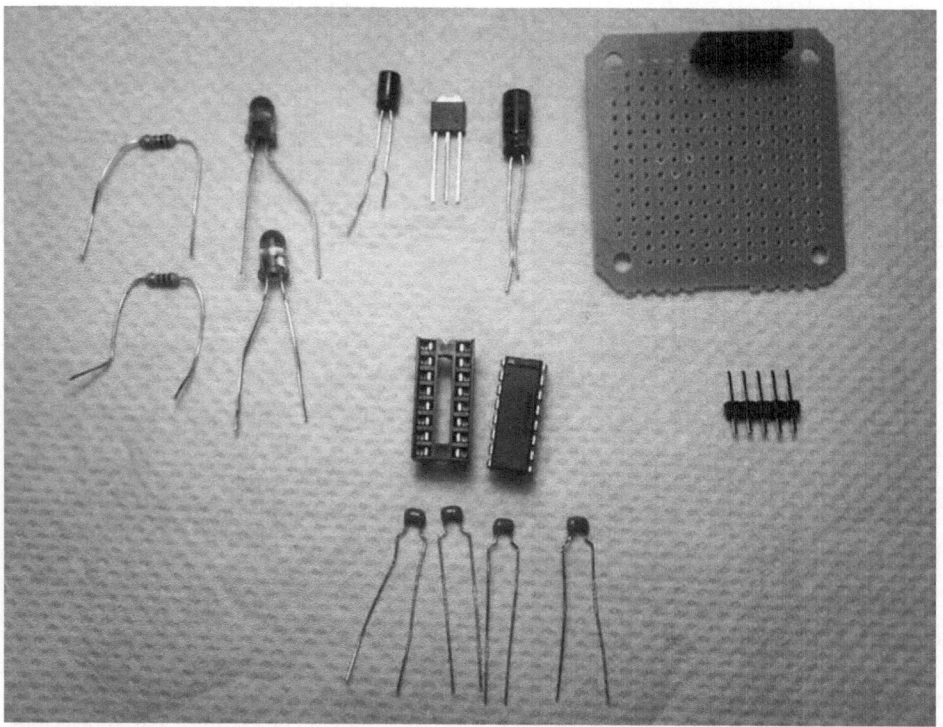

Figure 6-16. Components required for the MAX232 interface and power supply (the board has been prefit with the matching socket for the Arduino/sensor board)

Plan the Layout

The first thing you will want to do is make sure you have the header socket in the correct place. Figure 6-17A demonstrates how to check the placement by test assembling the two boards. You can go ahead and test fit everything by using some standoffs to screw the Arduino board and MAX232 board together. Fit the socket and solder it in place now.

Afterward, pull everything apart again and lay out where you want to place components, as shown in Figure 6-17B.

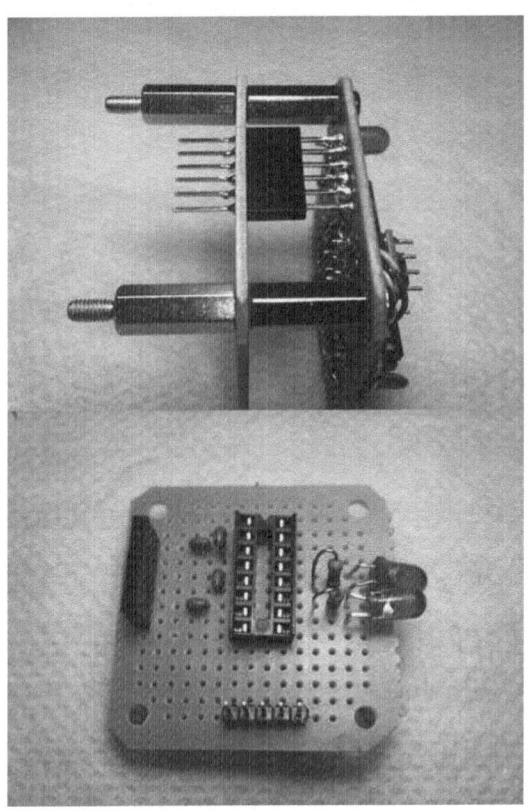

Figure 6-17. A: Preparing the socket placement of the RS232 interface board (left board) by mounting the Arduino board. B: Placing the components of the RS232 board.

Assembly of the board is a time-consuming process. Be sure to set aside a few hours to do the job. Take your time and double-check your work. There is a lot going on here. Study Figures 6-18, 6-19, and 6-20 carefully, and relate them to the schematic in Figure 6-15. Pay particular attention to the cable header. A common mistake is to connect TX and RX in the wrong order. If you find yourself scratching your head, wondering why your board does not communicate, you may need to swap the TX and RX wires.

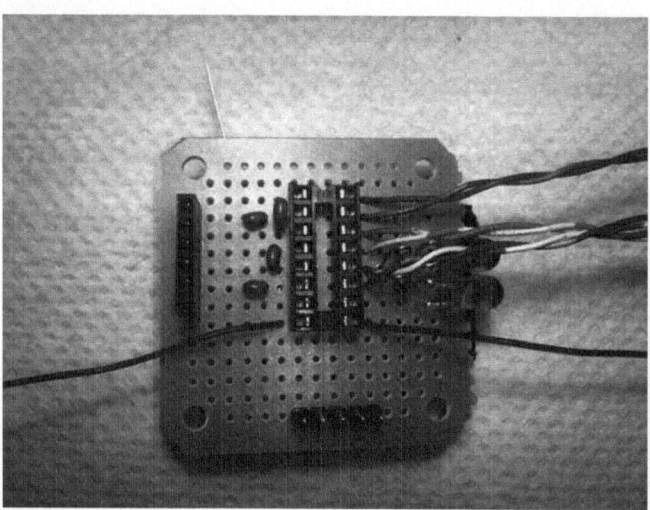

Figure 6-18. *Nearly complete: bundles of wire were cut from a short length of Ethernet cable, and pairs are color-coded and matched.*

Figure 6-19. *Completed sensor RS232 board. Left socket passes up to the Arduino board; bottom header pins will have wires from the Ethernet cable directly soldered to them. Between the header pins and the RS232 converter chip are the 5-volt regulator and associated capacitors.*

Figure 6-20. Completed board, bottom side (note the orientation compared with Figure 6-15). Header pins are at top, with the Arduino board socket on the left.

PC Side MAX232 Board

On the end of the cable that needs to connect to the PC, we need another MAX232 interface to step the higher voltage back down to TTL levels. They can then be connected to a TTL-USB adaptor. We will build much the same circuit (see Figure 6-21) as was installed in the sensor, except we don't need the 5 volt supply.

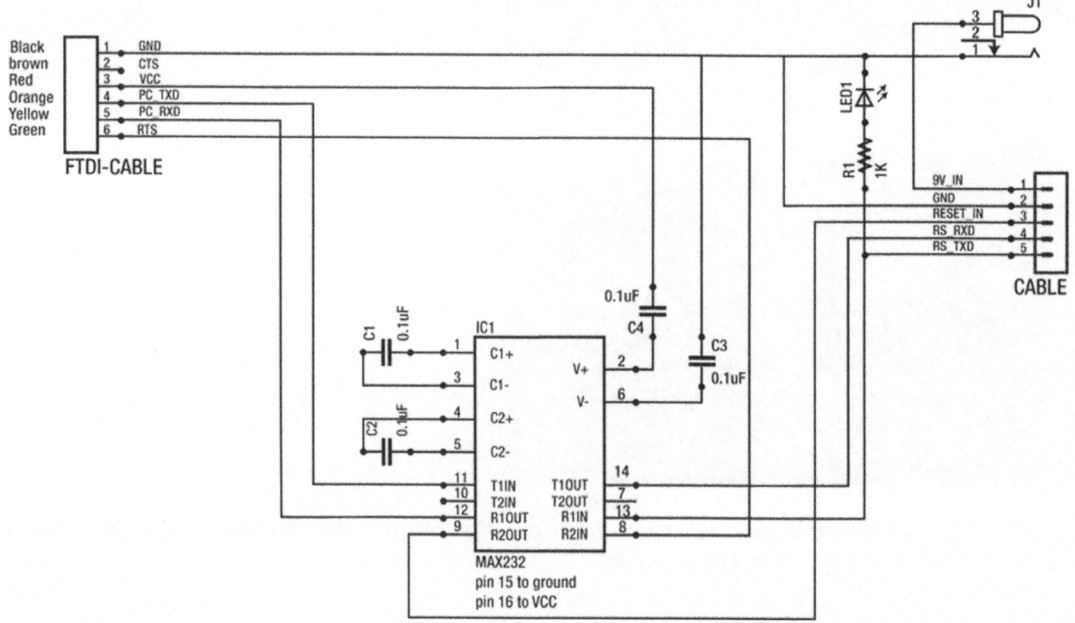

Figure 6-21. *PC side RS232 interface. Note that the FTDI USB-TTL cable connects on the left, and powers the MAX232 IC directly. The DC jack is connected directly to the Ethernet cable.*

You can also purchase a cable from FTDI that serves the function of converting USB directly to RS232, without the need for this step in the build. However, you still need to modify an Ethernet cable by attaching an DB9 connector on the PC side, as well as a barrel jack to connect and send 9 volts down to the sensor.

Be wary of using USB-to-RS232 adaptor cables from knockoff manufacturers. I initially attempted to save myself some time by shortcutting the final step, opting to use a USB-to-serial dongle. I actually went through three different units before I gave up completely and built the MAX232 adaptor board. Many of them simply don't work well.

Gather the Components

- Project box
- MAX232/ADM3202
- 14–pin DIP socket
- 4 x .1uF capacitors
- LED
- 1k Ohm resistor
- 2 x 6 pin headers or 1 each of 5 and 6 pins

- Panel mount DC barrel jack

- 7–9 volt wall wart power supply

- FTDI USB-TTL cable (TTL-232R-3V3 or TTL-232R-5V)

Plan the Layout

You can essentially copy the MAX232 board you built within the sensor. You will have some wires going to different pins, but it is very similar.

The only issue to be aware of is the placement of the connectors. Also, you want to position the LED so you can point it through a hole in the box, to serve as a visual indicator that it is receiving data (see Figure 6-22).

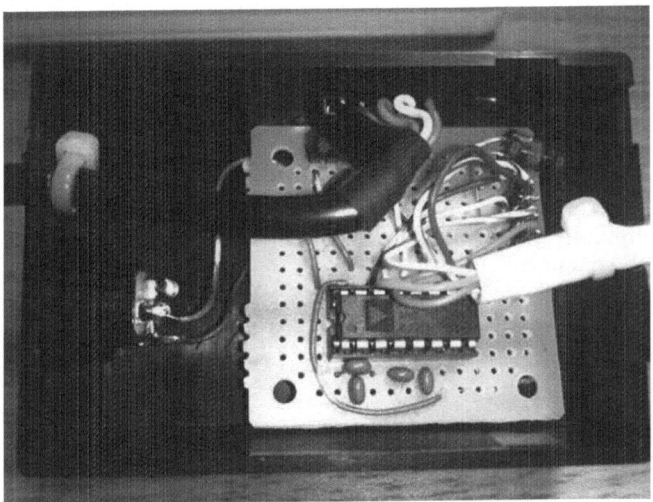

Figure 6-22. Inside the PC side box. Cable exiting on the left is the FTDI USB cable; below that is the DC jack. White cable exiting on the right is to the sensor.

Assembly

Before rushing ahead on this final piece of your seismometer kit, be sure to take a few moments to test fit everything in the box. Where will you point the LED? Where will the USB cable come in and the Ethernet cable go out? How about the panel jack? Measure twice; cut (and drill) once.

Because we covered the sensor side board in detail, I won't go into much more here because it is essentially the same board with a few wiring changes. You will need to connect all the ground connections within the box. The USB cable and the 9-volt supply need to share the same ground connection.

Testing and Assembly

The most frustrating part of this build is testing the communications. You might get lucky. More likely, you will have at least one set of wires in the communications chain crossed. To test everything, you could simply plug it in, go to the Arduino IDE, and open the serial monitor. If you get data right away, consider yourself an electronics master, on par with Yoda!

If you get a blank window staring back at you, you'll need to divide and conquer. Unplug everything and remove the top board of the sensor. With the Arduino board taken off, connect the system to your PC using the FTDI USB cable. Plug in the 9-volt wall wart power supply and connect it to the DC jack. At the sensor end of the cable, test the socket that connects to the Arduino board. First verify that you have 5 volts from the voltage regulator on the appropriate pins. If not, you will need to first double-check all the power connections. Go down to the cable at the sensor end and verify that you get voltage from the DC jack down to the sensor; then work your way back up to the connector.

Next, disconnect everything again, and insert a jumper between RX and TX on the socket for the Arduino board. We will do a basic serial test. With the jumper in place and the PC side box reconnected and powered up, anything coming down the receive line will be transmitted straight back. Open a serial terminal application on the PC and connect to the FTDI serial device. You may need to check your system hardware setting to verify the appropriate COM number on the PC or the device name on a Mac. Once properly connected, you should be able to type something into the serial port and see it come right back. In addition, both the LEDs on the sensor side should blink as data passes in and out. If not, carefully check all the connections for TX and RX throughout the chain.

You can work backward by disconnecting the sensor head and twisting the RS232 RX and TX lines and trying the test again. If the signal gets through, the problem is somewhere on the sensor level shifter board. If not, the problem is on the PC side of the chain. See Figure 6-23.

Figure 6-23. Mount the Sensor RS232 interface board first. The Ethernet cable enters through a hole in the lid under the board; solder directly to the headers.

Once you have confirmed a good signal all the way up to the Arduino board socket, it's time to get the complete system up and running. Once more, disconnect everything and plug in the Arduino and sensor board, but don't bother screwing it down yet. You may still have some bugs to work out. With the board in place, reconnect the system to the PC. You should see the LED on the Arduino board flash a few times. This is the Arduino starting up and waiting for new code to be transmitted. After a short period, the Arduino will jump into whatever program is resident in memory. If you have not placed the seismometer application on the board yet, the Arduino will simply idle.

Even if you have uploaded the seismometer code, it is a good idea to go ahead and upload the blink example from the Arduino IDE. We want to verify that the board can be reprogrammed remotely and reliably before putting it in the ground. If you have problems uploading the application, double-check both the final TX and RX connections, as well as the reset connection. If, upon attempting to upload code, the LED on the Arduino board flashes, but the transmit and receive lights on the MAX232 board do not flash, you know the reset pin is working, but the TX and RX lines may be crossed. Likewise, no flashing from the LED indicates that there is something wrong with the reset circuit. See Figure 6-24.

Figure 6-24. Insert the Arduino/sensor board and tighten the mounting screws.

Once you have verified that you can upload code to the Arduino with no problems, go ahead and install the final version of the sensor code. After the upload, the TX LED on the sensor stack should light continuously (actually, it is flashing with each transmission, but it happens so rapidly that it would appear as being continuously lit). Likewise, the RX LED in the box should be on as well. The sensor board is transmitting, and the PC side box is receiving data.

Fire up the Processing IDE and load the seismometer application. Hit run and you should see something like Figure 6-25. It is very possible that your traces are pegged near the top of the strip. Don't worry about that at the moment. Just shake the sensor around and make sure you see the traces dip down into view for each axis.

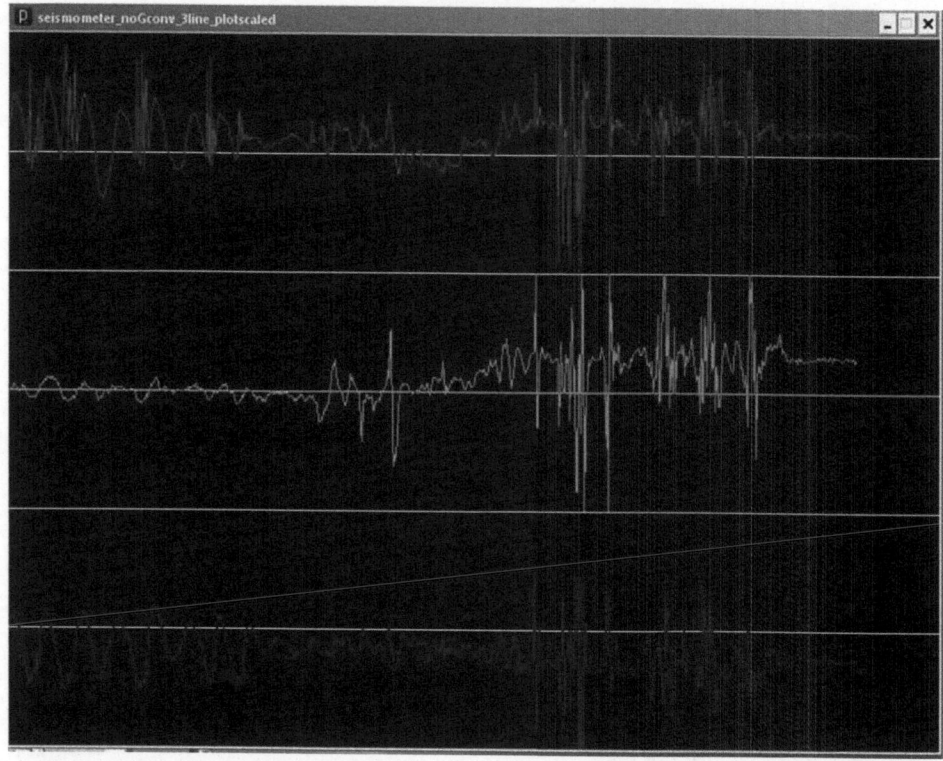

Figure 6-25. Output from the seismometer visualized by the Processing application.

Installation

In my opinion, installation is the most fun part of the build because it allows you to be the most creative. You could build a mount for the jar to strap it to a structural component such as a pylon or pier. For most typical users, however, the simplest option is to just bury it in the yard.

Dig a hole about two feet deep. Make a final check of the transducer. Be sure you have inserted a disilicat packet or two, the board is protected from moisture, and the screw and cable holes are sealed with silicon glue. Screw the lid down tight and wrap the joint with electrical tape to help keep water out. Alternatively, you could spread silicon glue around the neck of the jar just before screwing the lid on tight. This will lock the jar air and water tight.

Place the jar into the hole with the lid down. You might want to situate some material under the jar so you have a level surface to set the jar on. Look through the glass at the miniature compass. Rotate the jar so the compass (and thus the accelerometer) is oriented north. You might need to refer to the accelerometer module's data sheet to be sure you are pointing the Y-axis north. Pack a bit of dirt around the jar to hold it in place.

Make a final check of the orientation. It does not need to be perfect, but you should not be more than plus or minus 10 degrees off axis. Pack the remaining dirt over the jar, compressing and packing it as you go. Loose soil will not be an accurate foundation for the seismometer, and it may shake loose or change orientation over time. If at all possible, include some large heavy rocks or bricks around the sensor.

Be sure the cable is tended carefully all the way to the computer. You might want to dig a small trench (size depends on how aggressive your pets are at digging up wires) to bury the cable in. You can feed the cable in through a window or small hole in the house. If you are uncomfortable drilling holes, look around the building for the telephone input box. You can feed the cable through the same hole as the telephone lines.

If your cable is connected to the USB box via a jack, plug it into the box and connect power. Be sure the LED is flashing, indicating that the sensor is sending data. Connect the USB cable to your PC and start up the Processing application.

Just for fun, have someone stand over the sensor and jump around. Can you detect them?

With the sensor in place, it is now time to finally zero out all three axes and set up a permanent data-collection system. To zero out the axis, take a look at the Processing IDE debug window (that black window at the bottom of the code window). You should see data streaming through from the sensor as the draw window visualizes the data. If not, check the Processing application in the `serialEvent` function for the call to `printSensors()`. This should not be commented out yet (remove the `//` from before the code). Watch the stream for a few moments, making a mental average of the three axis values. Write them down for later.

Now run up to the top of the application, where the zero adjustments are. Enter the numbers you wrote down and run the application again. You should now see that the traces are right down the center line, or at least very close. You may need to tweak this a few times to get it just right.

Once you are satisfied with your zero adjustments, you can compile the application into native code. In the Processing IDE, go to File/Export Application. In the pop-up window, leave Full Window unchecked. Also uncheck any platforms you don't want to compile for. The application will appear in the same folder as the original code source. You can now move this executable file into your system startup folder, so when the computer boots, the seismometer starts automatically. The data folder will be in the same location as the application.

Going Further

The Processing application can use some improvements. For one thing, it is missing a calibration procedure. It would be nice if upon starting up, it took an initialization reading for a few moments, adjusted all axes to zero on that reading, and then started working.

It would also be nice to have a much longer backlog on the screen. For instance, from left to right represents five minutes of data instead of a few seconds. A scrollbar to view the whole hour would be fantastic.

Perhaps one of the biggest improvements would be to redesign the logging system so that it detects events and only logs them. Having had the sensor running for a few weeks, I found that 99 percent of my data was flat lines. It was tedious to find possible events, and it hogged a lot of disk space. It would be so much better to have the software maintain a rotating buffer of, say five minutes. We then do some threshold detection on each data reading. If one of the three axes exceeds a preset limit, the buffer dumps to a timestamped file, and the software continues to record. As long as it is detecting values above or below 3, for example, we continue recording. Once the signals go back to flatline, we record for a few more seconds and then close the file and return to using the five-minute buffer. This way, I only have files that contain events. If there are no files for the day, nothing significant happened. Also, I know exactly where to look in the file. The five-minute head and tail in the file might have minor precursors recorded in them that, by themselves may have not fired the trigger to start recording.

Finally, a second application should be written to read in log files and visualize them offline as well. The application as it stands is fine for recording, but gives you no chance to view data more than a few seconds old. I have yet to write such an application myself; instead, I have been importing data files into Microsoft Excel and doing my offline post-processing there. It is perfectly acceptable, but requires a lot of manual work for each and every file. It would be nice to have a custom-made application. Listing 6-7 shows the final code.

Listing 6-7. Final Processing Code

```
import processing.serial.*;

// Zero Adjustments (around 512 +- for mount angle offsets)
int xadj=-494;
int yadj=-509;
int zadj=-755;

int linefeed = 10;
// For storing serial port input
int sensors[] = new int[3];
// For line drawing purposes
int old_sensors[] = new int[3];
int xpos = 1;
// For dropping instances from the plot
int count = 0;
int count_limit = 15;

// logging
String dataFolder = "../data/Seismo/";
String folderName;
String logfilename;
PrintWriter logFile;
int logDay, logHour;
boolean logging = false;


Serial port;

void setup()
{
  // prep screen
  size(800,600,P2D);
  background(0);
  stroke(255,255,255);
  line(0,height*1/6,width,height*1/6);
  line(0,height*2/6,width,height*2/6);
  line(0,height*3/6,width,height*3/6);
  line(0,height*4/6,width,height*4/6);
  line(0,height*5/6,width,height*5/6);
```

```
  // prep serial port
  println(Serial.list());
  port = new Serial(this,Serial.list()[1],57600);
  port.bufferUntil(linefeed);

  // logging
  logDay = day();
  logHour = hour();
  folderName = dataFolder + nf(year(),4) + nf(month(),2)
  + nf(day(),2) + "/";

  logfilename = folderName + "Seismo-" + nf(year(),4)
  + nf(month(),2) + nf(day(),2) + "-" + nf(hour(),2)
  + nf(minute(),2) + nf(second(),2) + ".log";

  startLogging();
}

void draw()
{
  if (logDay != day())
  {
    logging = false;
    closeLogFile();
    logDay = day();
    logHour = hour();

    folderName = dataFolder + nf(year(),4) + nf(month(),2)
    + nf(day(),2) + "/";

    logfilename = folderName + "Seismo-" + nf(year(),4)
    + nf(month(),2) + nf(day(),2) + "-" + nf(hour(),2)
    + nf(minute(),2) + nf(second(),2) + ".log";

    openLogFile();
    logging = true;
  }
  if (logHour != hour())
  {
    logging = false;
    closeLogFile();
    logHour = hour();

    logfilename = folderName + "Seismo-" + nf(year(),4)
    + nf(month(),2) + nf(day(),2) + "-" + nf(hour(),2)
    + nf(minute(),2) + nf(second(),2) + ".log";

    openLogFile();
    logging = true;
  }
```

```
   if(count >= count_limit)
   {
     count = 0;
     plotSensors();
   }
}

void serialEvent(Serial port)
{
  String input = port.readStringUntil(linefeed);

  if(input != null)
  {
    input = trim(input);

    sensors = int(split(input,','));

    adjustSensors();
//    printData();
    plotSensors();
    writeLog();
    count++;
  }
}

void printData()
{
 for(int i=0; i<sensors.length; i++)
  {
    print(sensors[i]);
    print(" ");
  }
  println();
}

void adjustSensors()
{
  sensors[0] = sensors[0]+xadj;
  sensors[1] = sensors[1]+yadj;
  sensors[2] = sensors[2]+zadj;
}

void plotSensors()
{
  stroke(255,0,0);
  line(xpos-1,(height*1/6)-((old_sensors[0]*200)/1024), xpos,(height*1/6)-
((sensors[0]*200)/1024));
```

```
  stroke(0,255,0);
  line(xpos-1,(height*3/6)-((old_sensors[1]*200)/1024), xpos,(height*3/6)-
((sensors[1]*200)/1024));

  stroke(0,0,255);
  line(xpos-1,(height*5/6)-((old_sensors[2]*200)/1024), xpos,(height*5/6)-
((sensors[2]*200)/1024));

  old_sensors = sensors;

  if(xpos >= width)
  {
    xpos = 0;
    background(0);
    stroke(255,255,255);
    line(0,height*1/6,width,height*1/6);
    line(0,height*2/6,width,height*2/6);
    line(0,height*3/6,width,height*3/6);
    line(0,height*4/6,width,height*4/6);
    line(0,height*5/6,width,height*5/6);
  }
  else
  {
    xpos++;
  }
}

String formatLogEntry()
{
  String Hour, Minute, Second;
  Hour = nf(hour(),2);
  Minute = nf(minute(),2);
  Second = nf(second(),2);

  String log_entry =
    Hour + ":" + Minute + ":" + Second + "," +
    sensors[0] + "," + sensors[1] + "," + sensors[2];
  return log_entry;
}

void writeLog()
{
  if (logging)
  {
    String log_entry = formatLogEntry();
    logFile.println(log_entry);
    logFile.flush();
  }
}
```

```
void startLogging()
{
  // open file
  openLogFile();
  // start running
  logging = true;
  println("Started logging to " + logfilename);
}

void stopLogging()
{
  logging = false;
  closeLogFile();
  println("Stopped Logging.");
}

void openLogFile()
{
 // logfilename = logfileTextField.getText();
  if (logfilename.equals(""))
  {
    // set tentative file name
    logfilename = dataFolder + "Seismo-" + nf(year(),4) + nf(month(),2) + nf(day(),2)
      + "-" + nf(hour(),2) + nf(minute(),2) + nf(second(),2) + ".log";
  }
  logFile = createWriter(logfilename);
  println("Log file opened: " + logfilename);
}

void closeLogFile()
{
  logFile.flush();
  logFile.close();
  println("Log file close.");
  // set tentative file name
  logfilename = dataFolder + "Seismo-" + nf(year(),4) + nf(month(),2) + nf(day(),2)
    + "-" + nf(hour(),2) + nf(minute(),2) + nf(second(),2) + ".log";
}
```

References

- http://en.wikipedia.org/wiki/Seismic_waves#Surface_waves

- http://en.wikipedia.org/wiki/Richter_magnitude_scale

- http://en.wikipedia.org/wiki/Moment_magnitude_scale

- http://en.wikipedia.org/wiki/Japan_Meteorological_Agency_seismic_intensity
  _scale

- http://en.wikipedia.org/wiki/Lists_of_earthquakes#Largest_earthquakes_by_magnitude

- http://en.wikipedia.org/wiki/2011_Tōhoku_earthquake

- http://en.wikipedia.org/wiki/Peak_ground_acceleration

- http://en.wikipedia.org/wiki/Peak_ground_velocity

- Quake Catcher Network: http://qcn.stanford.edu/

- Freeware seismometer software:
  http://pods.binghamton.edu/~ajones/AmaSeis.html

- Introduction to measuring Earthquakes:
  http://faculty.weber.edu/bdattilo/shknbk/notes/msrngerthqks.htm

- KXM52 module from Akizuki Denshi: http://akizukidenshi.com/catalog/g/gI-01425/

- MMA7361 module from SparkFun: http://www.sparkfun.com/products/9652

CHAPTER 7

Staying Current

Keeping Track of Your Power Usage

Saving the world best begins in our own homes and backyards, and one way to get started is by monitoring, analyzing, and controlling our household energy usage. Energy consumption worldwide is on the rise, and local utility companies have started to roll out peak demand billing where your electricity costs more when you need it the most. Knowing when these rates occur and what you can do about them will hopefully help improve your energy efficiency and save you a few pennies in the process.

In this chapter, you will build an inexpensive open source modular energy monitor using the Arduino microcontroller and a handful of simple components. We will walk you through how to build this energy monitor, including a look at the sensors and displays needed to sense and monitor your energy usage. Once we have something built and working, we will then suggest a few things that can be done with your energy monitor to take it a little further, including storing the data on a memory card or connecting your monitor to the Web to gather and share your data. After building this project, you should have learned a little about how you use energy and what you can do to lower your energy bills—maybe you can lay to rest the debate over whether you should switch from incandescent lights to compact fluorescents.

This chapter draws heavily on and is deeply indebted to the work of the Open Energy Monitor project, which seeks to develop an open source energy monitoring system using the Arduino platform. We won't be going into quite as much complexity in our project, keeping to a relatively simple monitor just to get you going. For more information on the Open Energy Monitor, and to develop the project in this chapter in much greater depth, visit the project's web site at `http://openenergymonitor.org`.

What Is Alternating Current?

The project in this chapter is all about measuring the electric power of an *alternating current (AC)* power source, specifically that from our household mains. But what exactly are we talking about? Alternating current is a little different from the direct current or DC power sources that we have used in this book so far. Whereas a DC power supply, such as a battery or DC power adapter, provides a steady and constant current in one direction through a wire, AC power sources, like those coming out of the wall receptacle in our homes, alternates in both directions from positive to negative polarity. In the United States, this alternating polarity happens at a frequency of 60 hertz, or 60 times a second; in Europe the standard frequency is 50 hertz. The measure of the potential energy of a power source is called its *voltage* and is measured in volts. Our AC household mains voltage in the United States is standardized at 120 volts, although in Europe this ranges from 220–240 volts.

Because of these higher voltages and higher potential energy, AC is an ideal source for powering large devices such as refrigerators or clothes dryers, and even smaller devices such as bright light bulbs and televisions. Despite the best efforts of Thomas Edison, we adopted high-voltage AC current for our domestic power grid in the United States a long time ago, in part because it was easy to transmit power from large regional power stations over long distances to our homes.

In addition to its voltage, the next thing that we usually associate with our household energy use is the watt. For example, you probably already know that a 100-watt light bulb is a lot brighter than a 40-watt bulb because it's doing more work. The *watt (W)* is a measurement of the real power used by a load at any one time to convert potential electrical energy into light, heat, movement, or some other form of power. Where real power is the measurement of the amount of work a circuit can produce, a second component of AC power is its reactive power or the measurement of the electrical energy that is not used up by the devices in a circuit but rather circulates back and forth between the source and the load. Reactive power is found in circuits that contain capacitive or inductive loads such as motors and fluorescent light bulbs and is measured in *volts-amps-resistive (VAR)*. The third component of AC power is its apparent power or the sum total of a circuit's real power and reactive power and is measured in *volt-amps (VA)*. Apparent power is a kind of a maximum that can be expected by a circuit.

When we talk about the voltage or current of a circuit we are generally referring to its *RMS*, or the *root-mean-square* measurement of an AC sine wave. This is the measurement of the amount of AC voltage required to do the same amount of work as an equal DC voltage—a value of about 0.707 times the peak AC voltage. Given an RMS voltage for household mains in the United States of 120 volts, the peak voltage is actually 1.41 times this amount or 169.2 volts. We use the RMS values of voltage and current in our circuit to calculate the circuit's apparent power.

Apparent power is useful for knowing what the potential current in a circuit could be if connected to a purely resistive load such as an incandescent light bulb that uses nearly all its potential energy in one form or another. When comparing these two kinds of loads, a purely resistive load's reactive and apparent power will be nearly identical. On the other hand, the real power of a reactive load will almost always be lower than its apparent power. This relationship between real power in watts and apparent power in volt-amps, expressed in a percentage from 0 to 1, is called the *power factor* and it tells you how reactive or resistive your load really is.

Because most devices are a combination of resistive and reactive loads, real power in watts is generally a more useful measurement, and it's what your energy company will bill you for. However, power factor tells us how efficient an electrical device is.

You're probably more familiar with the *kilowatt-hour (kWh)* when you look at your energy bill every month. The kilowatt-hour is a measurement of your energy consumption in kilowatts, or 1,000 watts of power over one hour of time. For example, if a 100-watt incandescent light bulb is left on for 10 hours, it will have consumed 1 kilowatt-hour of electricity.

We will be working with all these measurements in our energy monitor project but because the higher voltages associated with AC loads are a lot more dangerous to work with than the low power DC sources that we are familiar with, we will be primarily concerned with finding ways to safely convert and measure our high–voltage power source using our low-voltage Arduino.

Let's now look at some of the hardware that will help to make this happen.

■ **Caution** For this project we are working closely with household mains voltages, which can be dangerous if you are not careful. Nothing in this project requires direct access to high voltages; however, you should as always proceed with caution.

Energy Monitor Hardware

For our simple energy monitor we will need some hardware both big and small beyond an Arduino-compatible microcontroller. This includes a current sensor, a safe source of alternating current, a display, some sort of extension cord or power strip, and a handful of other smaller components.

Before we get started building our energy monitor, though, let's first take a closer look at each of the main components in more detail and follow that up with a summary parts list for all the components needed to build this project.

Split-Core Current Transformer

At the heart of our energy monitor is the *split-core current transformer*. Also called a *CT sensor*, this is a noninvasive sensor that clips on to an AC power line to detect the flow of current through a wire. It does this through a process of induction: as the current passes through the wire it creates a magnetic field in the CT sensor's ferrite core. A secondary wire winding around this core creates a smaller current proportional to the load on the wire. Remember that the Arduino's ADC can only measure voltages, resistance, or current, so we need to combine our CT sensor with a small burden resistor to generate a voltage output that can be properly measured. The sensor we'll be using is shown in Figure 7-1, although you might have something that looks a little different.

Figure 7-1. A 100 amp, 333 millivolt output, split-core current transformer

Our CT sensor clips around an insulated wire, meaning that it does not require any work on the higher–voltage AC side of the circuit, and the low-current side of the CT is physically isolated from the high current side. This combines to make the CT sensor a safe and effective way to monitor energy consumption. In fact, the current flowing from the sensor is anywhere from 1500 to 2000 times less than the mains current because the secondary winding of the CT sensor typically numbers anywhere from 1500 to 2000 turns of wire. (This relationship is important to keep in mind when we discuss calibration.)

CT sensors can be purchased from a variety of venders and auction sites worldwide, although because there is so much variety in how the sensors work, you'll need to do some homework to find the specifications of your sensor and adjust some settings to get it to work correctly. There are two main types of CT sensor: those with a built-in burden resistor that outputs an alternating voltage, and those without that will need an external burden resistor added to the circuit to be used with the Arduino. The burden resistor also affects the overall range of current that can be measured by the CT sensor. A lower burden resistor allows for measuring a higher current at the loss of measurement resolution.

The specific CT sensor that we will be using for the project in this chapter has a burden resistor built in to the sensor housing. It has a fairly standard output of 333 millivolts, or 0.333 volts at its rated current of 100 amps. Because of the higher capacity of this sensor, it will even work for monitoring larger devices and appliances such as refrigerators or for whole-house monitoring with a little extra work and a second sensor (in the United States). On the other hand, it might not be the best choice for monitoring more energy-efficient and lower-drawing devices such as modern notebook computers, for example.

AC/AC Adapter

In addition to the CT sensor, the other major part of our current sensing setup is a low-voltage source of AC power. We use this to safely measure the household mains voltage to more accurately calculate the power consumption on our monitor. To avoid working with mains voltage directly, we use an off-the-shelf AC adapter or wall-wart to step down our source voltage, from 120 volts in the United States, for example, to a more reasonable range of anywhere from 9 to 12 volts AC.

AC-to-AC adapters are a little harder to come by than AC-to-DC adapters, but they can still be found through surplus outlets or major suppliers such as Digi-Key's part number T1004-ND. It's even possible, with some extra hardware, to power the Arduino directly from this power source, but to keep things simple we've decided to power the Arduino from a separate DC power supply.

Our particular AC-to-AC adapter is rated for 12 volts AC, but when measured with a digital multimeter, it usually outputs a little over 14 volts. That's to be expected because these transformers are not regulated power supplies and are not placed under any significant loads that might otherwise drop the total voltage output. We will calibrate for this in our code later; as long as your AC power source is somewhere in the vicinity of 9 to 12 volts it should work fine.

Liquid Crystal Display

There are lots of methods for displaying the information that we calculate from our two sensors including sending the data back to our computer through serial, storing the data on a memory card for review later, or even connecting our Arduino to the Web and sharing our data on sites such as Pachube (refer to Chapter 5) or services such as the former Google PowerMeter. To make our energy monitor as portable as possible, we will revisit the standard liquid crystal display (LCD) from earlier in this book to display the appropriate data in an easily readable format. The character display that we will use in this project is similar to what we used earlier except that it is only capable of displaying 16 characters wide by 2 characters tall. It uses the same industry standard interface controller called the HD44780 that is fairly easy to work with when combined with the Arduino's LiquidCrystal library.

Three-Wire Extension Cord

To measure the current of devices we need to be able to power them, and we need access to one of the wires that provide that power to clip on our CT sensor. Unlike DC, AC does not have a positive or negative polarity because the signal alternates polarity many times every second. A grounded AC power cord will have three wires inside of it; in the United States these wires are the hot or black wire, a neutral or white wire, and an earth ground or green wire; in the UK these wires are brown for the live wire, blue for the neutral, and yellow-black for earth ground. We are interested in the hot (no relation to temperature) or live wire that will need to pass through the CT sensor to measure the current of the attached devices, but somehow we have to get access to this wire. We could cut open the cable attached to our device, but that seems permanent and irreversible. Instead, we could wire up a new cable with a plug and outlet inside some kind of electrical box that would plug into the wall, providing power to the device to be measured. (I tend to avoid working with anything attached to the mains electrical if I can help it, so I would rather not build an outlet or cable.)

Our third option is to use an extension cord or power strip that we are not sentimentally attached to and, because our CT sensor is of the clip-on variety, All we need to do is cut into our power cord and clip on the sensor around the hot wire—no exposed copper to worry about.

For this project, I am using a short three-wire extension cord, meaning that the cord has the extra wire for connecting to earth ground, and it has three receptacles built into the cable. This allows us to connect a variety of devices to be monitored or to power our AC adapter from the cable as well. We will need to carefully cut into the outer insulation of the cable as explained later, without cutting into any of the wires inside, to get access to the hot or live wire so that we can clip on our CT sensor.

Parts List

Because every CT sensor and AC adapter is a little different you will need to experiment a little to find the appropriate parts that best match your sensor. The parts most likely to change from one instance of this project to the next are the resistors so you might need several different values of resistor other than those we list here. As such, it might be a good idea to get a package of assorted resistor values such as Radio Shack's 500-piece, 1/4-watt resistor assortment: part number 271-312. Because we can't list every possible part that might be required for every possible CT sensor and AC adapter, we will start with the parts we used for our example and show you how we went about putting it together.

Here is the parts list for this project:

- Arduino Uno or compatible

- 400-point solderless breadboard

- CT sensor, 333 millivolts at 100 amps

- 12-volt AC/AC power supply

- 16 x 2 character LCD

- Three-wire extension cord

- Power supply for the Arduino (USB or 9-volt DC adapter)

- 4 x 10 kilohm resistors

- 100 kilohm resistor

- 6.8 kilohm resistor

- 220 ohm resistor

- 10 kilohm potentiometer or trimpot

- 2 x 10 microfarad electrolytic capacitors

- 0.1-inch break away male pin headers

- 1/8-inch heat shrink tubing

Building it

Now that we have an idea of what's needed to build our energy monitor, let's move on to actually building it. The prototype for this project can be broken down into several main parts: the current and voltage sensing circuits, the display, and the physical connection to the AC power cable.

For the example here, I'm using the latest Arduino Uno, although any Arduino-compatible would work just as well. To keep things simple, we are going to leave our circuit on a breadboard using jumper wires to connect our devices to the Arduino, although feel free to transfer this design over to a more permanent solution such as an Arduino shield or circuit board, or build it into some form of enclosure at your convenience. Figure 7-2 shows the detailed schematic for building the energy monitor and connecting it to the Arduino.

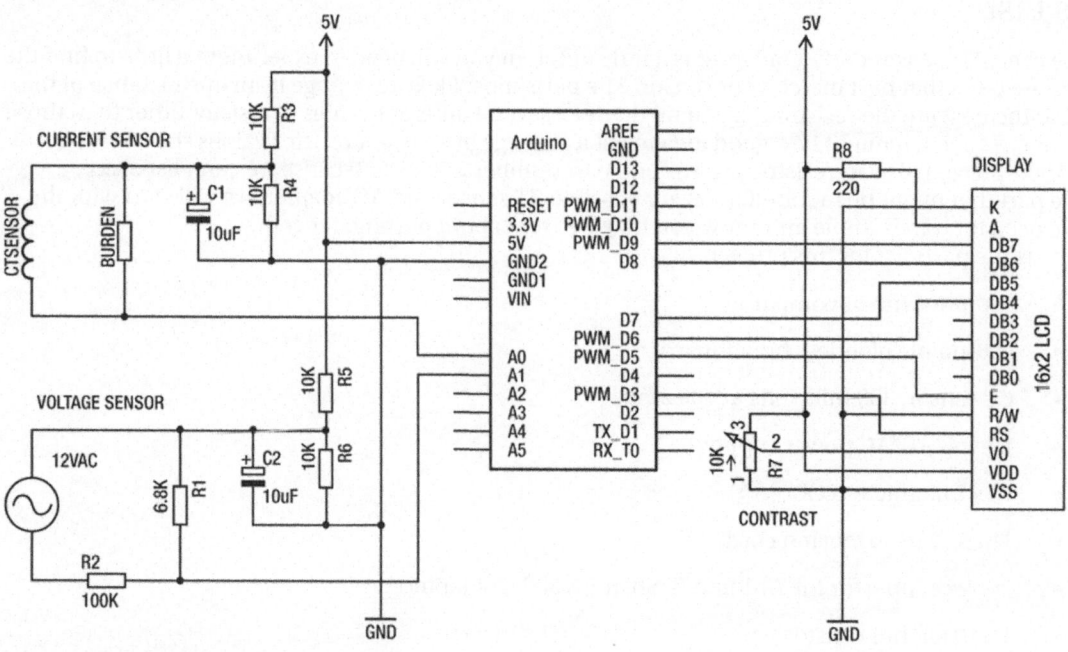

Figure 7-2. Energy monitor schematic

When this schematic is all wired up on the breadboard you should have something that looks like the energy monitor prototype shown in Figure 7-3. This should be fairly straightforward—all you need to do is follow the schematic, making sure that the parts as they are placed on the breadboard make the same connections that are shown in the schematic. In our example, we used a few short jumper wires from 24-gauge solid core insulated wire along with the power bus along the edge of the breadboard to get this done. Remember, a schematic is not a geographic map; its job is merely to show you how the individual components actually connect in the circuit.

Figure 7-3. Energy monitor prototype

Current and Voltage Sensing

The first thing we should do is build the current and voltage sensing components of our schematic. There are two parts to this: one to sense the current from our CT sensor and the other to sense the voltage from our AC power adapter. Beginning with the CT sensor in our schematic, this sensor is connected in parallel with the burden resistor. The burden resistor for our example is built into the CT sensor so that an external resistor is not needed. If your sensor does not have an internal burden resistor, you need to calculate the proper value for this resistor in relation to the number of turns of the secondary coil inside the CT sensor and the desired current range. For more information on choosing a burden resistor, refer to this web site: `http://openenergymonitor.org/emon/node/59`. We'll revisit this later in calibrating our system to determine the specifics of our sensor.

Once we have a CT sensor connected in parallel with a burden resistor that provides us with a voltage proportional to the amount of current passing through our AC load, we need to condition the output of our sensor's signal to make it more Arduino-friendly. We do this by providing a DC bias using a DC voltage divider (as discussed earlier in this book) created by resistors R3 and R4 to ensure that the output from our CT sensor is always a positive voltage in the range of the Arduino's ADC, which happens to be 0 to 5 volts for the Arduino Uno. Finally, we add the capacitor C1 to soak up some of the stray noise introduced in our signal to make for more reliable readings.

In addition to sensing current, we need to know what the mains AC voltage is to work out the final values for current and power. Because trying to sense 120 or 240 volts AC directly can be a little scary, we use an AC-to-AC adapter to step down the mains voltage to a safer level that we can work with. We will further reduce the incoming voltage to about 1 volt AC using an AC voltage divider discussed shortly in resistors R1 and R2. A second DC voltage divider in R5 and R6 is used to provide a DC bias, ensuring positive voltages that can be safely measured. Finally we add the capacitor C2 also to soak up some of the stray noise introduced in our signals.

We also need to find a way to easily plug the wires from the CT sensor and the AC adapter into the breadboard as well. Some CT sensors and AC adapters come with some form of barrel plug that isn't necessarily breadboard-friendly. Our sensor and adapter had bare wires that were both made of stranded copper and of a larger gauge that will not fit easily into the breadboard, either. To solve this, I soldered the end of each wire to a single .1-inch male pin header (clipped from a larger strip) and then covered this connection with a little section of heat shrink tubing, as shown in Figure 7-4.

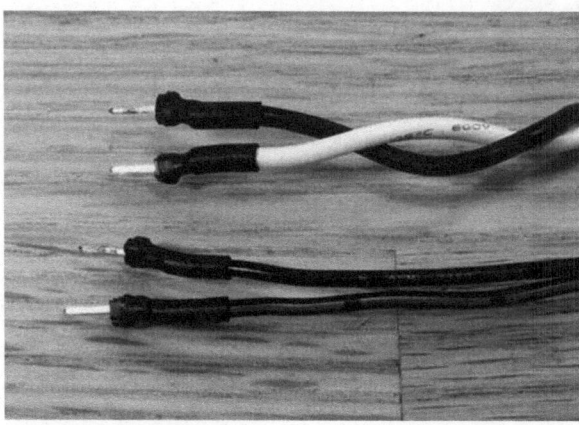

Figure 7-4. Pin headers soldered to wires

Now these wires easily and safely plug into the breadboard without creating any shorts in our circuit. You might instead solder the wires to short lengths of solid gauge wire or use some other form of connector of your preference. While I wouldn't worry too much about the CT sensor because it puts out such a low current and voltage, the AC adapter worries me a little so I would be especially careful to have this make a good connection to the breadboard.

Connecting the Display

Before we can begin to connect our display we need to solder some pin headers onto the LCD as well. This way we can plug it into the breadboard easily and connect the wires that will plug into the Arduino. To do this, it is probably easiest to break off as much of the .1-inch pin headers as you need for the LCD, insert them into your breadboard, and then place the LCD on top so that the short end of the pin headers poke through the 16 holes on the LCD. In the example shown in Figure 7-5, we used two shorter sections of headers with 6 pins each because we don't plan on using the middle 4 pins of the LCD, but feel free to use a single 16-pin section instead.

Figure 7-5. Breadboard close-up

With the pin headers soldered to the LCD so that the LCD lays flat on the breadboard, you can now start making the connections as shown in the schematic in Figure 7-2. The only tricky thing here is that the trimpot for setting the LCD's contrast has three pins on the bottom of it that cannot be seen. Figure 7-5 shows that the right-side pin shares a connection to ground with pin 1 of the LCD, while the middle pin has a small jumper wire that connects it to pin 3 on the LCD, and the left pin connects to +5 volts. The rest of the connections are fairly simple.

Building the Cable

Now that everything has been wired up on our breadboard we are almost ready to monitor a little current. The way CT sensors physically function means that we can't just clip the sensor around the entire three-wire cable because it just won't work. Instead we need to very carefully cut into the outer insulation, with the cable unplugged from the wall, without cutting into the wires inside, as shown in Figure 7-6, to find the hot or live wire inside.

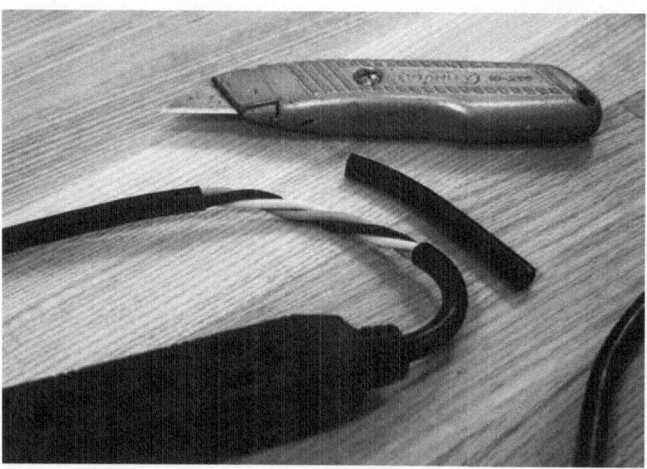

Figure 7-6. Outer insulation removed from power cable

Using an ordinary utility or hobby knife, carefully cut into the outer insulation without going too deeply. If you stretch or bend the cable at the point where you made the cut, you should be able to see whether you've cut through the insulation or not. Start with a circle around the circumference of the cable and then repeat about 3 inches down the cable. Once these cuts are made, you can carefully cut into the insulation lengthwise from one end to another, peeling away a small 3-inch section of outer insulation.

With this outer insulation removed, you should see three separately insulated wires inside. These wires will often be twisted together and will need to be slightly untwisted to slip the CT sensor in around the black or brown wire, as shown in Figure 7-7.

Figure 7-7. CT sensor clipped to the exposed hot wire

Remember that the CT sensor only clips around the one hot or live wire. It might also be necessary to reverse the direction of the CT sensor if, once you get everything connected up and the code installed on the Arduino, the readings come out a little weird. This isn't a problem with our sensor, but others can be directional.

Finishing it Up

With all the completed parts in place, your final project just needs something to monitor. As shown in Figure 7-8, we're using a small desk lamp with a 40-watt incandescent light bulb just to give us something to monitor.

Figure 7-8. Completed energy monitor

In this image we have the voltage and current sensing components and the display wired up on a solderless breadboard connected to the Arduino, the Arduino powered from a separated DC source (although USB could work just as well), the CT sensor is clipped around the hot wire in our power cable and plugs into the breadboard, the AC adapter is plugged into our power cable and is also plugged into the breadboard, and our little lamp is plugged into our power cable giving us a load of about 41 watts. While the lamp worked for this image, I'm sure you can find something more imaginative to connect your new energy monitor to, but now we need to give it some code to make it come to life.

Energy Monitor Code

With the hardware built, it's time to upload some code to our Arduino and get our current meter working. Listing 7-1 provides the source code for this project and we will follow this up with a discussion of the major elements in our sketch.

Listing 7-1. Energy Monitor Code

```
#include <LiquidCrystal.h>
LiquidCrystal lcd(3, 5, 6, 7, 8, 9);

const int voltageSensor = A0;
const int currentSensor = A1;

const int numberOfSamples = 3000;

// Calibration constants
const float AC_WALL_VOLTAGE      = 120.9;
const float AC_ADAPTER_VOLTAGE   = 14.1;
const float AC_VOLTAGE_DIV_VOUT  = 0.85;
const float CT_BURDEN_RESISTOR   = 40.2;
const float CT_TURNS             = 2280.0;

// Calibration coefficients
const float VCAL = 1.0;
const float ICAL = 1.0;
const float PHASECAL = 0.9;

// Calculated ratio constants, modified by VCAL/ICAL
const float AC_ADAPTER_RATIO = AC_WALL_VOLTAGE / AC_ADAPTER_VOLTAGE;
const float AC_VOLTAGE_DIV_RATIO = AC_ADAPTER_VOLTAGE / AC_VOLTAGE_DIV_VOUT;
const float V_RATIO = AC_ADAPTER_RATIO * AC_VOLTAGE_DIV_RATIO * 5 / 1024 * VCAL;
const float I_RATIO = CT_TURNS / CT_BURDEN_RESISTOR * 5 / 1024 * ICAL;

// Sample variables
int lastSampleV, lastSampleI, sampleV, sampleI;

// Filter variables
float lastFilteredV, lastFilteredI, filteredV, filteredI;

// Power sample totals
float sumI, sumV, sumP;

// Phase calibrated instantaneous voltage
float calibratedV;

// Calculated power variables
float realPower, apparentPower, powerFactor, voltageRMS, currentRMS;
unsigned long last_kWhTime, kWhTime;
float kilowattHour = 0.0;

void setup() {
 lcd.begin(16,2);
}
```

```
void loop() {
  calculatePower();
  displayPower();
}

void calculatePower() {
  for (int i = 0; i < numberOfSamples; i++) {
    // Used for voltage offset removal
    lastSampleV = sampleV;
    lastSampleI = sampleI;

    // Read voltage and current values
    sampleV = analogRead(voltageSensor);
    sampleI = analogRead(currentSensor);

    // Used for voltage offset removal
    lastFilteredV = filteredV;
    lastFilteredI = filteredI;

    // Digital high pass filters to remove 2.5V DC offset
    filteredV = 0.996 * (lastFilteredV + sampleV - lastSampleV);
    filteredI = 0.996 * (lastFilteredI + sampleI - lastSampleI);

    // Phase calibration
    calibratedV = lastFilteredV + PHASECAL * (filteredV - lastFilteredV);

    // Root-mean-square voltage
    sumV += calibratedV * calibratedV;

    // Root-mean-square current
    sumI += filteredI * filteredI;

    // Instantaneous Power
    sumP += abs(calibratedV * filteredI);
  }

  // Calculation of the root of the mean of the voltage and current squared (rms)
  // Calibration coeficients applied
  voltageRMS = V_RATIO * sqrt(sumV / numberOfSamples);
  currentRMS = I_RATIO * sqrt(sumI / numberOfSamples);

  // Calculate power values
  realPower = V_RATIO * I_RATIO * sumP / numberOfSamples;
  apparentPower = voltageRMS * currentRMS;
  powerFactor = realPower / apparentPower;

  // Calculate running total kilowatt hours
  // This value will reset in 50 days
  last_kWhTime = kWhTime;
  kWhTime = millis();
```

```
// Convert watts into kilowatts and multiply by the time since the last reading in ms
kilowattHour += (realPower / 1000) * ((kWhTime - last_kWhTime) / 3600000.0);

// Reset sample totals
sumV = 0;
sumI = 0;
sumP = 0;
}

void displayPower() {
  lcd.clear();
  lcd.print(realPower, 0);
  lcd.print("w ");
  lcd.print(apparentPower, 0);
  lcd.print("va ");
  lcd.print(powerFactor * 100, 0);
  lcd.print("%");
  lcd.setCursor(0,1);
  lcd.print(voltageRMS, 0);
  lcd.print("v ");
  lcd.print(currentRMS, 1);
  lcd.print("a ");
  lcd.print(kilowattHour, 4);
}
```

Constants

A significant amount of our code (just about everything before the setup() function, in fact) is spent setting up the global variables that will provide all the constants and variables that we will use in our power calculations. At the beginning of our code we start by including the library for the LCD display and set up the pin numbers that we will connect to the LCD as well as the current and voltage sensors:

```
#include <LiquidCrystal.h>
LiquidCrystal lcd(3, 5, 6, 7, 8, 9);

const int voltageSensor = A0;
const int currentSensor = A1;
```

In this case, our LCD is connected to Arduino's digital pins 3, 5, 6, 7, 8, and 9; while the voltage sensor is connected to analog input A0, and the current sensor is connected to analog input A1. We then tell the code how many times we want to quickly sample the sensors to get the most accurate readings that we can in this line:

```
const int numberOfSamples = 3000;
```

The sections labeled Calibration constants and Calibration coefficients will be used when we need to input some of our calibrated values, discussed in more detail shortly. The section Calculated ratio constants will take care of some of the initial maths so that we don't have to think about it, such as figuring out the ratio between the mains voltage and our AC adapter and converting the expected sensor inputs into a range usable by Arduino's ADC. The rest of the variables are used for the power calculations later.

You might have noticed that we're using the const (constant) variable qualifier for many of the constants found in this section of code. A variable labeled with this const keyword is still required to follow all the rules of Arduino's programming language for variables, specifically relating to a variable's scope, but the variable will not be allowed to be changed in the course of normal program flow and it saves us a little memory at the same time. This is not an absolute requirement, but it might help as we start to add to this code later.

setup() and loop()

Our setup() and loop() functions are about as simple as they get because we have put all the meat of this code into their own dedicated functions. All that is left to do is to start the LCD using the lcd.begin() function, and in the loop() function all that's needed is to call the calculatePower() and displayPower() functions. Writing our code this way helps to compartmentalize the sketch making it easier to add on to in the future.

calculatePower()

The calculatePower() function is where the action is at in our code. This function will sample our voltage and current sensors 3,000 times in quick succession, making calculations and averaging the results as it goes. We begin this function with a for loop to obtain the specified number of sample readings like this:

```
for (int i = 0; i < numberOfSamples; i++) {
```

Each time through this loop, we are keeping track of the last readings for our voltage and current values using these two lines:

```
lastSampleV = sampleV;
lastSampleI = sampleI;
```

This way, as we make new readings, the old and new values can be averaged out over time. To obtain the new readings we use the analogRead function as we did in these lines:

```
sampleV = analogRead(voltageSensor);
sampleI = analogRead(currentSensor);
```

We also use the calculatePower() function for sampling out the 2.5-volt DC bias that was introduced into our circuits by a pair of DC voltage dividers to create a positive DC signal, which is then sampled and factored into our RMS calculations:

```
filteredV = 0.996 * (lastFilteredV + sampleV - lastSampleV);
filteredI = 0.996 * (lastFilteredI + sampleI - lastSampleI);
```

After sampling our inputs for the number of times specified in the variable numberOfSamples, the function then calculates the final totals for the RMS voltage, RMS current, here:

```
voltageRMS = V_RATIO * sqrt(sumV / numberOfSamples);
currentRMS = I_RATIO * sqrt(sumI / numberOfSamples);
```

With the RMS values in hand, our code can now calculate real power, apparent power, and finally the power factor like this:

```
realPower = V_RATIO * I_RATIO * sumP / numberOfSamples;
apparentPower = voltageRMS * currentRMS;
powerFactor = realPower / apparentPower;
```

The last calculation that we need to make is the running total for kilowatt hours by checking how much time has passed in milliseconds using the `millis()` function, converting watts from the real power calculation into kilowatts, and then multiplying this value by the amount of time that has passed and adding the final value to the running total. This is all done in three lines of code:

```
last_kWhTime = kWhTime;
kWhTime = millis();
kilowattHour += (realPower / 1000) * ((kWhTime - last_kWhTime) / 3600000.0);
```

The value of kilowatt-hours will reset when the `millis()` function resets in 50 days, but that's a long enough time to monitor a device or two and get a good sampling over a month.

displayPower()

Once all the power calculations have been completed, we need to display these values on our LCD display. To do that, we have lumped all the functions that display this information into its own function, called `displayPower()`. This function is fairly simple and straightforward, beginning with clearing the display, which automatically sets the cursor to the top left of the screen using this one line:

```
lcd.clear();
```

Next we print from left to right on the LCD the value for real power followed by the character w for watts using the lcd.print() functions like this:

```
lcd.print(realPower, 0);
lcd.print("w ");
```

By specifying the variable name, `realPower`, and the number of decimal points, 0, the `print()` function will display the value of the variable with no decimal points. In the next line, however, we use the double quotation marks to tell the `print()` function to display the characters w and a space to create a label for our variable.

In a similar fashion, the `displayPower()` function will display the value for apparent power, followed by the characters va for volt-amps; and finally the value for power factor expressed as a percentage, followed by the character %. After this, we set the cursor to the second line using this function:

```
lcd.setCursor(0,1);
```

Starting on the second line of the display, we then print the value for RMS voltage followed by the character v for volts, the value for RMS current followed by the character a for amps, and finally the running total for kilowatt hours printed to three decimal points of precision. This last value doesn't have a label because it wouldn't fit on the screen. Depending on how long you run the monitor, it would just continue to move to the right of the screen and not be visible, anyway.

Calibrating

Chances are if you build this project as shown with parts that are reasonably close to those specified, your energy monitor will probably work fine, but the values will most likely be a little off. To get the best results from our energy monitor we will need to take some measurements using a digital multimeter and work out a few calculations to calibrate our settings in the code accordingly.

Current Settings

If you're smart or a little lucky, you'll purchase a CT sensor that has a data sheet from the manufacturer that will tell you all the specifics of your particular sensor so that you can skip some of the more unpleasant aspects of calibrating your sensor. My sensor didn't come with any of these details, so I had to do a little homework to determine a few figures that are necessary for accurate power calculations. From the seller's information about this sensor I knew it was rated for 100 amps with a 333 millivolts output at this rated current, but I still needed to know the value of the internal burden resistor and the number of turns on the secondary winding. So I began with the direct approach of opening up the case of the CT sensor shown in Figure 7-9.

Figure 7-9. The inside of a CT sensor

Fortunately, my CT sensor was easy enough to open with a few plastic clips holding it all together. After carefully removing the ferrite core and wire coil from the lower two-part housing, I discovered a little blue 40.2 ohm, 0.5% tolerance, built-in burden resistor hiding inside. With that I could work out the approximate number of turns for the secondary winding using a little math. By working backward from the examples provided on the Open Energy Monitor site, I knew that my burden resistor was 40.2 ohms and that the voltage over the burden resistor on our setup would be half of the reference voltage for the

Arduino Uno, or 2.5 volts, created from the DC voltage divider. This information would let me work out the peak current for the burden resistor:

burden resistor peak current = 2.5 volts ÷ 40.2 ohms = 0.062 amps

With the peak amps of the burden resistor solved, we then need to know the peak amps that our CT sensor is rated for because these two numbers are proportional to one another. I knew that my sensor was rated for 100 amps, but it's fairly safe to assume this is the RMS current—a sort of averaging of the potential current. What we needed, however, was to know the peak current of the sensor, a value that should be larger than the RMS current by a factor of the square root of 2, or 1.414 times the RMS current:

peak current = 100 amps × 1.414 = 141.4 amps

With those two equations out of the way, we now know the peak current for the burden resistor and the peak current from our CT sensor and because these two values are proportional to the windings, we can work out the number of windings in the secondary coil of the CT sensor like so:

number of turns = 141.4 amps ÷ 0.062 amps = 2280.64 turns

Armed with this information, we can provide our code with the specifics of our hardware to ensure reasonably accurate readings. The next thing we need to do is calibrate our voltage settings.

Voltage Settings

To calibrate the voltage settings, first we need to grab our digital multimeter and measure some voltages, specifically the mains voltage coming from our wall and the stepped-down voltage coming from our AC adapter. To do this, we need to set our digital multimeter for measuring AC voltages (marked with the letters AC and usually a wave symbol) and select a reasonable range, if we have a ranged multimeter, of fewer than 200 volts for measuring mains voltage in the United States and fewer than 20 if it has this option for measuring the AC adapter. With the meter properly set up, all we need to do is carefully insert the probes into the power outlet to measure the mains voltage and, with the adapter plugged into the wall, measure the two wires of the adapter as shown in Figures 7-10 and 7-11, respectively. Because AC oscillates between positive and negative voltages, AC power is not polarized so it's not important which probe contacts what wire.

Figure 7-10. *Measuring AC mains voltage*

Figure 7-11. *Measuring AC adapter voltage*

In the figures, both measurements exceeded the expected 120 volts from the wall and the 12 volts from the adapter. That's okay and is the whole point to calibrating our code to match the specifics of our location. In fact, these values can change depending on the time of day, day of the week, or location inside your house. For now, make a note of both of these voltages, and we will come back to them in a moment.

Next we calibrate our voltage divider for the AC sensing part of our circuit. In our example, we have a 12-volt AC adapter that generates a voltage closer to 14 volts, but what we actually need for our sensor is a signal of about 1 volt, or at least as close as we can get to it. To work this out, let's look at just the AC voltage divider part of our schematic, as shown in Figure 7-12.

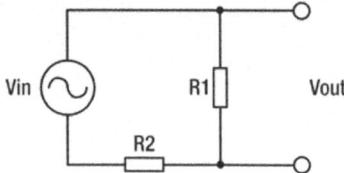

Figure 7-12. AC voltage divider schematic

In this simple circuit, we have a source of AC voltage marked Vin (in our case an AC power adapter) and two resistors labeled R1 and R2. The voltage output across resistor R1 labeled Vout can be calculated by the following equation:

Vout = (Vin × R1) ÷ (R1 + R2)

To get to 1 volt, we most likely need to adjust the values of one or both of these resistors. For AC adapters that provide anywhere from 7–12 volts, you can start with the values of 10 kilohm for R1 and 100 kilohm for R2, and adjust from there until Vout sits around 1 volt. In our project we used 6.8 kilohm for R1 and 100 kilohm for R2, using the following formula gives us a voltage reasonably close to 1 volt:

Vout = (14.1 volts × 6,800 ohms) ÷ (6,800 ohms + 100,000 ohms) = 0.897 volts

Alternatively, let's say that you have a 9-volt AC adapter and, rather than guessing at values, would like to use a little math to find an appropriate value for R1. To solve for this we could use the following formula:

R1 = (Vout × R2) ÷ (Vin – Vout)

So assuming that our 9-volt supply actually measures 9 volts, which it most likely doesn't, and sticking with 100 kilohm for R2, the value for R1 should equal somewhere near the following:

R1 = (1 volt × 100,000 ohms) ÷ (9 volts – 1 volt) = 12,500 ohms

Because a 12.5 kilohm resistor is a little hard to come by, we could use a 12 kilohm resistor instead because it's close enough. If we plug that value back into the formula to find Vout, it would look like this:

Vout = (9 volts × 12,000 ohms) ÷ (12,000 ohms + 100,000 ohms) = 0.964 volts

That's about as close to 1 volt as you're going to get. Now that we have a suitable voltage for Vout and the appropriate resistors for R1 and R2, you can swap out these new resistor values from those in our schematic in Figure 7-2. Next we should probably verify this output by measuring the AC voltage across R1 in the project schematic mainly because resistor values can be off by as much as 10 percent or more. Once you have a known voltage, add it to your calibration notes and let's proceed to entering these values into our code.

Entering the Constants

So far, we have collected lots of data about our energy monitor, so now it's time to put these numbers to use. As you have been measuring the different aspects of our setup you might be wondering how the calibration works in the first place when the values, AC mains voltages for example, continue to change over time. What's really important is to get a snapshot of the values at one moment in time. This will give you the best chance of having the ratios stay constant, giving you the most accurate readings possible.

Anyway, let's start with the block of code at the beginning of our sketch labeled `Calibration constants`. For clarity's sake, let's pull out this block of code:

```
// Calibration constants
const float AC_WALL_VOLTAGE      = 120.9;
const float AC_ADAPTER_VOLTAGE   = 14.1;
const float AC_VOLTAGE_DIV_VOUT  = 0.85;
const float CT_BURDEN_RESISTOR   = 40.2;
const float CT_TURNS             = 2280.0;
```

Each of these calibration values is of the float data type for floating-point numbers, so we need to remember to enter at least one digit on both sides of the decimal point even if that value is 0, as in 0.9 or 1.0. This will help ensure that any of the mathematical operations performed on the floating-point values will remain in the floating–point data type.

The first three of our calibration variables define the three different AC voltages that we are working with. The first, `AC_WALL_VOLTAGE`, is the voltage that we measured coming from our household mains voltage. The second is `AC_ADAPTER_VOLTAGE,` which is a measurement of the AC output of our AC-to-AC adapter, stepping down our high voltage to a safer low voltage source. The final value is `AC_VOLTAGE_DIV_OUT`, which is the voltage output that comes from our AC voltage divider and should be somewhere close to 1 volt AC.

The next two values relate to our CT sensor and are used for determining the amount of current that the sensor is reading. The constant variable `CT_BURDEN_RESISTOR` is the value of the resistor in ohms used to convert the current of the CT sensor to a voltage. This resistor might be built into your sensor as ours was, or it might need to be added to the circuit. The next value is the number of windings on the secondary coil of the CT sensor and is called `CT_TURNS`. This value should be in the thousands of turns.

Our next block of calibration values is labeled `Calibration coefficients`. Let's look at that block of code in more detail:

```
// Calibration coefficients
const float VCAL = 1.0;
const float ICAL = 1.0;
const float PHASECAL = 0.9;
```

If your measurements are reasonably accurate, you may not need to change any of these values. There are times, though, when a little nudge in one direction or another will help to make your final results that much more accurate. That's where `VCAL` and `ICAL` come in to adjust the RMS voltage and RMS current, respectively, by a small margin.

The last coefficient, `PHASECAL`, is an attempt to calibrate for phase offset that happens when a reactive load creates an off-phase AC signal and creates a significant divergence in the apparent power and real power. In practice, I haven't had much luck getting this value to do much in the way of significant changes, although your mileage may vary.

Wrapping it Up

With those calibration settings updated in your source code, your energy monitor should start providing some reasonably accurate results. Now you need to figure out what to start monitoring first!

Going Further

After all that, we now have a working energy monitor that will tell us at any given time what our power consumption looks like and will keep a running total of our kilowatt hours for as long as power is applied to the Arduino, and we don't keep it on for longer than 50 days.

The great thing about building our energy monitor around the Arduino is that we can customize it to do our bidding. Taking this project a step or two further, maybe you want it to control the color of an RGB LED to give you some very immediate feedback about your power consumption. Or maybe you want to set this up with a Twitter account to tweet your energy consumption every hour. Or maybe you want to log all this data being calculated on a permanent form of memory so the data can later be analyzed. Let's start there with the last one to see what's involved with storing our energy consumption data on a secure data or SD memory card and then analyze this data in something like Microsoft Excel, as shown in Figure 7-13.

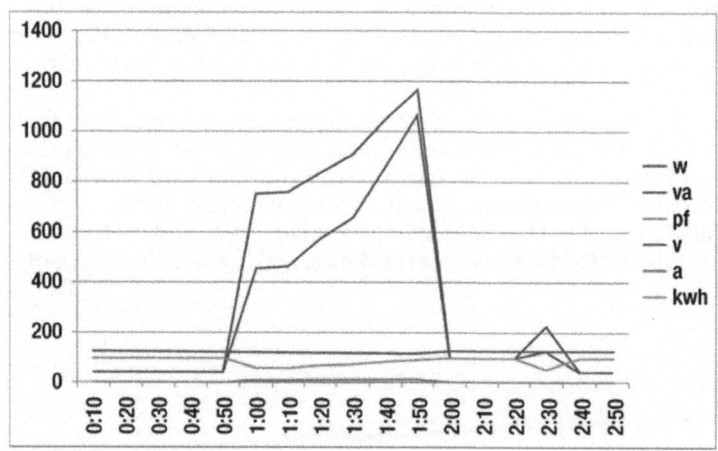

Figure 7-13. MS Excel data plot over three minutes of data logging

To take our project to this next step, we need some more hardware. Namely, we need a special kind of SD memory card breakout board that is designed to allow the Arduino to access a file on an SD card and write data to it. There are several online retailers offering such a board:

- Adafruit's MicroSD Breakout: `http://www.adafruit.com/products/254`

- Gravitech's MicroSD Card Adapter: `http://www.gravitech.us/micaad.html`

- Even better yet, we could use the Arduino Ethernet Shield, `http://www.adafruit.com/products/201`, because it has the MicroSD card connector built right into it and it might open up some later possibilities for a web-connected power meter.

Figure 7-14 shows what our project will look like when we swap in the Arduino Ethernet Shield.

Figure 7-14. Energy Monitor with Arduino Ethernet Shield

Another reason to use the Arduino Ethernet Shield is how easy it is to connect to the Arduino and get it going. All we need to do is unplug the jumper wires connecting our breadboard to the Arduino, plug the Ethernet Shield right on top of the Arduino and then reconnect the jumper wires to the exact same pins on the shield (as shown in the schematic). Now to get our SD data logging to work, we will need a properly formatted FAT16 microSD card (a small capacity works fine) and then we are ready for some new code.

Energy Monitor SD Code

To get you going with your own data–logging energy monitor, we will build off of the previous example code by adding a few additional lines of code that use Arduino's SD library to open a file named `data.txt` on an SD card and append new values to this file every ten seconds. Listing 7-2 provides the source code that makes this happen.

Listing 7-2. Energy Monitor SD Code

```
#include <LiquidCrystal.h>
#include <SD.h>

LiquidCrystal lcd(3, 5, 6, 7, 8, 9);
File file;

const int voltageSensor = A0;
const int currentSensor = A1;
const int SDcs = 4;

const int numberOfSamples = 3000;
```

```
// Calibration constants
const float AC_WALL_VOLTAGE      = 120.9;
const float AC_ADAPTER_VOLTAGE   = 14.1;
const float AC_VOLTAGE_DIV_VOUT  = 0.85;
const float CT_BURDEN_RESISTOR   = 40.2;
const float CT_TURNS             = 2280.0;

// Calibration coeficients
const float VCAL = 1.0;
const float ICAL = 1.0;
const float PHASECAL = 0.9;

// Calculated ratio constants, modified by VCAL/ICAL
const float AC_ADAPTER_RATIO = AC_WALL_VOLTAGE / AC_ADAPTER_VOLTAGE;
const float AC_VOLTAGE_DIV_RATIO = AC_ADAPTER_VOLTAGE / AC_VOLTAGE_DIV_VOUT;
const float V_RATIO = AC_ADAPTER_RATIO * AC_VOLTAGE_DIV_RATIO * 5 / 1024 * VCAL;
const float I_RATIO = CT_TURNS / CT_BURDEN_RESISTOR * 5 / 1024 * ICAL;

// Sample variables
int lastSampleV, lastSampleI, sampleV, sampleI;

// Filter variables
float lastFilteredV, lastFilteredI, filteredV, filteredI;

// Power sample totals
float sumI, sumV, sumP;

// Phase calibrated instantaneous voltage
float calibratedV;

// Calculated power variables
float realPower, apparentPower, powerFactor, voltageRMS, currentRMS;
unsigned long last_kWhTime, kWhTime;
float kilowattHour = 0.0;

unsigned long startTime = 0;
unsigned long interval = 10000;

void setup() {
 lcd.begin(16,2);
 Serial.begin(9600);

 // Starts the SD card
 Serial.print("Initializing SD card...");
 pinMode(10, OUTPUT);
```

```
  // Checks that the SD card is present
  if (!SD.begin(SDcs)) {
    Serial.println("initialization failed!");
    return;
  }
  Serial.println("initialization done.");
}

void loop() {
  calculatePower();
  displayPower();

  // Opens file on SD if interval has passed
  if (startTime + interval < millis()) {
    // Opens files and sets to write mode
    file = SD.open("data.txt", FILE_WRITE);

    // Writes values to file if present
    if (file) {
      Serial.print("Writing to data.txt... ");

      file.print(realPower);
      file.print(",");
      file.print(apparentPower);
      file.print(",");
      file.print(powerFactor * 100);
      file.print(",");
      file.print(voltageRMS);
      file.print(",");
      file.print(currentRMS);
      file.print(",");
      file.println(kilowattHour);

      Serial.println("done.");
      // Need to close a file to save the data
      file.close();
      Serial.println("File closed.");
    } else Serial.println("Error opening data.txt.");
    startTime = millis();
  }
}

void calculatePower() {
  for (int i = 0; i < numberOfSamples; i++) {
    // Used for voltage offset removal
    lastSampleV = sampleV;
    lastSampleI = sampleI;
```

```
  // Read voltage and current values
  sampleV = analogRead(voltageSensor);
  sampleI = analogRead(currentSensor);

  // Used for voltage offset removal
  lastFilteredV = filteredV;
  lastFilteredI = filteredI;

  // Digital high pass filters to remove 2.5V DC offset
  filteredV = 0.996 * (lastFilteredV + sampleV - lastSampleV);
  filteredI = 0.996 * (lastFilteredI + sampleI - lastSampleI);

  // Phase calibration
  calibratedV = lastFilteredV + PHASECAL * (filteredV - lastFilteredV);

  // Root-mean-square voltage
  sumV += calibratedV * calibratedV;

  // Root-mean-square current
  sumI += filteredI * filteredI;

  // Instantaneous Power
  sumP += abs(calibratedV * filteredI);
}

// Calculation of the root of the mean of the voltage and current squared (rms)
// Calibration coeficients applied
voltageRMS = V_RATIO * sqrt(sumV / numberOfSamples);
currentRMS = I_RATIO * sqrt(sumI / numberOfSamples);

// Calculate power values
realPower = V_RATIO * I_RATIO * sumP / numberOfSamples;
apparentPower = voltageRMS * currentRMS;
powerFactor = realPower / apparentPower;

// Calculate running total kilowatt hours
// This value will reset in 50 days
last_kWhTime = kWhTime;
kWhTime = millis();
// Convert watts into kilowatts and multiply by the time since the last reading
kilowattHour += (realPower / 1000) * ((kWhTime - last_kWhTime) / 3600000.0);

// Reset sample totals
sumV = 0;
sumI = 0;
sumP = 0;
}
```

```
void displayPower() {
  lcd.clear();
  lcd.print(realPower, 0);
  lcd.print("w ");
  lcd.print(apparentPower, 0);
  lcd.print("va ");
  lcd.print(powerFactor * 100, 0);
  lcd.print("%");
  lcd.setCursor(0,1);
  lcd.print(voltageRMS, 0);
  lcd.print("v ");
  lcd.print(currentRMS, 1);
  lcd.print("a ");
  lcd.print(kilowattHour, 4);
}
```

Code Summary

Now that might look a little intimidating at first, but not much has honestly changed. We need to include the SD library at the beginning of the code and create an instance for the library called `file`. Keep in mind that the SD card select uses pin 4 on the Arduino, and even if we are not using it, pin 10 needs to be set as an output for the Ethernet part of the shield. That's why our LCD has been set to use the pins 3, 5, 6, 7, 8, and 9; see, there is a method to my madness. After that, we've added some code to the `setup()` function to use Arduino's serial monitor for some feedback that we are writing to the SD card correctly.

The `loop()` function is where we did the most damage. Because there is no real reason to write data to the SD file too frequently, we set up a counter using the `millis()` function to know when the time specified in the `interval` variable, currently 10 seconds, has passed:

```
if (startTime + interval < millis()) {
```

When this condition is true, the code will open the file called `data.txt`, creating it if it doesn't already exist, and then set this file to write mode using this line of code:

```
file = SD.open("data.txt", FILE_WRITE);
```

Use the `print()` function like this:

```
file.print(realPower);
file.print(",");
```

We then add data to the end of the file the values for real power, apparent power, power factor, RMS voltage, RMS current, and the running total for kilowatt hours. To separate each value, a comma character is written to the file between the values, and a new line is created after the last value. When all is said and done, we have a file that looks like Listing 7-3.

Listing 7-3. Sample Data Log File

```
42.05,43.58,96.49,124.43,0.35,0.00
41.59,42.63,97.57,124.03,0.34,0.00
41.94,42.82,97.94,123.69,0.35,0.00
41.66,43.11,96.64,123.85,0.35,0.00
41.35,42.59,97.07,123.43,0.35,0.00
```

```
454.11,752.37,60.36,120.14,6.26,0.00
461.40,757.83,60.88,120.40,6.29,0.00
571.60,833.10,68.61,119.83,6.95,0.01
655.43,907.95,72.19,119.10,7.62,0.01
867.94,1047.79,82.83,117.35,8.93,0.01
1068.58,1167.77,91.51,116.99,9.98,0.01
96.69,97.91,98.76,125.15,0.78,0.01
96.23,97.23,98.97,124.97,0.78,0.01
96.10,97.06,99.01,124.86,0.78,0.01
121.87,225.12,54.13,124.57,1.81,0.01
42.29,43.55,97.12,125.42,0.35,0.02
42.38,43.69,97.00,125.46,0.35,0.02
```

While it might look like a bunch of gobbledygook in this form, this is the same file I used to create the line graph in Figure 7-13 and all in about 5 minutes. Because the data is in a format known as comma delimited, Excel and other spreadsheet programs can import this data easily enough and once the data is in spreadsheet format, it's only a matter of a few button clicks to provide column and row headings and generate a new graph. This could be a good way to monitor your energy consumption over an entire month and see how small changes to your energy habits could have a lasting effect on your energy consumption and your pocket book as well.

Further Still?

Not far enough? In that case, because we are running out of room for our chapter, here are a few more brief ideas to get you started as you explore new applications and new directions for your energy monitor.

Tweeting Energy Monitor

Now that you've got an Ethernet Shield hooked up to your energy monitor, why not set it up with its own Twitter account so it can tweet your energy usage? To get started tweeting with your Arduino, you should start with the Arduino Twitter and EthernetDNS Libraries that can be found at www.arduino.cc/playground/Code/TwitterLibrary. After that you will need to obtain a token to enable your Arduino to post a tweet from http://arduino-tweet.appspot.com.

With these three things in place, you could start with the SimplePost sketch that is a part of the Twitter library in the File ➤ Examples ➤ Twitter menu. To get started tweeting, you need to input the Ethernet Shield's MAC address, printed on a little label on the bottom of the shield, into the array `mac[]`. After that, you'll need to find an available IP address on your network and enter this into the `ip[]` array. Finally we need to take the token we obtained earlier and enter this into the Twitter `twitter()` object.

With all that in place and uploaded to your Arduino board, the Arduino will tweet this simple message: "Hello, World! I'm Arduino!" At this point, I'll leave you to figure out how to place your energy readings into the character string array `msg[]` and post this as a tweet. Should be fun!

Pachube and the Energy Monitor

Earlier in this book we looked at using the Arduino to talk to Processing to post data on the real-time data network site Pachube. With an Arduino Ethernet Shield in place, you should be able to post your energy monitor data straight to your own data feed with no computer needed. To get started, you'll need to use your Pachube account and set up a new data feed. For some code to get you started, check out the official Arduino tutorial at `http://arduino.cc/en/Tutorial/PachubeCient` and the Pachube tutorials at `http://community.pachube.com/node/112`. The rest is fairly similar to getting your Arduino to Tweet.

Whole House Monitoring

Rather than monitoring a device or three, with a sufficiently large enough CT sensor (or two), it's possible to monitor the energy consumption of your entire home. To do this, you will need to use 2 CT sensors tied in series of at least 100 amps in capacity each in the United States, or 1 CT sensor of 100 amps in the UK. These sensors need to be installed where the mains voltage enters your home—for example, the breaker box in a U.S. home.

Because this involves getting up close and personal with some scary amount of electricity it's probably a good idea to have a licensed electrician handle the installation of these components for you. Beyond that, measuring your household's current isn't much harder than measuring a 40 watt lamp. For a case example of whole house monitoring in the United States, check out the site `http://www.desert-home.com/p/test-html-code.html`; and see the wireless whole-house monitor developed by the folks at the Open Energy Monitor project here: `http://openenergymonitor.org/emon/emontx`.

Conclusion

In this chapter, we built a semiportable Arduino-based energy monitor; showed you how to calibrate the monitor to match the specifics of your installation; and introduced a few ways to expand your simple monitor to include data logging, tweeting, creating your own data feeds, and monitoring your entire household's energy usage.

Being able to monitor the energy draw in kilowatt hours of various household appliances and devices with a few simple and cheap components and your Arduino microcontroller will allow you to make better decisions about whether you should upgrade that old television or once and for all make the switch from incandescent light bulbs to compact fluorescents. Maybe your new energy monitor will save you a few pennies and save a little of the world in the process.

References

- Open Energy Monitor project: `http://openenergymonitor.org/`

- Original code by Trystan Lea: `https://github.com/openenergymonitor/MainsACv3`

- Arduino Twitter library: `http://www.arduino.cc/playground/Code/TwitterLibrary`

- Twitter authorization app: `http://arduino-tweet.appspot.com`

- Whole-house monitoring: `http://www.desert-home.com/p/test-html-code.html`

- emonTX energy monitoring node: `http://openenergymonitor.org/emon/emontx`

Index